500 Family Campsites

Credits

The information contained in this directory is sourced entirely from the AA's establishment database, Information Research, Hotel Services.

Cover photo: Photodisc.
All other photographs in this guide come from the AA World Travel Library, and were taken by: Steve Day (pg1 background), Nick Johnston (pg1 foreground) and Tony Souter (pg6).

Design by Jamie Wiltshire
Editor: Denise Laing
Typeset by iCandy Design Ltd, Basingstoke.
Printed and bound by Everbest, China

Published by AA Publishing, a trading name of Automobile Association Developments Limited, whose registered office is Southwood East, Apollo Rise, Farnborough, Hampshire, GU14 0JW.
Registered number 1878835

A CIP catalogue record for this book is available from the British Library
ISBN 07495 42721

A02039

Welcome to the Guide

This pocket guide is aimed at families with children looking for the right caravan or camping park for their holiday. Within its pages you will find parks of all kinds, from busy, action-packed holiday centres to small sites handily located near beaches or other attractions. All of them are child friendly, and all offer at minimum a playing ground and/or designated playing area where children can safely let off steam. Every park is inspected annually by an unannounced visit from an experienced AA inspector, and the information which appears in this Guide, is also updated every year. Do check with a park when booking that all of your requirements will be met.

The AA Campsite Classification Scheme

AA parks are classified on a 5-point scale according to their style and the range of facilities they offer. As the number of pennants increases, so the quality and variety of facilities is generally greater.

► One Pennant Parks offer a drinking water supply, chemical disposal point, and refuse collection. They may or may not have toilets and washing facilities

►► Two Pennant Parks additionally offer separate washrooms including at least 2 toilets and 2 wash basins per 30 pitches per sex, hot and cold water directly to each basin, and dishwashing facilities.

►►► Three Pennants Parks offer modern or modernised toilets with, additionally, at least one private shower cubicle per 35 pitches per sex, electric hook-ups, automatic laundry and children's playground.

►►►► Four Pennant Parks are of a very high quality, especially in the toilets which offer vanitory-style wash basins including some in lockable cubicles, some combined washing/toilet cubicles, or en suite shower/washing/toilet cubicles.

►►►► Five Pennant Parks are of an outstanding quality, and offer some fully-services pitches, first class toilet facilities including en suite cubicles.

 A separate HOLIDAY CENTRE category indicates that full day and night holiday entertainment is offered, including sports, leisure and recreational facilities, and a choice of eating outlets.

The quality percentage score shows a comparison between sites within the same pennant rating. The score runs between 50% and 80%.

How to Use this Guide

1 — **NEWTOWN**   **TL27**

The Caravan Park
2 — ▶▶▶ **68%**
Long Lane ABXX 4XX
☎ 01480 437566 📠 01480 437566
❻ camp@website.com
4 — **Dir:** Leave A14/A1 signed Newtown

★ ⌖ £12-£14 ⛺ £12-£14 ▲ £10-£12
Open all year (rs 31 Oct-1 Mar 10 pitches only
5 — plus 6 storage spaces) Booking Advisable all
bank hols & school hols Last arrival 22.00hrs
Last departure noon
*A small, friendly site in a pleasant setting
beside the river. Bay areas have been provided for caravans and motorhomes. A 4-acre site
with 50 touring pitches.*
Leisure: ⚐
Facilities: ⋔ ⊙ ❄ ✳ ————— **7**
Disabled facilities: toilet & washbasin
Services: ⛽ ⇕ ▣ → ⼁18 ✕ ☎ ♨ 🛒
6 — **Notes:** Dogs must be on leads, ball games on
field provided, no generators, one-way system
5mph, no cars by tents

1 **LOCATIONS**
The guide is listed in country, county
order, then by town/village
alphabetically. Counties are listed
down the side of each page. Map
references are based on the National
Grid.

2 AA PENNANT RATING Please see
page 3 for an explanation.

3 DIRECTIONS are shown where
provided by proprietors.

4 CHARGES
The prices given are the overnight
cost for one tent or caravan, and
one car with two adults, or one
motor caravan and two adults.
Some parks may charge separately
for some facilities, including
showers. There may be an extra

charge for pitches with electricity. Prices in the Republic of Ireland are given in Euros.

5 PITCHES

The brief description of the site includes the number of touring pitches and hardstanding, as well as the number of static van pitches which gives an indication of the size of the park. Static vans are not inspected, and are not part of the Pennant Scheme.

6 NOTES

These are any restrictions the park has told us about.

7 For Symbols & Abbreviations please see page 6

Useful Information

It is advisable to book in advance at peak holiday times. Check whether a reservation entitles you to a particular pitch. Speak to the person in charge immediately if you have any complaints. If this personal approach fails and the matter is serious, you may decide to approach the local authority or tourist board. **Chemical Disposal Point:** Most parks, except for those catering for tents only, will have one of these. It should have flushing, rinsing and soakaway facilities. **Electric Hook-Up:** Most parks offer these, but if it is important to you, check with the park when booking. Cables can usually be hired on a site, or a plug supplied to fit your own cable. **Restrictions:** On many parks, unaccompanied young people, single-sex groups, single adults, and motorcycle groups are not accepted. Most parks accept dogs, though some will refuse certain breeds.

Symbols & Abbreviations

Symbol	Description	Symbol	Description
△	tent		hairdryer
	caravan	✳	ice-pack facility
△	watersports	☎	public telephone
	indoor swimming pool		shop on site, or within 200 yards
◎	mini golf		BBQ area
◔	tennis court	⊼	picnic area
	outdoor swimming pool		dog exercise area
▢	separate TV room	→	facilities within 3 miles of the site
	boats for hire	∪	stables
	launderette	⌐18	golf course and number of holes
⅏	children's playground	♪	fishing
	games room	T	toilet fluid
✗	café/restaurant		fast food / takeaway
	cinema		baby care
	shower		electric hook up
	Calor Gaz	⚲	licensed bar
⌀	Camping Gaz		no dogs
	battery charging		
⊙	electric shaver		

6

RISELEY   SU76

Wellington Country Park ►►► 67%

RG7 1SP

☎ 0118 932 6444 🖹 0118 932 6445

🅴 info.wcp@wellington-country-park.co.uk

🆆 www.wellington-country-park.co.uk

Dir: Signed off A33 between Reading and Basingstoke, 4m S of M4 J11

★ 🚐 £11.75-£20.75 🚐 £11.75-£20.75

🅰 £10-£18

Open Mar-Nov Booking Advisable peak periods Last arrival 17.30hrs Last departure 13.00hrs

A peaceful woodland site set within extensive country park, which comes complete with lakes, nature trails, deer farm and boating. Ideal for M4 travellers. A 80-acre site with 72 touring pitches, 10 hardstandings.
Boating, fishing, miniature railway

Leisure: 🅰

Facilities: 🅽 ⊙ ℚ ✳ Ꮭ 🐾 🏇 ㅠ ㅐ

Services: ✕ 🚐 🖻 🝙 🔌 → ∪ ⚡ 🝙 ◎ ◬

Notes: No single sex groups

▨▨ ▨▨ ▨▨ 🔌 🔊

COMBERTON   TL35

Highfield Farm Touring Park ►►►► 77%

Long Road CB3 7DG

☎ 01223 262308 🖹 01223 262308

🅴 enquiries@highfieldfarmtouringpark.co.uk

🆆 www.highfieldfarmtouringpark.co.uk

Dir: From M11 J12, take A603 (Sandy) for 0.5m, then R onto B1046 to Comberton

★ 🚐 £8.50-£12 🚐 £8.50-£12 🅰 £8.25-£12

Open Apr-Oct Booking Advisable bank hols wknds Last arrival 22.00hrs Last departure 14.00hrs

Run by a very efficient and friendly family, the park is on a well-sheltered hilltop, with spacious pitches including a cosy backpackers/cyclists area, and separate sections for couples and families. There is a 1.5m marked walk around the family farm, with stunning views. A 8-acre site with 120 touring pitches, 52 hardstandings.
Postbox

Leisure: 🅰

Facilities: 🅽 ⊙ ℚ ✳ 🝙 Ꮭ 🏇 ㅐ

Services: 🔲 🚐 🖻 🝙 🔌 🔳 → ∪ ╎18 🝙

GRAFHAM TL16

Old Manor Caravan Park
▶▶▶▶ 72%

Church Road PE28 0BB
☎ 01480 810264 📠 01480 819099
[E] camping@old-manor.co.uk
[W] www.old-manor.co.uk

Dir: Signed off A1, S of Huntingdon at Buckden and from A14, W of Huntingdon at Ellington

★ 🚐 £12.50-£15.50 🚌 £12.50-£15.50
⛺ £12.50-£15.50

Open all year (rs Nov-Feb on site shop closed) Booking Advisable wknds & peak times Last arrival 21.30hrs Last departure 18.00hrs

A secluded, well screened park in attractive gardens surrounding a 17th-century cottage. Pitches have lovely views of the countryside and Grafham Water is only a mile away. The enthusiastic owners continue to upgrade every area of the park. A 6.5-acre site with 84 touring pitches, 7 hardstandings and 8 static.

Leisure: 🏊 🛝
Facilities: 🚿 ⊙ ✱ 📞 🛒
Disabled facilities: toilet and wash basin in purpose built unit with ramp access
Services: [T] 🍴 ⛽ 🔒 → ⛳18 ✈ 🎣 ⛵
Notes: Dogs on leads

💳 VISA [S]

GREAT SHELFORD TL45

Camping & Caravanning Club Site
▶▶▶ 66%

19 Cabbage Moor CB2 5NB
☎ 01223 841185
[W] www.campingandcaravanningclub.co.uk

Dir: M11 J11 onto B1309 signposted Cambridge. At 1st set of lights turn R. After 0.5m follow site sign on L, pointing down lane

★ 🚐 £12.95-£16.35 🚌 £12.95-£16.35
⛺ £12.95-£16.35

Open Mar-Nov Booking Advisable bank hols & peak periods Last arrival 21.00hrs Last departure noon

A popular, open site close to Cambridge and the M11, surrounded by high hedging and trees, with well-maintained toilet facilities. The large rally field is well used. A 11-acre site with 120 touring pitches.

Leisure: 🛝
Facilities: 🚿 ⊙ ✱ 📞 🛒 🐕
Disabled facilities: toilet, shower, washbasin, razor point
Services: [T] ⛽ 🔒 → ⛳9 🎣 🛒

💳 VISA Barclays CONNECT [S]

The Willows Caravan Park
▶▶▶ 68%

Bromholme Lane Brampton PE28 4NE
☎ 01480 437566 📠 01480 437566
📧 willows@willows33.freeserve.co.uk

Dir: Leave A14/A1 signed Brampton, follow signs for Huntingdon. Site on R close to Brampton Mill pub

★ 🚐 £12-£14 🚐 £12-£14 ▲ £10-£12
Open all year (rs 31 Oct-1 Mar 10 pitches only plus 6 storage spaces) Booking Advisable all bank hols & school hols Last arrival 22.00hrs Last departure noon
A small, friendly site in a pleasant setting beside the River Ouse, on the Ouse Valley Walk. Bay areas have been provided for caravans and motorhomes, and planting for screening is maturing. There are launching facilities beside the site, and free river fishing. A 4-acre site with 50 touring pitches.
Free book lending

Leisure: 🅰
Facilities: 🕰 ⊙ ✳
Disabled facilities: toilet & washbasin
Services: 🖾 ⅋ 🖹 → ⅋18 ⅍ 🍽 ⅃ 🖳
Notes: Dogs must be on leads, ball games on field provided, no generators, one-way system 5mph, eco-friendly groundsheets, no cars by tents

Trevarth Holiday Park ▶▶▶ 68%
TR4 8HR
☎ 01872 560266 📠 01872 560379
📧 trevarth@lineone.net

Dir: Leave A30 at Chiverton rdbt onto unclass rd signed Blackwater. Site on R in 200mtrs

★ 🚐 £8-£11 🚐 £8-£11 ▲ £8-£11
Open Etr or Apr-Oct Booking Advisable Jul-Aug Last arrival 22.00hrs Last departure noon
A neat and compact park with touring pitches laid out on attractive, well-screened high ground adjacent to A30/A39 junction. This pleasant little park is centrally located for touring, and is maintained to a very good standard. A 4-acre site with 30 touring pitches, 2 hardstandings and 21 static.
Baby changing facilities

Leisure: 🔦 🅰
Facilities: 🕰 ⊙ 🖾 ✳ 🕰 🖳
Services: 🖾 🖾 ⓘ ⌀ 🖹 → ⅃ 🖳

BOLVENTOR SX17

Colliford Tavern Campsite
▶▶▶▶ 66%

Colliford Lake St Neot PL14 6PZ
☎ 01208 821335 📠 01208 821335
📧 info@colliford.com
🌐 www.colliford.com

Dir: Leave A30 1.25m W of Bolventor onto unclass rd signed Colliford Lake. Site 0.25m on L

🚐 🚙 🅰

Open Etr-Sep Booking Advisable bank hols & Jul-Aug Last arrival 22.30hrs Last departure 11.00hrs

An oasis on Bodmin Moor, a small site with spacious grassy pitches and very good quality facilities. The park is surrounded by mature trees and very sheltered in the centre of Bodmin Moor. Fly fishing is available at nearby Colliford Lake. A 3.5-acre site with 40 touring pitches.

Leisure: 🅰

Facilities: 🍳 ⊙ 🖤 ✳ 🕻 🏕

Disabled facilities: toilet & washbasin

Services: ✕ 🍴 🖁 ♀ 🖐 ∅ → 🍴

Notes: Dogs must be kept on leads

🔲 🔲 🔲 🔲 🔲 🔲

BOSWINGER SW94

Sea View International Caravan & Camping Park ▶▶▶▶▶ 78%

PL26 6LL
☎ 01726 843425 📠 01726 843358
📧 holidays@seaviewinternational.com
🌐 www.seaviewinternational.com

Dir: From St Austell take B3273 signed Mevagissey. Turn R before entering village and follow brown tourist signs to site

★ 🚐 £7-£25 🚙 £7-£25 🅰 £7-£25

Open all year (rs Oct-1 Apr shop & takeaway closed) Booking Advisable Jul-Sept Last arrival 21.00hrs Last departure 11.00hrs

This attractive holiday park is set in a beautiful environment overlooking Veryan Bay, with colourful landscaping including attractive flowers and shrubs. Many times a winner of AA awards for its beautiful environment and its dedication to high standards of maintenance under previous owners, it continues to offer an outstanding holiday experience. The beach and sea are just half a mile away. A 28-acre site with 189 touring pitches, 13 hardstandings and 38 static.

Crazy golf, volleyball, badminton, cycle hire

Leisure: 🏃 🔍 🏐 🅰

Facilities: 🍴 🍳 ⊙ 🖤 ✳ 🕻 🖁 🎣 🎿 🏕

Disabled facilities: toilets, baths & showers

Services: 🍺 🖁 🚽 🖁 🖐 ∅ → ⊚ ⌂ ↓ 🍴

Notes: No single sex groups, certain breeds of dog not permitted

🔲 🔲 🔲 🔲 🔲

Sandymouth Bay Holiday Park ⌂ 66%

Sandymouth Bay EX23 9HW
☎ 01288 352563 📄 01288 354822
📧 sandymouthbay@aol.com
🌐 www.sandymouthbay.co.uk

Dir: Signed off A39 approx 0.5m S of Kilkhampton, 4m N of Bude

★ ⛺ £7.50-£20 🚐 £7.50-£20 ⛺ £7.50-£20

Open Apr-Oct Booking Advisable Jul & Aug Last arrival 22.00hrs Last departure 10.00hrs
A friendly holiday park with glorious and extensive sea views. Many on-site facilities, and an extensive entertainment programme for all ages. A 4-acre site with 100 touring pitches, and 158 static.
Sauna, solarium, crazy golf

Leisure: 🏊 🎱 ⚲
Facilities: 🏪 ⊙ 🔲 ☀ 🚿 🛁 🏬
Disabled facilities: toilet & shower
Services: 🚽 ✖ 🍺 🚐 🔋 🎿 🧴 ∅ 🔲 → ∪ ⌂ 18 ⚓ ☕

💳 💳 💳 💳 💳

Wooda Farm Park ▶▶▶▶▶ 74%

Poughill EX23 9HJ
☎ 01288 352069 📄 01288 355258
📧 enquiries@wooda.co.uk
🌐 www.wooda.co.uk

Dir: 2m E. From A39 at edge of Stratton follow unclass Coombe Valley road

★ ⛺ £8.50-£13.50 🚐 £8.50-£13.50

⛺ £8.50-£13.50

Open Apr-Oct (rs Apr-end May & mid Sep-end Oct shop & restaurant hours limited) Booking Advisable Jul-Aug Last arrival 20.00hrs Last departure noon
Attractive park set on raised ground overlooking Bude Bay, with lovely sea views. The park is divided into paddocks by hedges and mature trees, and offers high quality facilities and a variety of activities. The sandy surfing beaches are a short drive away. A 12-acre site with 200 touring pitches, 60 hardstandings and 55 static.
Coarse fishing, clay pigeon shooting, pets corner

Leisure: 🎱 ⚲ 🎮
Facilities: ➡ 🏪 ⊙ 🔲 ☀ 🚿 🛁 🏓 🐾
Disabled facilities: toilets & showers
Services: 🚽 ✖ ➡ 🚐 🔋 🎿 🧴 ∅ 🔲 → ∪ ⌂ 18 ⚓ ☕ ☕
Notes: No single sex groups of 3 or more

💳 💳 💳 💳 💳

CORNWALL

BUDE SS20

Budemeadows Touring Holiday Park ►►►► 68%

EX23 0NA
☎ 01288 361646 📠 01288 361646
[E] wendyjo@globalnet.co.uk
[W] www.budemeadows.com

Dir: 3m S of Bude on A39. Park entered via layby

★ 🚐 £6.60-£15.40 🚙 £6.60-£15.40 ⛺ £6.60-£15.40

Open all year (rs Sep-Spring BH shop, bar & pool closed) Booking Advisable Jul-Aug Last arrival 21.00hrs Last departure 11.00hrs

A very well kept site of distinction, with good quality facilities. Budemeadows is set on a gentle sheltered slope in nine acres of naturally landscaped parkland, surrounded by mature hedges. Just one mile from Widemouth Bay, and three miles from the unspoilt resort of Bude. A 9-acre site with 144 touring pitches, 24 hardstandings.

Table tennis, giant chess, baby changing facility

Leisure: 🏊 🔍 ⛺ 📺
Facilities: 🛁 🚿 ⊙ 🧺 ✳ 📞 🛒 🍖 ⛩ 🐕
Disabled facilities: bathroom facilities
Services: 🏕 🚐 🍸 🗑 🍷 🧯 🌿 ⊞ → U ⛳18 ✈ 🎥 🎣 ◎ ⛵

💳 💳 💳 💳 [S]

BUDE SS20

Upper Lynstone Caravan Park ►►► 66%

Lynstone EX23 0LP
☎ 01288 352017 📠 01288 359034
[E] reception@upperlynstone.co.uk
[W] www.upperlynstone.co.uk

Dir: 0.75m S of Bude on coastal road to Widemouth Bay

★ 🚐 £7.50-£14 🚙 £7.50-£14 ⛺ £7.50-£14

Open Apr-Oct Last arrival 22.00hrs Last departure 10.00hrs

There are extensive views over Bude to be enjoyed from this quiet family-run park set on sheltered ground. There is a small shop selling camping spares, and a children's playground. A path leads directly to the coastal footpath with its stunning sea views, and the old Bude Canal is a stroll away. A 6-acre site with 65 touring pitches, and 41 static.

Baby changing room

Leisure: ⛺
Facilities: 🚿 ⊙ 🧺 ✳ 📞 🛒 ⛩
Disabled facilities: toilet and hand basin
Services: [T] 🚐 🗑 🧯 🌿 ⊞ → U ⛳18 ✈ 🎥 🎣 ◎

⛵ **Notes:** No groups

💳 💳 [S]

CAMELFORD   SX18

Juliot's Well Holiday Park
▶▶▶ 67%

PL32 9RF
☎ 01840 213302 📄 01840 212700
📧 juliotswell@travelsmith.co.uk
🌐 www.holidaysincornwall.net

Dir: Through Camelford, A39 at Valley Truckle
turn R onto B3266, then 1st L signed Lanteglos,
site 300yds on R

🏕 £5-£10 🚐 £5-£10 ⛺ £5-£10
Open all year (rs Nov-Feb Bar/restaurant not
open daily) Booking Advisable all year Last
arrival 20.00hrs Last departure 11.00hrs
*Set in the wooded grounds of an old manor
house, this quiet site enjoys lovely and
extensive views across the countryside. A
rustic inn on site offers occasional
entertainment, and there is plenty to do both
on and in the vicinity of the park. A 31-acre
site with 60 touring pitches.*
Putting green

Leisure: ⚡ ⚲ 🎣 𝄞
Facilities: ⬅🅿⊙🅀✳🎠🛁🛒🏧🍴🐾
Services: ✕🛒🚐🔲🔾 → ∪🅁18
Notes: Single sex groups by prior
arrangement only

▦▦ VISA

CARLYON BAY   SX05

Carlyon Bay Caravan & Camping
Park ▶▶▶▶ 75%

Bethesda Cypress Avenue PL25 3RE
☎ 01726 812735 📄 01726 815496
📧 holidays@carlyonbay.net
🌐 www.carlyonbay.net

Dir: Off A390 W of St Blazey, turn L on A3092
for Par, and R again in 0.5m. On private road to
Carlyon Bay

★ 🏕 £11-£20 🚐 £11-£20 ⛺ £9-£18
Open Etr-3 Oct (rs Etr-mid May & mid Sep-3
Oct swimming pool, take-away & shop closed)
Booking Advisable mid Jul-mid Aug Last
arrival 21.00hrs hrs Last departure 11.00hrs
*An attractive, secluded site set amongst a belt
of trees with background woodland. The
spacious grassy park offers plenty of on-site
attractions, with occasional family
entertainment, and it is less than 0.5m from a
sandy beach. The Eden Project is only 2m
away. A 35-acre site with 180 touring pitches,
6 hardstandings.*
Crazy golf, children's entertainment in Jul &
Aug

Leisure: ⚡ ⚲ 🎣 𝄞 🎱
Facilities: 🅿⊙🅀✳🛁🛒🐾
Services: 🔲🛒⬅🚐🔲🍴🗑🔾 → ∪🅁18⚓📺
🎵

▦▦ VISA ▦▦ ▦▦ 🆂

CORNWALL

CRANTOCK (NEAR NEWQUAY) SW76

Trevella Tourist Park ►►►► 69%

TR8 5EW
☎ 01637 830308 🖹 01637 830155
📧 trevellapark@aol.com
🌐 www.trevella.co.uk

Dir: Between Crantock and A3075

★ 🚐 £7.60-£13 🚐 £6.80-£12 ▲ £7.60-£13

Open Etr-Oct Booking Advisable BH's & Jul-Aug

A well established and very well run family site, with outstanding floral displays. Set in a rural area close to Newquay, this attractive park boasts three teeming fishing lakes for the experienced and novice angler, and a superb outdoor swimming pool and paddling section. All areas are neat and clean. A 15-acre site with 295 touring pitches, 53 hardstandings and 50 static.

Crazy golf, fishing & badminton

Leisure: 🎿 🎣 🎢 🎱

Facilities: 🌂 ⊙ 🎇 ✳ 🔥 🗻 📷 🐾

Disabled facilities: specially adapted 6-berth holiday home

Services: 🔟 ✕ 🧺 🕹 ⅏ 🔥 🖊 ⊘ 🖃 → ∪ ∩18 ♈ ♨ ♪ ◎ ⟁

▨ ▨ ▨ ▨ ▨ ▨ 🗾

CRANTOCK (NEAR NEWQUAY) SW76

Treago Farm Caravan Site ►►► 67%

TR8 5QS
☎ 01637 830277 🖹 01637 830277

Dir: From A3075 W of Newquay turn R for Crantock. Site signed beyond village

★ 🚐 £8-£12 🚐 £8-£12 ▲ £8-£12

Open mid May-mid Sep (rs Apr-mid May & Oct no shop or bar) Booking Advisable Jun-Aug Last arrival 22.00hrs Last departure 18.00hrs

A grass site in open farmland in a south-facing sheltered valley. This friendly family park has direct access to Crantock and Polly Joke beaches, National Trust Land and many natural beauty spots. A 5-acre site with 90 touring pitches, and 10 static.

Leisure: 🎣 🎱

Facilities: 🌂 ⊙ 🎇 ✳ 🔥 🗻 📷 🐾

Services: 🔟 🖊 🕹 🟦 🕹 ⊘ 🖃 → ∪ ∩18 ♈ ♪ ◎ ⟁

DAVIDSTOW   SX18

Inny Vale Holiday Village
▶▶▶ 67%

PL32 9XN
☎ 01840 261248 📄 01840 261740
🔵 jn.c@which.net
🔵 www.innyvale.com

Dir: Signed off A395 on single track road to Tremail, approx 1m from jct with A39

★ 🚐 £10.50-£17 🚐 £12.50-£17 ▲ £10.50-£13.25

Open Etr-Oct Booking Advisable Jul & Aug Last arrival 16.00hrs Last departure 10.00hrs
A sheltered park with a stream running through the level grounds. A smartly-refurbished toilet block and a new café have greatly improved the facilities, and the site is attached to a small holiday bungalow village. A 2-acre site with 27 touring pitches, 2 hardstandings.

Leisure: ⚘ ⚲ 🏊
Facilities: 🏪 ⊙ ⚙ ☀ ⚡ 🛁 🎦 🗮
Disabled facilities: toilet & shower
Services: ✗ 🚐 🗄 🛢 🚰 ⊞ → ∪ ⋔18 🎵
Notes: No single sex groups, no groups of under 21yrs

🔲 🔲 🔲 ⑤

FALMOUTH   SW83

Tregedna Farm Touring Caravan & Tent Park ▶▶ 69%

Maenporth TR11 5HL
☎ 01326 250529

Dir: Take A39 from Truro to Falmouth. Turn off R at Hill-Head rdbt. Campsite 2.5m on R

★ 🚐 £8-£8.50 🚐 £8-£8.50 ▲ £8-£8.50

Open Jun-Sep Last arrival 23.00hrs Last departure 13.00hrs
Set in the picturesque Maen Valley, this gently-sloping, south-facing park is part of a 100-acre farm. It is surrounded by beautiful wooded countryside just minutes from the beach, with spacious pitches and well-kept facilities. A 12-acre site with 40 touring pitches.

Leisure: 🏊
Facilities: 🏪 ⊙ ☀ ⚡ 🛁 🗮
Services: 🚐 🛢 🚰 → ⅋ 🎵 ⚴ 🗄 ◎
Notes: One dog only per pitch

FOWEY — SX15

Penhale Caravan & Camping Park
▶▶▶ 65%

PL23 1JU
☎ 01726 833425 📄 01726 833425
📧 info@penhale-fowey.co.uk
🕸 www.penhale-fowey.co.uk

Dir: Off A3082, 0.5m before jct with B3269

★ 🚐 £5.75-£10.50 🚐 £5.75-£10.50
🛖 £5.75-£10.50
Open Etr/Apr-Oct
Set on a working farm 1.5m from a sandy beach and the town of Fowey, this grassy park has stunning coastal and country views. Pitches are well spaced, and there is an indoor room for wet weather. A 4.5-acre site with 56 touring pitches, and 15 static.

Leisure: ♦
Facilities: 🌂 ⊙ 🖤 ❄ 🕻 🗜
Services: 🖴 🖽 🛢 🔌 → ∪ 🏊18 ⛵ 🜂 ⛆

GOONHAVERN — SW75

Penrose Farm Touring Park
▶▶▶▶ 70%

TR4 9QF
☎ 01872 573185 📄 01872 571972
🕸 www.penrosefarm.co.uk

Dir: From Exeter, take A30, past Bodmin and Indian Queens. After Wind Farm take B3285 towards Perranporth. Park on L on entering Goonhavern

🚐 🚐 🛖
Open Apr-Oct Booking Advisable Jul & Aug Last arrival 21.30hrs
A quiet sheltered park set in five paddocks divided by hedges and shrubs, only a short walk from the village. Lovely floral displays enhance the park's appearance, and the grass and hedges are neatly trimmed. Four en suite family rooms are very popular, and there is a good laundry. A 9-acre site with 100 touring pitches, 8 hardstandings.

Leisure: 🎢
Facilities: 🌂 ⊙ 🖤 ❄ 🕻 🗜 🖽 🎋 🕇
Disabled facilities: disabled toilet
Services: 🖳 🖴 🖽 🛢 🔌 🖹 → ∪ 🏊18 ⛵

GOONHAVERN   SW75

Silverbow Park ▶▶▶▶ 71%

Perranwell TR4 9NX
☎ 01872 572347 📄 01872 572347

Dir: Adjacent to A3075, 0.5m S of village

🏕 🚐 ⛺

Open mid May-mid Sep (rs mid Sep-Oct & Etr-
mid May swimming pool & shop closed)
Booking Advisable Jul-Aug Last arrival
22.00hrs Last departure noon
This park has a quiet garden atmosphere, and
appeals to families with young children. The
landscaped grounds and good quality toilet
facilities - including four en suite family rooms
- are maintained to a very high standard with
attention paid to detail. A 14-acre site with
100 touring pitches, 18 hardstandings and 15
static.
Badminton courts, short mat bowls rink

Leisure: ⚡ ⚲ ⚫ ⚁
Facilities: 🚿 📶 ⊙ 🗑 ✳ 🔒 🚻 📮 🐾
Disabled facilities: toilet, shower
& washbasin
Services: 🎛 🚐 🔲 📦 🗑 ⊠ → ∪ ⌐18 🎵
Notes: No unaccompanied teenagers

HAYLE   SW53

St Ives Bay Holiday Park 🏕 68%

73 Loggans Road Upton Towans TR27 5BH
☎ 01736 752274 📄 01736 754523
📧 stivesbay@btconnect.com
🌐 www.stivesbay.co.uk

Dir: Exit A30 at Hayle. Immediate R at mini-
rdbts. Park entrance 0.5m on L

🏕 🚐 ⛺

Open May-1 Oct (rs Etr-1 May & 25 Sep-25
Oct no entertainment, food & bar service)
Booking Advisable Jan-Mar Last arrival
23.00hrs Last departure 9.00hrs
An extremely well maintained holiday park
with a relaxed atmosphere, built on sand
dunes adjacent to a 3-mile-long beach. The
touring section forms a number of separate
locations in amongst the statics. The park is
specially geared for families and couples, and
as well as the large indoor swimming pool
there are two pubs with seasonal
entertainment. Dogs are not allowed. A 90-
acre site with 240 touring pitches, and 250
static.
Crazy golf, video room

Leisure: ⚡ ⚲ ⚫ ⚁ ▭
Facilities: 📶 ⊙ 🗑 ✳ 🔒 🚻
Disabled facilities: toilets
Services: 🎛 ✖ 🛒 🚐 🔲 🍽 📦 🗑 ⊠ → ∪ ⌐18 🎵
Notes: ✖

HAYLE — SW53

Treglisson Camping & Caravan Park ▶▶▶ 65%

Wheal Alfred Road TR27 5JT
☎ 01736 753141
🄴 enquiries@treglisson.co.uk
🄦 www.treglisson.co.uk

Dir: 4th exit off rdbt on A30 at Hayle. Continue 100mtrs and at 1st mini rdbt turn L. Follow road 1.5km past golf course and Treglisson sign visible on L

★ �caravan £8-£12 �caravan £8-£12 ▲ £8-£12

Open Etr-Oct Booking Advisable Jul-Aug Last arrival 20.00hrs Last departure 11.00hrs
A small secluded site in a peaceful wooded meadow, a former apple and pear orchard. This quiet rural site has a well-planned modern toilet block and level grass pitches, and is just 2 miles from the glorious beach at Hayle with its vast stretch of golden sand. A 3-acre site with 30 touring pitches.
Tourist information available. Milkman delivers

Leisure: ⚄ 𝕸
Facilities: 🛈⊙🛇❄🛇🖾🗟🛪
Disabled facilities: toilet & wash room
Services: 🚐🖻🖫→🇵12 🌙▲🛱
Notes: Max 6 people to a pitch, dogs must be on lead at all times

HELSTON — SW62

Lower Polladras Touring Park ▶▶▶ 67%

Carleen Breage TR13 9NX
☎ 01736 762220 🖷 01736 762220
🄴 polladras@hotmail.com
🄦 www.lower-polladras.co.uk

Dir: From Helston take A394 turn onto B3302 Hayle road at Hilltop Garage, take 2nd turning on L to Carleen, site 2m on R

★ 🚐 £8.50-£12.50 🚐 £8.50-£12.50
▲ £6.50-£10.50

Open Apr-Oct Booking Advisable Jul-Aug Last arrival 22.00hrs Last departure noon
A rural park with extensive views over the fields, appealing to families who enjoy the countryside. Newly-planted trees and shrubs are maturing, and help to divide the area into paddocks with spacious grassy pitches. A 4-acre site with 60 touring pitches.
Caravan and boat storage area

Leisure: 𝕸
Facilities: 🛈⊙🛇❄🖾🗟🛪🖫
Services: 🛈🚐〰🖻🛈🖉🖫→∪🇵18 ⚠◎
🛪🍴🌙

Trelowarren Caravan & Camping Park ▶▶▶ 65%

Mawgan TR12 6AF
☎ 01326 221637 📄 01326 221427
🌐 www.trelowarren.co.uk

Dir: From Helston on A3083 turn L past Culdrose Naval Air Station onto B3293. Site signed on L in 1.5m

🚐 🚐 ⚠

Open Apr-Sep Booking Advisable bank hols & Jul-Aughrs Last departure noon
A very attractive setting in the extensive park of Trelowarren House. The superb location is over a mile from the nearest road, and visitors can explore the gardens and follow several woodland walks. A bar and bistro are popular attractions. A 20-acre site with 225 touring pitches, 14 hardstandings.

Leisure: 🔍 🎢
Facilities: 🚿 🖍 ⊙ 🔯 ✳ 🗞 🗊 🥢
Disabled facilities: toilet & shower
Services: 🔢 ✕ 📠 🚐 🔌 🗊 🍽 🍴 🗊 → ∪ ⌂18
🏪

Holywell Bay Holiday Park 🏚 66%

TR8 5PR
☎ 01637 871111 📄 01637 850818
📧 enquiries@parkdean.com
🌐 www.parkdean.com

Dir: Leave A30 onto A392, take A3075 signed Redruth, then L in 2m signed Holywell/Cubert. Follow road through Cubert past Trevornick to park on L

★ 🚐 £9-£26 🚐 £9-£26 ⚠ £7-£23

Open Mar-Oct Booking Advisable Jun-Aug Last arrival 21.00hrs Last departure 10.00hrs
Close to lovely local beaches in a rural location, this level grassy park borders on National Trust land, and is only a short distance from the Cornish Coastal Path. The park provides a popular entertainment programme for the whole family. A 40-acre site with 68 touring pitches, and 144 static.

Leisure: 🎿 🎢
Facilities: 🖍 ⊙ 🔌 🗞 🗊 🗊
Disabled facilities: adapted caravan, disabled toilet
Services: 🔢 📠 🚐 🔌 🗊 🍴 🗊 → ∪ ⌂18 🎵 ◎ ♨
Notes: 🐾 No single sex groups under 25yrs

CORNWALL

HOLYWELL BAY SW75

Trevornick Holiday Park 73%

TR8 5PW
☎ 01637 830531 📠 01637 831 000
[E] info@trevornick.co.uk
[W] www.trevornick.co.uk

Dir: 3m from Newquay off A3075 Newquay to Redruth road. Follow signs to Cubert & Holywell Bay

★ 🚐 £9.60-£16 🚌 £8.60-£15 ⛺ £9.60-£16

Open Etr & mid May-mid Sep Booking Advisable Jul-Aug Last arrival 21.00hrs Last departure 10.00hrs

A large seaside holiday complex with excellent facilities and amenities. There is plenty of entertainment including a children's club and an evening cabaret, adding up to a full holiday experience for all the family. A sandy beach is a 15-minute footpath walk away. The park has 68 ready-erected tents for hire. A 20-acre site with 450 touring pitches, 6 hardstandings.

Fishing, golf course, entertainment

Leisure: 🧒 🎱 🛝
Facilities: 🛁 🚿 ⊙ 🧺 ✳ 📞 🛒 🪑 🐕
Disabled facilities: special bathroom
Services: [T] 🍴 🍟 🚐 🗑 🍸 🧯 🥫 [E] → 🐎 ⛳18 ✈ 🎣 ◎ ⛵
Notes: Families and couples only

American Express · Mastercard · Visa · Barclays Connect · Switch

KILKHAMPTON SS21

Penstowe Caravan & Camping Park ▶▶▶▶ 74%

Penstowe Manor EX23 9QY
☎ 01288 321354 📠 01288 321273
[E] info@penstoweleisure.co.uk
[W] www.penstoweleisure.co.uk

Dir: A39 4m N of Bude, turn L to Sandymouth site, 200yds on R

★ 🚐 £10-£16 🚌 £10-£16 ⛺ £8-£14

Open Apr-Oct Booking Advisable Aug Last arrival 22.00hrs Last departure 10.00hrs

An all-touring park with quality facilities located about 2 miles from Sandymouth Bay with its beaches and surf. The mixture of grass and hardstanding are all level. Visitors can take advantage of the adjoining Penstowe Leisure Club, accessed via a private road on the estate. Some of the amenities require a small membership charge. A 6-acre site with 80 touring pitches, 25 hardstandings.

Sports facilities, tenpin bowling, green bowls

Leisure: 🏊 🧒 🎾 🎱 🛝
Facilities: 🚿 ⊙ 🧺 ✳ 📞 🛒 🪑 🐕
Disabled facilities: toilet
Services: 🍴 🍟 🚐 ⚡ 🗑 🍸 🧯 🥫 → 🐎 ⛳18 🎣

American Express · Visa · Barclays Connect · Delta · Switch

CORNWALL

KILKHAMPTON SS21

Tamar Lake ▶▶ 64%

Upper Tamar Lake
☎ 01288 321712
[W] www.swlakestrust.org.uk

Dir: From A39 at Kilkhampton turn onto B3254, turn L in 0.5m onto unclass road and follow signs for approx 4m to site

★ fr £10 fr £10 ▲ fr £10

Open 31 Mar-Oct

A well-trimmed, slightly sloping site overlooking the lake and countryside, with several signed walks. The site benefits from the excellent facilities provided for the watersports centre and coarse anglers, with a rescue launch on the lake when the flags are flying. A good family site, with Bude's beaches and surfing waves only 8m away. A 2-acre site with 36 touring pitches.

Watersports centre, canoeing, sailing & windsurfing

Leisure:

Facilities:

Disabled facilities: toilet & access to teashop

Services: →

Notes: Dogs must be kept on a lead

LANIVET SX06

Mena Caravan & Camping Site ▶▶ 70%

Mena Farm PL30 5HW
☎ 01208 831845
[E] mena@campsitesincornwall.co.uk
[W] www.campsitesincornwall.co.uk

Dir: Turn off A30 Innes Downs rdbt onto A391, signed St Austell. After 0.5m 1st L, then after 0.75m turn R (before bridge) signed Fowey/Lanhydrock. 0.5m to staggered jct and monument stone, turn sharp R, 0.5m downhill turn R into site.

★ £7.50-£10 £7.50-£10 ▲ £7.50-£10

Open May-Sept Booking Advisable mid Jul-Aug Last arrival 10.00hrs Last departure noon

Set in a secluded, elevated location with high hedges for shelter, and plenty of peace. This grassy site is about 4 miles from the Eden Project, and midway between N and S coasts. On site is a small coarse fishing lake. A 4-acre site with 25 touring pitches, and 2 static.

Leisure:

Facilities:

Disabled facilities: shower/wc/washbasin

Services: → 18

LEEDSTOWN (NEAR HAYLE) SW63

Calloose Caravan & Camping Park
▶▶▶ 71%

TR27 5ET
☎ 01736 850431 📄 01736 850431
📧 calloose@hotmail.com
🌐 www.calloose.co.uk

Dir: From Hayle take B3302 to Leedstown, turn L opp village hall, before entering village, park 0.5m on L at bottom of hill

🚐 🚐 ▲

Open Mar-Nov, Xmas & New Year (rs Mar-mid May & late Sep-Nov swimming pool closed) Booking Advisable Etr, May bank hols & Jun-Aug Last arrival 22.00hrs Last departure 11.00hrs
A comprehensively equipped leisure park in a remote rural setting in a small river valley. This very good park is busy and bustling, and offers bright and clean facilities. A 12.50-acre site with 120 touring pitches, and 17 static.
Crazy golf, skittle alley

Leisure: 🎿 🏊 🎱 ⚲ 🏛 ▢
Facilities: 🏠 ⊙ 🖉 🖾 ☀ 📞 🛒 🏧 🐕 🗙
Disabled facilities: toilets & access ramps to lounge bar
Services: 🆔 🗙 🛒 🚐 🗄 🛢 🖉 🗄 → 🔧
Notes: No single sex groups

▨ ▨ ▨ ▧ 5

LOOE SX25

Tencreek Holiday Park ⌂66%

Polperro Road PL13 2JR
☎ 01503 262447 📄 01503 262760
📧 reception@tencreek.co.uk
🌐 www.dolphinholidays.co.uk

Dir: Take A387 1.25m from Looe. Site on left

★ 🚐 £8.50-£16.50 🚐 £8.50-£16.50
▲ £8.50-£16.50

Open all year Booking Advisable Jul & Aug Last arrival 23.00hrs Last departure 10.00hrs
Occupying a lovely position with extensive countryside and sea views, this holiday centre is in a rural spot but close to Looe and Polperro. There is a full family entertainment programme, with indoor and outdoor swimming pools and an adventure playground, and an exciting children's club. A 14-acre site with 254 touring pitches, and 101 static.
Nightly entertainment, solarium, 45mtr pool flume

Leisure: 🏊 🎿 🎱 ⚲
Facilities: 🏠 ⊙ 🖉 ☀ 📞 🛒 🐕
Disabled facilities: toilet & ramp to shop
Services: 🆔 🗙 🛒 🚐 🗄 🛢 🖉 🗄 → 🔧 ⌂18 ✦ 🍴 🔧 △
Notes: Families & couples only

▨ ▨ ▨ ▧ 5

Polborder House Caravan & Camping Park ►►► 69%

Bucklawren Road St Martins PL13 1QR
☎ 01503 240265
📧 rlf.polborder@virgin.net
🌐 www.peaceful-polborder.co.uk

Dir: On approaching Looe from E on A387, follow B3253 for 1m, then bear L at signpost to Polborder & Monkey Sanctuary. Site 0.5m on R

★ 🚐 £8.20-£11.50 🚙 £8.20-£11.50

🛖 £8.20-£11.50

Open Etr or Apr-Oct Booking Advisable Jul-Aug Last arrival 22.00hrs Last departure noon
A very neat and well-kept small grassy site on high ground above Looe in a peaceful rural setting. Friendly and enthusiastic owners. A 3-acre site with 31 touring pitches, 13 hardstandings.
Washing/food prep sinks, off-licence, Info Centre

Leisure: ⚴
Facilities: ♠⊙♥✲ᴄ🛒🎋
Disabled facilities: toilet, sink & shower
Services: 🔲 ➡ 🚐 🗟 ⅄ ∅ 🞢 → ⅌18 ⅄ ➴ ⬙
Notes: No trade vehicles, no single sex groups

▨ ▨ ▨ 𝒮

Talland Caravan Park ►►► 67%

Talland Bay PL13 2JA
☎ 01503 272715 📠 01503 272224
📧 tallandcaravan@btconnect.com
🌐 www.tallandcaravanpark.co.uk

Dir: 1m from A387 on unclass road to Talland Bay

★ 🚐 £9-£16 🚙 £7.50-£14 🛖 £7-£16

Open Apr-Oct Booking Advisable School hols Last arrival 20.00hrs Last departure noon
Overlooking the sea just 300 yards from Talland Bay's two beaches, this quiet park has an elevated touring area with sea views. Surrounded by unspoilt countryside and with direct access to the coastal footpath, it is approximately halfway between Looe and Polperro. A 4-acre site with 80 touring pitches, and 46 static.

Leisure: ⚴ ⚴
Facilities: ♠⊙♥✲ᴄ🛒🎋🎋
Disabled facilities: separate shower and handbasin
Services: 🔲 ✕ ♨ 🚐 🗟 ⅄ ⅄ ∅ 🞢 → ⅌18 ⅄ ➴ ⬙
Notes: Single sex groups only by prior arrangement

▨ ▨ ▨ 𝒮

LOSTWITHIEL SX15

Powderham Castle Tourist Park
▶▶▶ 65%

PL30 5BU

☎ 01208 872277

🅴 powderhamcastletp@tiscali.co.uk

🆆 www.powderhamcastletouristpark.co.uk

Dir: 1.5m SW of Lostwithiel on A390 turn R at brown/white signpost in 400mtrs

★ 🚐 £7.50-£14 🚑 £7.50-£14 ▲ £7.50-£14

Open Etr or Apr-Oct Booking Advisable peak periods Last arrival 22.00hrs Last departure 11.30hrs

A very quiet and well-run site in a good touring location, set in mature parkland and well screened. A 12-acre site with 75 touring pitches, 7 hardstandings and 38 static.
Badminton & soft tennis, putting green

Leisure: ◆ ⚲ ▱

Facilities: �🜨 ⊙ ⦵ ✱ ⚲ ☰

Services: 🞔 🗑 🛢 🖉 🗄 → ∪ ⬚18 ↘ ⤵ ◎ ◬ ⚱

Notes: No unaccompanied groups of young adults

LUXULYAN SX05

Croft Farm Holiday Park
▶▶▶ 70%

PL30 5EQ

☎ 01726 850228 📠 01726 850498

🅴 lynpick@ukonline.co.uk

🆆 www.croftfarm.co.uk

Dir: Leave A30 at Bodmin for A391 towards St Austell. In 7m L at double rdbt onto unclass road towards Luxulyan/Eden Project, continue to T-jct, turn L signed Luxulyan. Croft Farm 1m on L. Do not approach any other way as roads are very narrow

★ 🚐 £9.20-£13.20 🚑 £9.20-£13.20

▲ £3.20-£13.20

Open 21 Mar-21 Jan Booking Advisable Jul & Aug Last arrival 18.00hrs Last departure noon

A peaceful, picturesque setting at the edge of a wooded valley, and only 1 mile from 'The Eden Project', Cornwall's biomodes. A 5-acre site with 52 touring pitches, 10 hardstandings and 35 static.
Mother & baby room, washing up area, info centre

Leisure: ◆ ⚲

Facilities: ➔ 🜨 ⊙ ⦵ ✱ ⚲ ⚱ ☰ ☰

Services: 🅣 🞔 🗑 🛢 🖉 🗄 → ∪ ⤵

MARAZION SW53

Wheal Rodney ▶▶▶ 66%

Gwallon Lane TR17 0HL
☎ 01736 710605
🅔 reception@whealrodney.co.uk
🆆 www.whealrodney.co.uk

Dir: Turn off A30 at Crowlas, signed Rospeath. Site 1.5m on R. From Marazion centre turn opposite Fire Engine Inn, site 500mtrs on L.

★ 🚐 £9-£15 🚎 £9-£15 ▲ £9-£13

Open all year Booking Advisable Xmas & Etr-Oct Last arrival 21.00hrs Last departure 11.00hrs

Set in a quiet rural location surrounded by farmland, with level grass pitches and well-kept facilities. Just half a mile away are the beach at Marazion and the causeway or ferry to St Michael's Mount. A cycle route is just 400 yds away. A 2.5-acre site with 30 touring pitches.

Sauna room

Leisure: ⚒
Facilities: ♙⊙🔍❄🔌
Services: 🔌🔋🔀➔ ∪⊓18 🗲⊙⚤⚓🗲
Notes: No groups under 25yrs

▨ ▨ ▨ 🗐

MAWGAN PORTH SW86

Sun Haven Valley Holiday Park
▶▶▶▶ 67%

TR8 4BQ
☎ 01637 860373 📠 01637 860373
🅔 traceyhealey@hotmail.com
🆆 www.sunhavenvalley.co.uk

Dir: From B3276 in Newquay take Padstow road, turn R onto unclass rd just after petrol station complex & park in 1.75m

★ 🚐 £9-£15 🚎 £9-£15 ▲ £9-£15

Open Apr-Oct (rs Oct-Mar Chalets only) Booking Advisable Jul-Aug Last arrival 22.00hrs Last departure 11.00hrs

An attractive site with level pitches on the side of a river valley. The very high quality facilities include a TV lounge and a games room in a Swedish-style chalet, and a well-kept adventure playground. Trees and hedges fringe the park, and the ground is well drained. A 5-acre site with 118 touring pitches, 36 static.

Leisure: ⚒ 🅰 ⛶
Facilities: ➡♙⊙🔍❄🔌⚓🏕
Disabled facilities: toilet & washing facilities
Services: 🔲🔌🔋🗲⚖➔ ∪⊓18 🗲⊙
Notes: Families and couples only

▨ ▨ ▨ 🗐

MAWGAN PORTH SW86

Trevarrian Holiday Park ▶▶▶ 62%

TR8 4AQ
☎ 01637 860381

Dir: From A39 at St Columb rdbt turn R onto A3059 towards Newquay. Fork R in approx 2m for St Mawgan onto B3276. Turn R and site on L

🚐 🚌 ⛺

Open Etr-Sep Booking Advisable Jun-Aug Last arrival 22.00hrs Last departure 11.00hrs

A well-established and well-run holiday park overlooking Mawgan Porth beach. This park has a wide range of attractions including a free entertainment programme in peak season. A 7-acre site with 185 touring pitches.

Sports field & pitch 'n' putt

Leisure: 🏊 🎾 ● ⛹ 📺

Facilities: 🛁 🚿 ⊙ 🧺 ✳ 📞 🏪

Services: [T] 🍴 🚐 🗑 🍷 🔒 🍃 ⊞ → U ⛳18 ✈ 👥 🎣 ◎

💳 💳

MULLION SW61

Mullion Holiday Park 🏖 67%

Ruan Minor TR12 7LJ
☎ 01326 240428 📠 01326 241141
[E] bookings@weststarholidays.co.uk
[W] www.weststarholidays.co.uk

Dir: From A30 take A39 from Fraddon to Truro and continue on the Falmouth road. Take A394 to Helston then take A3083 for the Lizard. Park is on L after 7m, opposite Mullion turning.

★ 🚐 £12.50-£28.50 🚌 £12.50-£28.50
⛺ £12.50-£28.50

Open 22 May-11 Sept Booking Advisable Jul-Aug & bank holidays Last arrival 22.00hrs Last departure 10.00hrs

A comprehensively-equipped leisure park geared mainly for self-catering holidays, set in rugged moorland on the Lizard peninsula. There is plenty of on-site entertainment for all ages, with indoor and outdoor pools. A 49-acre site with 150 touring pitches, 8 hardstandings and 347 static.

Adventure playground, scuba diving, football pitch

Leisure: 🏊 🏊 ● ⛹ 📺

Facilities: 🚿 ⊙ 🧺 ✳ 📞 🏪 🚼 ⛩ 🐕

Disabled facilities: toilets & ramps

Services: 🍴 🍟 🚐 🗑 🍷 🔒 🍃 → U ⛳9 🎣 ◎ ⛵

Notes: No unaccompanied persons under 21yrs or single sex groups

💳 💳 💳 💳 💳

Hendra Holiday Park 69%

TR8 4NY
☎ 01637 875778 📠 01637 879017
📧 hendra-uk@dial-pipex.com
🌐 www.hendra-holidays.com

Dir: Leave A30 onto A392 signed Newquay. At Quintrell Downs over rdbt, signed Lane, 0.5m on L

★ 🚐 £8.45-£14 🚎 £8.45-£14 ▲ £8.45-£14

Open Feb-Oct (rs Apr-Spring bank hol)
Booking Advisable Jul-Aug Last arrival dusk Last departure noon

A large complex with superb facilities including an indoor fun pool and an outdoor pool. There is a children's club for the over 6s, and evening entertainment during high season. The touring pitches are set amongst mature trees and shrubs, and some have fully-serviced facilities. All amenities are open to the public. A 46-acre site with 600 touring pitches, and 188 static.

Solarium, fish bar, sauna, kids' club, train rides

Leisure: 🏊 🏊 ⚓ 🎱 ♟

Facilities: 🅿 ☉ ⚒ ❄ 🔥 🖳 🛒 🎍 🐕 🕆

Disabled facilities: toilets & showers

Services: ℡ ✕ 🚽 🍺 🚚 🚐 🅱 🍴 🖊 🔌 → ∪ ∩ 18

🕆 🎪 ⚓ ◎ △

Notes: Families and couples only

[payment card logos]

Newquay Holiday Park 66%

TR8 4HS
☎ 01637 871111 📠 01637 850818
📧 enquiries@parkdean.com
🌐 www.parkdean.com

Dir: From Bodmin on A30 pass under low bridge and turn R towards RAF St Mawgan. Take A3059 towards Newquay, and site past Treloy Golf Club

🚐 £9-£26 🚎 £7-£26 ▲ £7-£23

Open Mar-Oct Booking Advisable Jun-Aug Last arrival 21.00hrs Last departure 10.00hrs

A well-maintained park with a wide range of indoor and outdoor activities. A children's playground and café/take-away have enhanced the facilities, and the club and bars have been extended, offering quality entertainment. A 60-acre site with 300 touring pitches, 10 hardstandings and 164 static.

Snooker, pool table, 9-hole pitch & putt, crazy golf

Leisure: 🏊 ⚓ 🎱 ♟

Facilities: 🅿 ☉ 🍳 ❄ 🔥 🖳 🛒 🎍

Services: ℡ ✕ 🚽 🍺 🚐 🅱 🍴 🖊 🔌 🅱 → ∪ ∩ 18 🕆

🍴

Notes: ✗ No single sex groups under 25yrs

[payment card logos]

Trencreek Holiday Park
►►►► 70%

Hillcrest Higher Trencreek TR8 4NS
☎ 01637 874210 📄 01637 874210
🅴 enquiries@trencreekholidaypark.co.uk
🅦 www.trencreekholidaypark.co.uk

Dir: A392 to Quintrell Downs, turn R towards of Newquay, turn L at 2 mini rdbts into Trevenson Road to park

🚐 £9.50-£13.50 🚙 £9.50-£13.50 ▲ £9.50-£13.50

Open Whit-mid Sep (rs Etr, Apr-May & late Sep swimming pool, cafe & bar closed) Booking Advisable Jul-Aug Last arrival 22.00hrs Last departure noon
An attractively landscaped park in the village of Trencreek, with modern re-styled and upgraded toilet facilities of a very high standard. Two well-stocked fishing lakes, and evening entertainment in the licensed clubhouse, are extra draws. Located about 2 miles from Newquay with its beaches and surfing. A 10-acre site with 194 touring pitches, 8 hardstandings and 6 static.
Coarse fishing on site

Leisure: ⚡ ◆ ⚄ ⏢
Facilities: ⚲ ⊙ ✳ ☾ ⅏ 淼 戸
Disabled facilities: toilets
Services: ⊡ ✕ ♨ 🔟 ⊡ ♀ 📧 ⌀ ⊞ → ∪ ⌂18 ⅄ ⅃ 🔟 ◎ △ ⅏
Notes: ✖

Porth Beach Tourist Park
►►► 73%

Porth TR7 3NH
☎ 01637 876531 📄 01637 871227
🅴 info@porthbeach.co.uk
🅦 www.porthbeach.co.uk

Dir: 1m NE off B3276 towards Padstow

★ 🚐 £11-£23.60 🚙 £10-£20.60
▲ £9-£16.60

Open Mar-Nov Booking Advisable Jul-Aug Last arrival 18.00hrs Last departure 10.00hrs
This attractive, popular park offers level, grassy pitches in neat and tidy surroundings. A well-run site set in meadowland and adjacent to sea and a fine sandy beach. A 6-acre site with 201 touring pitches, and 19 hardstandings.

Leisure: ⚄
Facilities: ⚲ ⊙ ☾ ⅏
Disabled facilities: toilet and washing facilities
Services: ♨ ⅊ ⊡ 🔟 ⌀ ⊞ → ∪ ⌂18 ⅄ ⅃ ◎
△ Notes: Families and couples only

Treloy Tourist Park ►►► 70%

TR8 4JN
☎ 01637 872063 📠 01637 872063
📧 holidays@treloy.co.uk
🌐 www.treloy.co.uk

Dir: Off A3059, St Columb Major to
Newquay road

★ 🛒 £8-£13 🚐 £8-£13 ▲ £8-£13

Open Apr-Sep (rs Apr & Sep swimming pool &
bar closed) Booking Advisable Jul-Aug Last
arrival 23.00hrs Last departure 10.00hrs
*Attractive site with fine countryside views,
within easy reach of resorts and beaches. The
pitches are set in four paddocks with mainly
level but some slightly sloping grassy areas.
Maintenance and cleanliness are very high. A
12-acre site with 119 touring pitches, 24
hardstandings.*
Concessionary green fees for golf,
entertainment

Leisure: 🎣 ♠ ⚲ ▢
Facilities: ℝ ⊙ ℚ ✳ ⅊ ⅃ ⅌ 🐾
Disabled facilities: shower/toilet/washbasin
Services: ▯ ✗ 🍺 🛒 🔋 ♨ 🍴 ▢ → ∪ ⅂18 ⅃
♪ Notes: No single sex groups

▬ ▬ ▬ 𝒮

Trethiggey Touring Park ►►►
67%

Quintrell Downs TR8 4QR
☎ 01637 877672 📠 01637 879706
📧 enquiries@trethiggey.co.uk
🌐 www.trethiggey.co.uk

Dir: From A30 take A392 signed Newquay at
Quintrell Downs rdbt, turn L onto A3058 past
pearl centre to site 0.5m on L

🛒 🚐 ▲

Open Mar-Dec Booking Advisable Jul-Aug
*A family-owned park in a rural setting that is
ideal for touring this part of Cornwall.
Pleasantly divided into paddocks with
maturing trees and shrubs, and offering
coarse fishing and tackle hire. A 15-acre site
with 145 touring pitches, 35 hardstandings
and 12 static.*
Off licence, dishwashing sink, recreation field

Leisure: ♠ ⚲ ▢
Facilities: ℝ ⊙ ℚ ✳ ⅊ 🐾 🎿 🏓 🐾
Disabled facilities: toilet & shower
Services: ▯ 🍺 🛒 🔋 ♨ 🍴 ▢ → ∪ ⅂18 ⅃ ♪ ◎
▲ ▬ ▬ ▬ ▬ 𝒮

NOTTER BRIDGE — SX36

Notter Bridge Caravan & Camping Park ▶▶▶ 74%

PL12 4RW
☎ 01752 842318
e holidays@notterbridge.co.uk
w www.notterbridge.co.uk

Dir: On A38, 3.5m W of Tamar Bridge (do not enter Saltash)

★ ⛟ £7-£10 ⛺ £7-£10 ▲ £7-£8

Open Etr-Sep Booking Advisable Jul-Aug Last arrival 21.30hrs Last departure 11.00hrs
A sheltered valley park surrounded by woodland, and flanked on one side by the River Lynher. The friendly owners maintain the facilities to a high standard, and there are plenty of hard pitches with electric and TV hook-up. A good base for visiting nearby beaches, with a country pub close by. A 6.25-acre site with 30 touring pitches, 24 hardstandings and 24 static.
Games field, river frontage & fishing

Leisure: ⚲
Facilities: ⬤ ⊙ ✱
Disabled facilities: unisex shower/wc/washbasin, level site
Services: ⬤ ⊞ → Ɽ18 ♪ ⬤ ⛟ ⬳
Notes: Groups & commercial vehicles only by prior arrangement

OTTERHAM — SX19

St Tinney Farm Holidays ▶▶▶ 64%

PL32 9TA
☎ 01840 261274 📠 01840 261575
e info@st-tinney.co.uk
w www.st-tinney.co.uk

Dir: Signposted 1m off A39 via unclass road signed Otterham

★ ⛟ £6-£9.90 ⛺ £6-£9.90 ▲ £6-£9.90

Open Etr-Oct (rs Nov-Etr self catering lodges/static. caravan only) Booking Advisable Spring BH & Jul-Aug Last arrival 21.00hrs Last departure 11.00hrs
A family-run farm site in a rural area, with nature trails, lakes, valleys and complete seclusion. Visitors are free to walk around the farmland lakes and lose themselves in the countryside. A 34-acre site with 20 touring pitches.
Coarse fishing, horse/donkey rides, pony trekking

Leisure: ⚲ ⚲
Facilities: ⬤ ⊙ ⬤ ✱ ⬤ ⬤ ⊞ ⛟
Services: ✖ ⬤ ⬤ ⊞ ⬤ ⬤ ⊞ → ∪ ⛟ ♪

Pentewan Sands Holiday Park
71%

PL26 6BT
☎ 01726 843485 📠 01726 844142
📧 info@pentewan.co.uk
🌐 www.pentewan.co.uk

Dir: On B3273 4m S of St Austell

★ ⊕ £9.95-£24.15 ⊕ £9.95-£24.15
▲ £9.95-£24.15
Open Apr-Oct (rs Apr-14 May & 15 Sep-Oct
shop, pool, clubhouse closed, boats launching)
Booking Advisable Jul-Aug Last arrival
22.00hrs Last departure 10.30hrs
*A large holiday park with a wide range of
amenities, set on the dunes adjacent to a
private beach where plenty of aquatic
activities are available. A short stroll leads to
the pretty village of Pentewan, and other
attractions are a short drive away. A club on
site offers evening entertainment. A 32-acre
site with 500 touring pitches, 120 static.
Cycles, boat launch, water sports, caravan
store*

Leisure: ⎔ ◦ ◦ ⚲ ⋔
Facilities: ↦ ⋒ ⊙ ⊕ ⌑ ⌗
Disabled facilities: toilet & shower, ramps
Services: 🚇 ✕ 🛒 🔌 ⌂ ☐ ⌘ 🔧 ⊘ ☐ → ∪ ⌂18
⌇ 🔧 ◎ △
Notes: ✈ No single-sex groups, no jet skis
▬ ▬ ▨ ▧ 🄢

Sun Valley Holiday Park
▶▶▶▶▶ **75%**

Pentewan Road PL26 6DJ
☎ 01726 843266 📠 01726 843266
📧 reception@sunvalleyholidays.co.uk
🌐 www.sunvalleyholidays.co.uk

Dir: From St Austell take B3273 towards
Mevagissey. Park is 2m on R

★ ⊕ £12-£26 ⊕ £12-£26 ▲ £12-£26
Open Apr (or Etr if earlier)-Oct Booking
Advisable May-Sep Last arrival 22.00hrs Last
departure noon
*In a picturesque valley amongst woodland,
this neat park is kept to an exceptionally high
standard. The extensive amenities include
tennis courts, indoor swimming pool, licensed
clubhouse and restaurant. The sea is 1m
away, and can be accessed via a footpath and
cycle path along the river bank. A 4-acre site
with 22 touring pitches, and 75 static.*

Leisure: ⎔ ◦ ⚲ ⋔
Facilities: ⋒ ⊙ ⊕ ⌑ ⌂ 🔌 ⌗ 🐾
Services: ✕ 🛒 🔌 ⌂ ☐ ⌘ 🔧 ⊘ ☐ → ∪ ⌂18 ♣
⌇
Notes: No single sex groups
▬ ▬ ▧ 🄢

PENTEWAN — SX04

Heligan Woods ▶▶▶ 66%

PL26 6BT
☎ 01726 842714 📄 01726 844142
🄴 info@pentewan.co.uk
🅦 www.pentewan.co.uk

Dir: From A390 take B3273 for Mevagissey at x-roads signed 'No caravans beyond this point'. R onto unclass road towards Gorran, site 0.75m on L

★ 🚐 £9.35-£21.45 🚍 £9.35-£21.45

🅰 £9.35-£21.45

Open Apr-1 Nov Booking Advisable late July & Aug

A pleasant peaceful park adjacent to the Lost Gardens of Heligan, with views over St Austell Bay, and well-maintained facilities. Guests can also use the extensive amenities at the sister park, Pentewan Sands. A 12-acre site with 89 touring pitches, 30 static.

Leisure: 🄰
Facilities: 🄽 ⊙ ⚒ 🦺 🐾
Services: 🚰 ⚡ 🖾 🅿 ⊞ → ∪ ❙ 18 ✕ ♨ ⏚
Notes: No single sex groups

▬ ▬ ▦ ▨ 🆂

PENTEWAN — SX04

Penhaven Touring Park ▶▶▶ 62%

PL26 6DL
☎ 01726 843687 📄 01726 843870
🄴 enquiries@penhaventouring.co.uk
🅦 www.penhaventouring.co.uk

Dir: S from St Austell on B3273 towards Mevagissey. Site on L,1m after village of London Apprentice

🚐 🚍 🅰

Open Apr-Oct Booking Advisable public hols & end Jul-Aug Last arrival 21.00hrs Last departure 10.00hrs

An open park in a wooded valley with a river running past. The sandy beach at Pentewan is just a mile away, and can be accessed by a footpath and cycle path along the river bank directly from the park. A 13-acre site with 105 touring pitches, 12 hardstandings.

Off-licence, motorvan service point

Leisure: ⚴ 🄰
Facilities: 🄽 ⊙ ⚒ ❄ 🦺 🐾
Disabled facilities: toilet, shower & washbasin
Services: 🅃 🧺 🚰 🖾 🅿 🅐 ⊞ → ❙ 18 ✕ ♨ ⏚

▬ ▬ ▦ ▨ 🆂

Perran Sands Holiday Park 70%

TR6 0AQ
☎ 01872 573742
ⓦ www.havenholidays.com

Dir: Leave A30 onto B3285 towards Perranporth, site on R in 1.5m after Goonhavern

Open Mar-Oct Last arrival 22.00hrs Last departure noon

Nestling amid 500 acres of protected dune grassland, and with a footpath through to the surf and 3 miles of golden sandy beach, this lively park is set in a large village-style complex. It offers a complete range of on-site facilities and entertainment for all the family which make it an extremely popular park. A 550-acre site with 412 touring pitches, 395 static.

Leisure: 🏊 🎾 ♦ 🎡 🏓
Facilities: 🚿
Services: ✗ 🛒 🔲 🍺 🔌

Tollgate Farm Caravan & Camping Park ▶▶▶ 69%

Budnick Hill TR6 0AD
☎ 01872 572130
ⓔ enquiries@tollgatefarm.co.uk
ⓦ www.tollgatefarm.co.uk

Dir: Off A30 onto B3285 to Perranporth. Site on R 1.5m after Goonhavern

★ 🚐 £8.50-£14 🚙 £8.50-£14 ▲ £8.50-£14

Open Etr-Oct Booking Advisable Jul-Aug Last arrival 21.00hrs Last departure 11.30hrs
A quiet site in a rural location with spectacular coastal views. Pitches are divided into four paddocks sheltered and screened by mature hedges. Children will enjoy the play equipment and pets' corner. The three miles of sand at Perran Bay are just a walk away through the sand dunes, or a 0.75m drive. A 10-acre site with 140 touring pitches.
Breakfast bar & animal area

Leisure: 🎡
Facilities: 🌳 ⊙ 🔍 ❄ 🍴 🚿 🚻 🏓 🐾 🐕
Disabled facilities: toilet & shower
Services: 🔲 🛒 🚐 🔲 🔲 🍴 ∅ 🔌 → ∪ ◗18 ⅄ ✈
© ⚠ Notes: No large, young or single sex groups

CORNWALL

POLPERRO SX25

Killigarth Manor Holiday Centre
△ 65%

PL13 2JQ
☎ 01503 272216 📠 01503 272065
📧 killigarthmanor@breathemail.net
🌐 www.killigarth.co.uk

Dir: Leave A38 at Trerulefoot rdbt onto A387, through Looe, over bridge signed Polperro. In 3.5m turn L past shelter/phone box. Park 400yds on L

🚐 🚃 ▲

Open Etr-Oct Booking Advisable 3rd wk Jul-Aug Last arrival 20.00hrs Last departure noon
Set on high ground at the approach to the historic fishing village, this large holiday centre offers a wide variety of leisure activities based around the indoor complex. In the evening the entertainment centres around the lively Harbour Lights Club. A 7-acre site with 202 touring pitches, 147 static.
Amusement arcade, pool table & table tennis

Leisure: 🏊 🎾 🎣 🎮 🏓

Facilities: 🛉 ⊙ 🖳 ⚶ ⚓ 🚻 🗑 🏪

Disabled facilities: showers & toilets

Services: 🅣 ✕ 🛒 🚐 🔵 🅨 🎱 ⊘ 🖃 → ⋃ �│18 ⅍ 🐕 🎵 ⊘ 🐾 Notes: 🐕

▬▬ ▬▬ ▬▬ 🔀 🟲

POLRUAN SX15

Polruan Holidays - Camping & Caravanning ►►► 72%

Polruan-by-Fowey PL23 1QH
☎ 01726 870263 📠 01726 870263
📧 polholiday@aol.com

Dir: A38 to Dobwalls, L onto A390 to East Taphouse then L onto B3359. After 4.5m turn R signposted Polruan

★ 🚐 £9-£13 🚃 £9-£13 ▲ £7-£13

Open Etr-Sept Booking Advisable Jul, Aug & bank hols Last arrival 21.00hrs Last departure noon
A very rural and quiet site in a lovely elevated position above the village, with good views of the sea. The River Fowey passenger ferry is close by, and the site has a good shop, and barbecues to borrow. A 3-acre site with 47 touring pitches, 7 hardstandings and 11 static.
Tourist information

Leisure: 🏓

Facilities: 🛉 ⊙ 🖳 ⚶ ⚓ 🚻 🗑 🏪

Services: 🅣 🚐 🔵 ⊘ 🖃 → ⋃ ⅍ 🎵 ⊘

PORTHTOWAN — SW64

Porthtowan Tourist Park ▶▶▶ 74%

Mile Hill TR4 8TY
☎ 01209 890256 📠 01209 890256
📧 admin@porthtowantouristpark.co.uk
🌐 www.porthtowantouristpark.co.uk

> **Dir:** Leave A30 at exit signed
> Redruth/Porthtowan. 3rd exit from rdbt, follow
> road for 2m. R at T-jct. Park on L at top of hill

★ 🚐 £7-£11.50 🚙 £7-£11.50 ▲ £7-£11.50

Open Etr-Oct Booking Advisable Jul-Aug Last
arrival 21.30hrs Last departure 11.00hrs
*A neat, level grassy site on high ground above
Porthtowan, with plenty of shelter from
mature trees and shrubs. Superb toilet
facilities are provided at this peaceful rural
park, which is almost midway between the
small seaside resorts of Portreath and
Porthtowan, with their beaches and surfing. A
5-acre site with 50 touring pitches, and 4
hardstandings.*

Leisure: 🔦 ⚙
Facilities: 🌂 ⊙ ⊕ ☀ ℃ 🗝 ⧉ ★
Disabled facilities: toilet, shower
& washbasin
Services: 🗊 🚰 🛢 ⌀ ⊞ → ∪ Ⱶ18 ⚡ ☰ ⤵ 🗑 △

REDRUTH — SW64

Cambrose Touring Park ▶▶▶ 65%

Portreath Road TR16 4HT
☎ 01209 890747 📠 01209 891665
📧 cambrosetouringpark@supanet.com
🌐 www.cambrosetouringpark.co.uk

> **Dir:** Leave A30 onto B3300 towards Portreath.
> Approx 0.75m at 1st rdbt R onto B3300. Take
> unclass rd on R signed Porthtowan. Site 200yds
> on L

🚐 🚙 ▲

Open Apr-Oct Booking Advisable Jul-Aug Last
arrival 22.00hrs Last departure 11.30hrs
*Situated in a rural setting surrounded by trees
and shrubs, this park is divided into grassy
paddocks. About two miles from the harbour
village of Portreath. A 6-acre site with 60
touring pitches.*
Mini football pitch

Leisure: ⸚ 🔦 ⚙
Facilities: 🌂 ⊙ ⊕ ☀ ℃ 🗝 ★
Disabled facilities: toilets, shower
& washbasin
Services: 🗊 🚰 🚰 🛢 ⌀ ⊞ → ∪ Ⱶ18 ⚡ ⤵ ◎

REDRUTH SW64

Lanyon Holiday Park ▶▶▶ 66%

Loscombe Lane Four Lanes TR16 6LP
☎ 01209 313474 📄 01209 313422
📧 jamierielly@btconnect.com
🌐 www.lanyonholidaypark.co.uk

Dir: Signed 0.5m off B2397 on Helston side of
Four Lanes village

★ 🚐 £12-£16 🚐 £12-£16 ⚠ £6-£10

Open Mar-Oct Booking Advisable Jul & Aug
Last arrival 22.00hrs Last departure noon
*Small, friendly rural park in elevated position
with fine views to distant St Ives Bay. This
family owned and run park is being upgraded
in all areas, and is close to a cycling trail.
Stithian's Reservoir for fishing, sailing and
windsurfing is two miles away. A 14-acre site
with 25 touring pitches, 49 static.*
Take-away service, all day games room

Leisure: ⚑ ⚓ ⚙ ▢
Facilities: ⬅ ⚑ ⊙ ⚑ ⚒ ❋ ⛺ ⚘ ⛱ ⅋
Services: ✗ ⬛ ⚑ ⊡ ⚑ ⚡ ⅋ ⊡ → ∪ ⒄18 ⅋ ⚒
♪ ◎ ⚐

Notes: No single sex groups

▨ ▨ ▨ 🆔 ▨ ▨ 𝒮

REJERRAH SW75

Monkey Tree Touring Park 🏠 64%

Scotland Road TR8 5QR
☎ 01872 572032 📄 01872 571602
📧 enquiries@monkeytreeholidaypark.co.uk
🌐 www.monkeytreeholidaypark.co.uk

Dir: Turn R off A30 onto B3285 to Perranporth,
in 0.25m turn R into Scotland Rd, site on L in
1.5m

★ 🚐 £5-£11.90 🚐 £5-£11.90 ⚠ £5-£11.90

Open Apr-Sep Booking Advisable Jul & Aug
Last arrival 22.00hrs Last departure from
10.00hrs
*A busy holiday park with plenty of activities
and a jolly holiday atmosphere. Set close to
lovely beaches between Newquay and
Perranporth, it offers an outdoor swimming
pool, children's playground, two bars with
entertainment, and a good choice of eating
outlets including a restaurant and a takeaway.
A 56-acre site with 450 touring pitches, 41
static.*
Sauna, solarium, mountain bike hire & football
pitch

Leisure: ⚑ ⚓ ⚙ ▢
Facilities: ⚑ ⊙ ❋ ⚹ ⚒ ⛱ ⚘ ⅋
Disabled facilities: toilets & shower
Services: ⒄ ✗ ⬛ ⚑ ⊡ ⚡ ⚑ ⅋ ⊘ ⊡ → ∪ ⒄18 ⅋
♪ ⚐

▨ ▨ ▨ ▨ ▨ 𝒮

REJERRAH   SW75

Newperran Holiday Park
▶▶▶ 73%

TR8 5QJ
☎ 01872 572407 📠 01872 571254
📧 holidays@newperran.co.uk
🌐 www.newperran.co.uk

Dir: 4m SE of Newquay & 1m S of Rejerrah on A3075

★ 🚐 £8.90-£14 🚐 £8.90-£14 ▲ £8.90-£14

Open Etr-Oct Booking Advisable Jul-Aug
A family site in a lovely rural position near several beaches and bays. This airy park offers screening to some pitches, and there is plenty to occupy all the family. Newquay and Perranporth are about 4 miles away. A 25-acre site with 270 touring pitches, and 18 hardstandings.
Crazy golf, adventure playground & pool

Leisure: ⚛ ◕ ⚠ ☐
Facilities: ➔ ⋔ ⊙ ⬚ ※ ⚲ ⚟ ⟊
Disabled facilities: toilets & shower
Services: 🔟 ✕ ⚙ 🔲 ⚙ ♈ ⬛ ⬀ ∪ ⋔ 18 ⚥
⚌ ⬛ ⚙ ◯ △

ROSUDGEON   SW52

Kenneggy Cove Holiday Park
▶▶▶ 65%

Higher Kenneggy TR20 9AU
☎ 01736 763453
📧 enquiries@kenneggycove.co.uk
🌐 www.kenneggycove.co.uk

Dir: On A394 between Penzance & Helston, turn S into signed lane to site & Higher Kenneggy

★ 🚐 £7-£15 🚐 £7-£15 ▲ £7-£15

Open Apr-Nov Booking Advisable Jul-Aug Last arrival 21.00hrs Last departure 11.00hrs
Set in an Area of Outstanding Natural Beauty with spectacular sea views, this family-owned park is quiet and well kept. A short walk along a country footpath leads to the Cornish Coastal Path, and on to the golden sandy beach at Kenneggy Cove. A 4-acre site with 60 touring pitches, 9 static.
Fresh bakery, cooked breakfasts, evening meals

Leisure: ⚠
Facilities: ➔ ⋔ ⊙ ⬚ ※ ⚲ ⚟ ⚏
Services: 🔟 ⚙ 🚐 🔲 ⚙ ♈ ⬛ ⬀ ∪ ⋔ 9 ⚥ ⚌ △
Notes: No unaccompanied teenagers, large or single sex groups

River Valley Holiday Park
▶▶▶▶ 71%

London Apprentice PL26 7AP
☎ 01726 73533 📠 01726 73533
ⓔ river.valley@tesco.net

ⓦ www.cornwall-holidays.co.uk

Dir: Direct access to park signed on B3273 from St Austell at London Apprentice

★ 🚐 £7-£20 🚗 £7-£20 ▲ £7-£20

Open end Mar-Sep Booking Advisable Jul-Aug Last arrival 22.00hrs Last departure 11.00hrs
A neat, well-maintained family-run park set in a pleasant river valley. The quality toilet block and attractively landscaped grounds make this a delightful base for a holiday. A 2-acre site with 45 touring pitches, 40 static.
Cycle trail

Leisure: 🏊 🎣 ⚂

Facilities: 🅝 ⊙ ⌦ ✳ 🛈 🐕

Disabled facilities: shower and toilet

Services: 🛒 🔌 🗑 → ⌦18 🛒 🚲 🔧 △

▦ ▦ 🅢

Camping & Caravanning Club Site
▶▶▶ 66%

Higher Tregiffian Farm TR19 6JB
☎ 01736 871588

ⓦ www.campingandcaravanningclub.co.uk

Dir: Follow A30 towards Lands End. R onto A3306 St Just/Pendeen road. Site 50yds on L

★ 🚐 £11.75-£15.35 🚗 £11.75-£15.35

▲ £11.75-£15.35

Open Apr-Oct Booking Advisable bank hols & peak periods Last arrival 21.00hrs Last departure noon
Set in a rural area with distant views of Carn Brae and the coast just 2m from Land's End, this very good club site is well run with modern, clean facilities. It offers a children's playfield, late arrivals area and a dog-exercising paddock. A 4-acre site with 75 touring pitches, 6 hardstandings.

Leisure: ⚂

Facilities: 🅝 ⊙ ⌦ ✳ ⌂ 🐕

Disabled facilities: toilet, shower, washbasin & razor point

Services: 🔲 🔌 🚿 🗑 🛈 ⌀ ⊞ → 🔧 🚲

▦ ▦ ▦ ▦ 🅢

ST ISSEY   SW97

Trewince Farm Holiday Park
▶▶▶▶ 71%

PL27 7RL

☎ 01208 812830 📠 01208 812835

Dir: From Wadebridge on A39 take A389 signed Padstow. Site 2m on L

🏕 🚐 ⚠

Open Etr-Oct Booking Advisable anytime Last departure 11.00hrs

A family-owned park run to high standards amongst rolling farmland close to the coast. Part of a working farm, Trewince has been beautifully landscaped and offers good facilities. This comfortable and friendly park has a relaxed feel, and is only three miles from Padstow. A 6-acre site with 120 touring pitches, 35 static.

Crazy golf, farm rides in summer, near Camel Trail

Leisure: ⚲ �’ ⚘ ⚠

Facilities: ⚙ ⚐ ⊙ ⚒ ✳ ⚖ ⚎ 🛒 📷 🐾

Disabled facilities: toilet & shower

Services: 🔌 ⚐ ⚐ ⚕ ⚘ → ∪ ⋔18 ⚒ 🍴 ⚲

ST IVES   SW54

Polmanter Tourist Park
▶▶▶▶▶ 72%

Halsetown TR26 3LX

🟢 01736 795640 📠 01736 795640

⚙ reception@polmanter.com

   www.polmanter.com

Dir: Signed off B3311 at Halsetown

★ 🚐 £10-£17 🚐 £10-£17 ⚠ £10-£17

Open Whit-10 Sep (rs Mar-Whit & 12 Sep-Oct shop, pool, bar & takeaway food closed) Booking Advisable Jul-Aug Last arrival 21.00hrs Last departure 10.00hrs

A well-developed touring park on high ground, Polmanter offers high quality in all areas, from the immaculate modern toilet blocks to the outdoor swimming pool and hard tennis courts. Pitches are individually marked and sited in meadows, and the park has been tastefully landscaped. The fishing port and beaches of St Ives are just 1.5m away, and there is a bus service in high season. A 20-acre site with 240 touring pitches.

Putting, sports field, two family shower rooms

Leisure: ⚲ ⚘ ⚘ ⚠

Facilities: ⚙ ⊙ ⚒ ✳ ⚖ 🐾

Services: 🔤 ✖ ⚖ ⚐ 🔌 ⚿ ⚐ ⚋ ⚕ ⚘ → ∪ ⋔18 ⚒ 🍴 ⚲ ◎ ⚠

Notes: No single sex groups

ST IVES

SW54

Ayr Holiday Park ►►► 68%

TR26 1EJ
☎ 01736 795855 📠 01736 798797
🅔 recept@ayrholidaypark.co.uk
🅦 www.ayrholidaypark.co.uk

Dir: From A30 follow St Ives 'large vehicles' route via B3311 through Halsetown onto B3306. Park signed towards St Ives town centre

🚐 £12-£21 🚐 £12-£21 ▲ £12-£21

Open all year Booking Advisable Jun-Aug Last arrival 22.00hrs Last departure 10.00hrs
A well-established park on a cliffside overlooking St Ives Bay, with a heated toilet block making winter holidaying more attractive. There are stunning views from most pitches, and the town centre, harbour and beach are only 0.5m away, with direct access to the coastal footpath. A 4-acre site with 40 touring pitches, 20 hardstandings and 50 static.

Leisure: ♠ ⚲
Facilities: ⇥ ⛱ ⊙ ⚲ ☀ ⚷ 🛒 ▣ 🎋 🐾
Disabled facilities: disabled toilet/shower
Services: 🚽 🚐 ⬒ ⚡ 🗑 ⬛ ⊘ 🗄 → ⋃ ⌗18 ⚓ 🍴
🍴 ⬭

Notes: No teenage or single sex groups
⬛ ⬛ ⬛ ⬛ 🅢

ST IVES

SW54

Penderleath Caravan & Camping Park ►►► 69%

Towednack TR26 3AF
☎ 01736 798403
🅦 www.penderleath.co.uk

Dir: From A30 take A3074 towards St Ives. At 2nd mini rdbt, turn L and follow road to T-jct, approx 3m. Turn L and then immediately R, turn L at next fork

★ 🚐 £8.50-£14 🚐 £8.50-£14 ▲ £8.50-£14

Open Spring BH-Sep Booking Advisable Jul-Aug Last arrival 21.00hrs Last departure 10.30hrs
Set in a rugged rural location, this tranquil park has extensive views towards St Ives Bay and the north coast. Facilities are all housed in modernised granite barns, and include a quiet licensed bar with beer garden, breakfast room and bar meals. The owners are welcoming and helpful. A 10-acre site with 75 touring pitches.

Leisure: ♠ ⚲
Facilities: ⛱ ⊙ ⚲ ☀ ⚷ 🛒
Disabled facilities: toilet, washbasin, wall bars & mirror
Services: 🚽 ✖ 🚐 ⬒ ⚡ ⚡ ⊘ 🗄 → ⋃ ⌗18 ⚓ 🍴
🍴 ◎ ⬭

Notes: Dogs must be well behaved & kept on leads

ST IVES SW54

Trevalgan Touring Park ►►► 65%

Trevalgan TR26 3BJ
☎ 01736 796433 🖹 01736 796433
🅔 recept@trevalgantouringpark.co.uk
🆆 www.trevalgantouringpark.co.uk

Dir: From A30 follow brown tourist signs (B3311). Climb hill to T-jct. Turn R onto B3311. At jct with B3306 turn left. Site 0.5m on R.

★ 🚐 £11-£18 🚍 £11-£18 ▲ £11-£18

Open Etr-Sep (rs Etr-June & Sept shop & takeaway closed) Booking Advisable mid Jul-Aug Last arrival 22.00hrs Last departure 10.00hrs
An open park next to a working farm in a rural area on the coastal road from St Ives to Zennor. The park is surrounded by mature hedges, but there are extensive views out over the sea. There is a good range of facilities. A 4.9-acre site with 120 touring pitches.
Farm trail, pets' corner, mini golf

Leisure: 🅡 🄊 ▢
Facilities: 🅡 ⊙ 🅡 ☀ 🅛 🅛 🄌 🅡
Services: 🅣 ✕ 🛒 🚽 🅡 🖢 🖪 🅡 🄌 🖪 → ∪ 🅡9
🄌 🍴 🅙 🛆
Notes: No single sex groups in high season
▨▨ ▨▨ ▨▨ ▨▨ 🅖

ST JUST (NEAR LAND'S END) SW33

Kelynack Caravan & Camping Park ►►► 64%

Kelynack TR19 7RE
☎ 01736 787633 🖹 01736 787633
🅔 steve@kelynackholidays.co.uk
🆆 www.ukparks.co.uk/kelynack

Dir: 1m S of St Just 5m N of Land's End on B3306

★ 🚐 fr £7 🚍 fr £7 ▲ fr £7

Open Apr-Oct Booking Advisable Jul-Aug Last arrival 22.00hrs Last departure noon
A small secluded park nestling alongside a stream in an unspoilt rural location. The level grass pitches are in two areas, and the park is close to many coves, beaches and ancient villages. A 2-acre site with 20 touring pitches, 5 hardstandings and 13 static.
Dining & cooking shelter

Leisure: 🅡 🄊
Facilities: 🅡 ⊙ 🅡 ☀ 🅛 🅛 🄌 🅡 🅡
Disabled facilities: shower, toilet, washhand basin
Services: 🅣 🅡 🖢 🄌 🖪 → 🅡18 🅙 🖪

Roselands Caravan Park
▶▶▶ 68%

Dowran TR19 7RS
☎ 01736 788571
📧 camping@roseland84.freeserve.co.uk
🌐 www.roselands.co.uk

Dir: From A30 Penzance bypass turn R for St Just on A3071. Continue for 5m, turn L after Tin Mine Chimney at sign, follow signs to park

★ ☗ £7.10 ☗ £7.10 ▲ £5.80

Open Jan-Oct Booking Advisable Jun-Sep Last arrival 21.00hrs Last departure 11.00hrs
A small, friendly park in a sheltered rural setting, an ideal location for a quiet family holiday. The owners are continuing to upgrade the park, and in addition to the attractive little bar there is an indoor games room, children's playground, and good toilet facilities. A 3-acre site with 15 touring pitches, 15 static.
Cycle hire

Leisure: ◕ ⚲

Facilities: ℟ ⊙ ℺ ✻ ℃ ℥ ⊓ ✝

Services: ✗ ⬥ ☗ ▣ ♀ 🛢 ⌀ → ∪ ⌐18 ♪

Notes: No single sex groups, no cars by caravans

Trevaylor Caravan & Camping Park
▶▶▶ 65%

Botallack TR19 7PU
☎ 01736 787016
📧 bookings@trevaylor.com
🌐 www.trevaylor.com

Dir: On B3306 St Just to St Ives road, campsite on R 0.75m from St Just

★ ☗ £8.50-£9 ☗ £8.50-£9 ▲ £8.50-£9

Open Etr or 1 Apr-Oct Booking Advisable Jul & Aughrs Last departure noon
A sheltered grassy site located off the beaten track in a peaceful location at the western tip of Cornwall. The dramatic coastline and the pretty villages nearby are truly unspoilt. Clean, well-maintained facilities and a good shop are offered along with a bar serving tasty bar meals. A 6-acre site with 50 touring pitches.

Leisure: ◕ ⚲

Facilities: ℟ ⊙ ℺ ✻ ℥

Services: ▣ ✗ ☗ ▣ ♀ 🛢 ⌀ ⊞ → ⌐18 ♪

CORNWALL

ST JUST-IN-ROSELAND   SW83

Trethem Mill Touring Park
▶▶▶ 76%

TR2 5JF
☎ 01872 580504 📠 01872 580968
📧 reception@trethem.com
🌐 www.trethem.com

Dir: From Tregony follow A3078 to St Mawes. 2m after passing through Trewithian, follow signs to park

★ 🚐 £9-£13 🚃 £9-£13 ▲ £9-£13

Open Apr-Oct Booking Advisable Jul-Aug Last arrival 21.00hrs Last departure 11.00hrs
A carefully-tended and sheltered park in a rural setting, with spacious pitches separated by young trees and shrubs. This quiet park is personally run by a very keen family. A 11-acre site with 84 touring pitches, 15 hardstandings.
Info centre

Leisure: ◕ /⋀\
Facilities: ⋒ ⊙ ⊕ ✻ ┗ ⣺ ☓
Disabled facilities: disabled shower suite
Services: 🅣 🚐 🗑 🚿 ∅ ⊟ → ∪ ┷ ⤳ △

◼ ◼ ◼ ◪ ⑤

ST MABYN   SX07

Glenmorris Park ▶▶▶ 71%

Longstone Road PL30 3BY
☎ 01208 841677 📠 01208 841677
📧 info@glenmorris.co.uk
🌐 www.glenmorris.co.uk

Dir: S of Camelford on A39, L after BP garage to B3266 to Bodmin, 6m to Longstone, R at x-rds to St Mabyn, site 400mtrs R.

🚐 🚃 ▲
Open Etr-Oct Booking Advisable Jul-Aug, all year for statics Last arrival 11.30hrs Last departure 10.30hrs
A very good, mainly level park in a peaceful rural location offering clean and well-maintained facilities - a small games room, heated outdoor swimming pool, sunbathing area, and shop. An ideal location for visiting this unspoilt area. A 11-acre site with 80 touring pitches, 12 hardstandings and 6 static.

Leisure: ⋋ ◕ /⋀\
Facilities: ⋒ ⊙ ⊕ ✻ ┗ ⣺ ⌿
Disabled facilities: ramps to chalet, toilets & laundry
Services: 🅣 🚐 🗑 🚿 ∅ → ∪ ⋔⁹ ⤳
Notes: Quiet after 10pm

ST MERRYN (NEAR PADSTOW) SW87

Carnevas Farm Holiday Park & Cottages ▶▶▶ 67%

Carnevas Farm PL28 8PN
☎ 01841 520230 ▤ 01841 520230

Dir: Leave St Merryn village on B3276 towards Porthcothan Bay, after 2m turn R at site sign into unclass road opposite Tredrea Inn, site in 0.25m on R

★ ⊕ £6.46-£12.33 ⊕ £6.46-£12.33
▲ £6.46-£12.33

Open Apr-Oct (rs Apr-Whit & mid Sep-Oct shop, bar & restaurant closed) Booking Advisable Jul-Aug

A family-run park on a working farm, divided into four paddocks on slightly sloping grass. The toilets are central to all areas, and there is a small licensed bar serving bar meals. A 8-acre site with 195 touring pitches, 14 static.

Leisure: ♦ ⚙
Facilities: ⋔ ⊙ ☜ ☼ ᘉ ᒼ ⏚ ⋔
Disabled facilities: toilet & shower room
Services: ⊺ ✗ ⊕ ▣ ☉ ⏉ ⏚ ⊟ → ∪ ⏰18 ⏚ ◬

ST MINVER SW97

St Minver Holiday Park ⌂ 62%

PL27 6RR
☎ 01208 862305 & 0870 420 2991
▤ 01208 862265
📧 enquiries@parkdeanholidays.com
🌐 www.parkdeanholidays.com

Dir: From A39 N of Wadebridge take B3314 Port Isaac road. Site signed on L in 3m

⊕ £9-£26 ⊕ £7-£26 ▲ £7-£23

Open Etr-27 Oct Booking Advisable Jul-Sep Last arrival mdnt Last departure 10.00hrs

A large holiday park set around St Minver House in sylvan surroundings. The park offers a wide range of holiday activities, including crazy golf, table tennis, and large indoor fun pool and waterslide. A programme of family entertainment is offered during evenings in the high season. A 40-acre site with 120 touring pitches, 264 static.

Crazy golf, free evening entertainment, amusements

Leisure: ☜ ♦ ⚙
Facilities: ⋔ ⊙ ☜ ☼ ᘉ ᒼ ⏚ ⋔
Services: ⊺ ✗ ⛟ ⊕ ▣ ☉ ⏉ ⏚ ⊟ → ⏰18 ⛩ ◬
Notes: No single-sex groups under 25yrs, no mixed groups under 21yrs

▰▰ ▰▰ ▰▰ ▰ ᔕ

ST MINVER   SW97

Gunvenna Caravan Park
▶▶▶▶ 67%

PL27 6QN

☎ 01208 862405   🖷 01208 862405

Dir: From A39 N of Wadebridge take Port Isaac road B3314, park 4m on R

★ 🛖 £5.50-£15 🚐 £5.50-£15 ▲ £5.50-£15

Open Etr-Oct Booking Advisable Jul-Aug Last arrival 21.00hrs Last departure 11.00hrs
Attractive park with extensive rural views in a quiet country location, yet within three miles of Polzeath. This popular park is family owned and run, and provides good facilities in an ideal position for touring north Cornwall. A 10-acre site with 75 touring pitches, 25 static.

Leisure: 🎐 🎣 /A

Facilities: ➡ 🏮 ⊙ ⊙ 🔌 ☀ ⸇ ⅏ 🎋 🎋 ⼊

Disabled facilities: toilet & washbasin

Services: 🕒 ⅋ 🖥 ⅋ ⅋ → ∪ ⌐18 ⅄ ⅏ ⅃

△ Notes: No single sex groups

TINTAGEL   SX08

Headland Caravan & Camping Park
▶▶▶ 65%

Atlantic Road PL34 0DE

☎ 01840 770239   🖷 01840 770925

🌐 headland.cp@virgin.net

🕸 www.headlandcaravanpark.co.uk

Dir: From B3263 follow brown tourist signs through village to Headland

★ 🛖 £10-£12 🚐 £9-£11 ▲ £9-£12

Open Etr-Oct Booking Advisable Jul-Aug Last arrival 21.00hrs
A peaceful family-run site in the mystical village of Tintagel, close to the ruins of King Arthur's Castle. The Cornish coastal path and the spectacular scenery are just two of the attractions here, and there are safe bathing beaches nearby. A 5-acre site with 62 touring pitches, 28 static.

Leisure: /A

Facilities: 🏮 ⊙ 🔌 ☀ ⸇ ⅏ 🎋

Disabled facilities: toilet, shower & washroom

Services: 🆣 ⅋ ⅋ 🖥 ⅋ ⅋ 🖾 → ∪ ⅄ ⅃ △

Notes: Dogs must be kept on short leads & exercised off park, quiet after 23.00 hrs

CORNWALL

TRURO   SW84

Carnon Downs Caravan & Camping Park ▶▶▶▶ 75%

Carnon Downs TR3 6JJ
☎ 01872 862283
🅔 info@carnon-downs-caravanpark.co.uk
🆆 www.carnon-downs-caravanpark.co.uk

Dir: Take A39 from Truro towards Falmouth. Site just off the main Carnon Downs rdbt, on L

★ 🚐 £12-£17.50 🚍 £12-£17.50

🅰 £10-£15.50

Open all year Booking Advisable Jul-Aug Last arrival 22.00hrs Last departure 11.00hrs
A mature park with a high standard of landscaping, set in meadowland and woodland close to the village amenities of Carnon Downs. The toilet facilities provide quality and comfort in an en suite environment. A 33-acre site with 110 touring pitches, 55 hardstandings and 1 static.
Baby & child bathroom, 3 family bathrooms

Leisure: 🅐 🖵
Facilities: ➡ 🅝 ☉ ℚ ✳ 🅲 🖂 🅉
Disabled facilities: disabled bathroom
Services: 🆃 🎇 ⅋ 🖳 🅸 🅀 🖃 → ∪ ﬁ18 ↯ 🎪 🖉 △ 🆉
Notes: No single sex groups

VERYAN   SW93

Camping & Caravanning Club Site ▶▶▶ 67%

Tretheake Manor TR2 5PP
☎ 01872 501658
🆆 www.campingandcaravanningclub.co.uk

Dir: Left off A3078 at filling station signed Veryan/Portloe on unclass road. Site signed on L

★ 🚐 £12.95-£16.35 🚍 £12.95-£16.35

🅰 £12.95-£16.35

Open Mar-Nov Booking Advisable BH's & peak periods Last arrival 21.00hrs Last departure noon
A quiet park on slightly undulating land with pleasant countryside views. A tranquil fishing lake holds appeal for anglers, and the site is just 2.5 miles from one of Cornwall's finest sandy beaches. A 9-acre site with 150 touring pitches, 14 hardstandings.

Leisure: 🅠 🅐
Facilities: 🅝 ☉ ℚ ✳ 🅲 🛁 🅉
Disabled facilities: toilet, shower, washbasin & razor point
Services: 🆃 🎇 ⅋ 🖳 🅸 🅀 🖃 → ∪ 🖉 △ 🆉

The Laurels Holiday Park
▶▶▶ 71%

Padstow Road Whitecross PL27 7JQ
☎ 01208 813341 📠 01208 816590
📧 anicholson@thelaurelsholidaypark.co.uk
🌐 www.thelaurelsholidaypark.co.uk

Dir: Off A389 Padstow road near jct with A39,
W of Wadebridge

★ 🚐 £5-£14 🚍 £5-£14 ▲ £5-£14

Open Apr/Etr-Oct Booking Advisable Jul-Sep
Last arrival 20.00hrs Last departure 11.00hrs
*A very smart and well-equipped park with
individual pitches screened by hedges and
young shrubs. The keen and friendly owners
keep the park in very good condition,
including facilities like the laundry, reception
and dish wash area. A dog walk is of great
benefit to pet owners, and the Camel cycle
trail and Padstow are not far away. A 2.2-acre
site with 30 touring pitches.*

Leisure: ⚓
Facilities: ⬛ ⊙ ⬛ ✳ ⬛ ⬛ ⬛
Services: 🔌 ⬛ ⬛ → ∪ 🅿18 ↳ ⬛ ⬛ ⬛
Notes: Dogs must be kept on leads,
no single sex groups

Little Bodieve Holiday Park
▶▶▶ 64%

Bodieve Road PL27 6EG
☎ 01208 812323
📧 berry@littlebodieveholidaypark.fsnet.co.uk
🌐 www.littlebodieve.co.uk

Dir: From A39 rdbt on Wadebridge by-pass take
B3314 signed Rock/Port Isaac, site 0.25m on R

🚐 £8.80-£14.50 🚍 £8.80-£14.50
▲ £8.80-£14.50

Open Apr-Oct (rs early & late season pool,
shop & clubhouse closed) Booking Advisable
Jul-Aug Last arrival 20.00hrs Last departure
11.00hrs
*Set in a rural area with pitches located in
three large paddocks of mostly level grass,
this family park is close to the Camel Estuary.
The licensed clubhouse provides bar meals,
with an entertainment programme in high
season, and there is a swimming pool with
sun terrace, and a separate waterslide and
splash pool. A 20-acre site with 195 touring
pitches, 75 static.*
Crazy golf, water shute/splash pool & pets'
corner

Leisure: ⚓ ⬛ ⚓
Facilities: ⬛ ⬛ ⊙ ⬛ ✳ ⬛ ⬛ ⬛
Disabled facilities: bathroom
Services: ⬛ ✕ ⬛ 🔌 ⬛ ⬛ ⬛ ⬛ ⬛ → ∪ 🅿18 ⬛
⬛ △ Notes: No single sex groups

⬛ ⬛ ⬛ ⬛

WATERGATE BAY   SW86

Watergate Bay Tourist Park
▶▶▶ *72%*

Watergate Bay TR8 4AD
☎ 01637 860387 📠 01637 860387
📧 watergatebay@email.com
🌐 www.watergatebaytouringpark.co.uk

Dir: 4m N of Newquay on B3276 coast road at Watergate Bay

★ 🚐 £8-£13 🚙 £8-£13 ▲ £8-£13

Open Mar-Oct (rs Mar-22 May & 13 Sep-Nov restricted bar, café, shop & swimming pool) Booking Advisable Jul-Aug Last arrival 22.00hrs Last departure noon

A well-established park set on high ground above Watergate Bay, with its acres of golden sands and many rock pools. The toilet facilities have been refurbished to a superb standard in two out of three blocks, and there is a regular entertainment programme in the clubhouse. A 32-acre site with 171 touring pitches, 14 hardstandings.

Entertainment, free minibus to beach

Leisure: 🏊 🎣 🎮 🎱

Facilities: 🚿 🏪 ⊙ 🚰 🐕 🛒 ℁ 🏪

Disabled facilities: toilet, bath, shower & washbasin

Services: 🅣 🗙 🚮 🔌 🛢 🖙 🛒 🗑 → 🅟9 🔧 ◎
🔺 ⚠ ▭ ▭ ▭ ▭ 🔧 🔄

WHITE CROSS   SW85

White Acres Holiday Park 🏖 *70%*

TR8 4LW
☎ 01726 862100 & 0870 420 2991
📠 01726 860777
📧 reception@parkdeanholidays.co.uk
🌐 www.parkdeanholidays.co.uk

Dir: From A30 at Indian Queens take A392 signed Newquay. Site 2m on R

★ 🚐 £12.50-£32 🚙 £8.50-£32 ▲ £8.50-£28

Open all year (rs Nov) Booking Advisable high season Last arrival 21.00hrs Last departure 10.00hrs

A high quality holiday park with upmarket facilities and plenty of leisure activities and entertainment for the whole family. Boasting one of the best coarse fishing centres in the South West, it also offers a heated indoor swimming pool, sauna, jacuzzi and gym, coffee bar, restaurant and pub, and clubs for children. The touring area is partly terraced, and the setting of 100 rural acres is very attractive. A 167-acre site with 40 touring pitches, 6 hardstandings.

Entertainment, sauna, solarium, fishing, gym, bowling

Leisure: 🏊 🎣 🎮 Facilities: 🏪 ⊙ 🚰 ℁ 🔌
🛒 🎋 Disabled facilities: toilets & holiday homes with disabled access

Services: 🗙 🚮 🔌 🛢 🖙 🔄 → ∪ 🔧 ◎

Notes: No single sex groups under 25yrs, no mixed groups under 21yrs

▭ ▭ ▭ 🔧 🔄

WHITE CROSS   SW85

Summer Lodge Holiday Park
►►► 64%

TR8 4LW

☎ 01726 860415 🖷 01726 861490

🖃 summer.lodge@snootyfoxresorts.co.uk

🌐 www.snootyfoxresorts.co.uk

> **Dir:** From Indian Queens on A30 take A392 to Newquay. Site on L at Whitecross in 2.5m

★ 🚐 £9.50-£17 🚐 £9.50-£17 ▲ £6-£10

Open Mar-Oct (rs Etr-Whit & Sep-Oct shop cafe closed) Booking Advisable Jul-Aughrs Last departure 10.00hrs

Small holiday complex offering use of good facilities. This park has a nightly cabaret in the licensed pub, plus other on-site entertainment. A 26-acre site with 100 touring pitches, 118 static.

Crazy golf

Leisure: ⚲ ⚄ ⚲

Facilities: ⬤⊙⬤⚹⚻⬤⚲⬛

Disabled facilities: toilet & shower, ramps to all amenity buildings

Services: 🔲✕⬤⬤⬤⬤⬤⬤⬤→∪⬤

Notes: ✗

⬛ ⬛ ⬛ VISA ⬛ 🟩

WIDEMOUTH BAY   SS20

Widemouth Bay Caravan Park
66%

EX23 0DF

☎ 01288 361208 🖷 01271 866791

🖃 bookings@jfhols.co.uk

🌐 www.johnfowlerholidays.com

> **Dir:** take Widemouth Bay coastal road off A39, turn L. Park on L

★ 🚐 £8-£20 🚐 £8-£20 ▲ £6-£18

Open Mar-Oct Last departure 10.00hrs

A partly sloping rural site set in countryside overlooking the sea and one of Cornwall's finest beaches. Nightly entertainment in high season with emphasis on children's and family club programmes. This park is located less than half a mile from the sandy beaches of Widemouth Bay. A 58-acre site with 220 touring pitches, 90 hardstandings and 200 static.

Leisure: ⚲ ⚄

Facilities: ⬤⊙⬤⚹⚻⬤⚲⬛⚲

Services: ✕⬤⬤⬤⬤→∪⬤18⚲⬤⬤◎

⚠ Notes: No single sex groups

WIDEMOUTH BAY SS20

Penhalt Farm Holiday Park

▶▶▶ 64%

EX23 0DG

☎ 01288 361210 🖷 01288 361210

[E] denandjennie@penhaltfarm.fsnet.co.uk

[W] www.holidaybank.co.uk/penhaltfarmholidaypark

Dir: From Bude take Widemouth Bay road off A39, L at end signed Millook onto coastal road. Site 0.75m on L

★ 🚐 £6.50-£14 🚙 £6.50-£14 ⛺ £6-£11

Open Etr-Oct Booking Advisable Jul & Aug

Splendid views of the sea and coast can be enjoyed from all pitches on this sloping but partly level site, set in a lovely rural area on a working farm. About one mile away is one of Cornwall's finest beaches which is popular with all the family as well as surfers. A 8-acre site with 100 touring pitches.

Pool table, netball & football posts

Leisure: ● /Λ\

Facilities: 🚿 ⊙ 🧺 ✲ 📞 🏪 🐕

Disabled facilities: toilet

Services: ➜ 🚐 🔒 ⊘ [≡] → U ⛳9 ✈ 🎥 ⛵ 🎣

💳 💳 💳 [S]

AMBLESIDE NY30

Skelwith Fold Caravan Park

▶▶▶▶ 74%

LA22 0HX

☎ 015394 32277 🖷 015394 34344

[E] info@skelwith.com

[W] www.skelwith.com

Dir: Leave Ambleside on A593 towards Coniston, turn L at Clappersgate onto B5286 Hawkshead road. Park 1m on R

★ 🚐 £12.50-£15 🚙 £12.50-£15

Open Mar-15 Nov Booking Advisable public hols & Jul-Aug Last arrival dusk Last departure noon

In the grounds of a former mansion, this park is in a beautiful setting close to Lake Windermere. Touring areas are dotted in paddocks around the extensively wooded grounds, and the all-weather pitches are set close to the many facility buildings. There is a 5-acre family recreation area which has spectacular views of Loughrigg Fell. A 130-acre site with 150 touring pitches, 150 hardstandings and 300 static.

Family recreation area

Leisure: /Λ\

Facilities: 🚿 ⊙ 🧺 ✲ 📞 🏪 🏠 ⛩ 🐕

Disabled facilities: toliets, shower & washbasin

Services: [T] 🚐 🗑 🔒 ⊘ [≡] → U ⛳18 ✈ 🎥 🎣 ⛵

💳 💳 💳 💳 [S]

AMBLESIDE NY30

Low Wray National Trust Campsite ▶▶▶ 65%

Low Wray LA22 0JA
☎ 015394 32810 📠 015394 32684
ⓔ lowwraycampsite@nationaltrust.org.uk
ⓦ www.nationaltrust.org.uk

Dir: 3m SW of Ambleside on A593 to Clappersgate, then B5286 for approx 1m. Turn L at the sign for Wray. Site is less than 1m on the L

★ ▲ £10.50

Open wk before Etr-Oct Last arrival 21.00hrs Last departure 11.00hrs
Picturesquely set on the wooded shores of Lake Windermere, this site is a favourite with tenters and watersports enthusiasts. The well-maintained facilities are housed in wooden cabins, and tents can be pitched in wooded glades with lake views or open grassland. Off-road biking, walks and pub food are all nearby. A 10-acre site with 200 touring pitches.
Launching for sailing

Leisure: ⚙
Facilities: ⬤⊙ⓒ🗲
Disabled facilities: toilet, shower & washing facilities
Services: →⅄🖦🍴🗑ⓢ🗲♨
Notes: No single sex groups of more than three/large mixed groups

▬▬ ▭▭ ▦▦ ▨▨ ⑤

APPLEBY-IN-WESTMORLAND NY62

Wild Rose Park ▶▶▶▶▶ 77%

Ormside CA16 6EJ
☎ 017683 51077 📠 017683 52551
ⓔ hs@wildrose.co.uk
ⓦ www.wildrose.co.uk

Dir: Signed on unclass road to Great Ormside, off B6260

★ ⟐ £10.50-£17.90 ⟐ £10.50-£17.90
▲ £10.50-£17.90

Open all year (rs Nov-Mar shop & swimming pool closed) Booking Advisable bank & school hols Last arrival 22.00hrs Last departure noon
Situated in the Eden Valley, this large family-run park has been carefully landscaped and offers superb facilities maintained to an extremely high standard. There are several individual pitches, and extensive views from most areas of the park. Traditional stone walls and the planting of lots of indigenous trees help it to blend into the environment, and wildlife is actively encouraged. A 40-acre site with 240 touring pitches, 140 hardstandings and 279 static.
Tourist Information, pitch and putt

Leisure: ⟑⚫⚙⌑
Facilities: ⬤⊙⚏☀ⓒ🗲🏒
Disabled facilities: toilets, access to facilities, shower, shop/mobility vehicle
Services: 🅣✗♨⚙⤵🗑🝙⊘⊞→🍴18 🗲
Notes: No unaccompanied teenagers, no dangerous dogs

▬▬ ▭▭ ▦▦ ▨▨ ⑤

CUMBRIA

BARROW-IN-FURNESS   SD26

South End Caravan Park
▶▶▶ 70%

Walney Island LA14 3YQ
☎ 01229 472823 📄 01229 472822
🄴 kathmulgrew@aol.com
🅦 www.walney-island-caravan-park.co.uk

Dir: A590 in Barrow follow signs for Walney Island. Turn L after crossing bridge. 4m S

★ 🚐 £14-£18 🚐 £12-£18 ▲ £12-£18

Open Mar-Oct Booking Advisable Jul-Aug Last arrival 22.00hrs Last departure noon
Mainly level grass site adjacent to sea, and close to a nature reserve, on southern end of Walney Island. This friendly family-owned and run park offers an extensive range of good quality amenities and high standards of cleanliness and maintenance. A 7-acre site with 60 touring pitches, 100 static.
Bowling green

Leisure: 🦢 🔌 🚣 ▦ ▢
Facilities: ℕ ⊙ ✳ ℂ ♨ ⚑
Disabled facilities: toilet & shower
Services: ♨ 🚐 🄱 ♨ 🄰 🖽 → ∪ ⋈ 8 ⚻ 🖌 🄱 🛒
Notes: No single sex groups

▭ ▭ ▧ 🅂

DALSTON   NY35

Dalston Hall Caravan Park
▶▶▶ 69%

Dalston Hall Estate CA5 7JX
☎ 01228 710165
Dir: 2.5m SW of Carlisle, just off B5299 & signed

★ 🚐 £11-£12 🚐 £11-£12 ▲ £7.50-£8.50

Open Mar-Oct Booking Advisable Jul-Aug Last arrival 21.00hrs Last departure 13.00hrs
A neat, well-maintained site on level grass in the grounds of an estate located between Carlisle and Dalston. All facilities are to a very high standard, and amenities include a 9-hole golf course, a bar and clubhouse serving breakfast and bar meals, and salmon and trout fly fishing. A 3-acre site with 60 touring pitches, 26 hardstandings and 17 static.
9-hole golf course & fly fishing

Leisure: ▦
Facilities: ℕ ⊙ ℂ ✳ ℂ ⴲ ⚑
Services: 🄣 ✕ ♨ 🚐 🄱 ♨ 🄰 🖽 → ⋈9 ⚻ 🖌

FLOOKBURGH SD37

Lakeland Leisure Park 62%

Moor Lane LA11 7LT
☎ 015395 58556 🖹 015395 58559

Dir: Approach on B5277 through Grange-over-Sands to Flookburgh, turn L at village square and park 1m

Open late Mar-early Nov Booking Advisable May-Oct Last arrival 21.00hrs Last departure 11.00hrs

A complete leisure park with full range of activities and entertainments, making this flat, grassy site ideal for families. The touring area is quietly situated away from the main amenities, but the swimming pools, all-weather bowling green and evening entertainment are just a short stroll away. A 105-acre site with 125 touring pitches, 740 static.

Horse riding

Leisure: ⛳ ✈ ◕ ♣ /🖽

Facilities: 🖍 ⊙ ✳ 🔥 🖫 🛒 🎄 ⊓ 🏲

Disabled facilities: toilets & ramps

Services: 🆃 ✗ 🖦 ⊞ 🖾 ♀ ∅ ⊠ → ∪ Γ18 ♪ ◎

GREAT LANGDALE NY20

Great Langdale National Trust Campsite ►►► 64%

LA22 9JU
☎ 015394 37668 🖹 015394 37668
🄴 langdale.camp@nationaltrust.org.uk
🄦 www.langdalecampsite.org.uk

Dir: Take A593 to Skelwith Bridge, turn R onto B5343 for 5m to the New Dungeon Ghyll Hotel, and site entrance on L in 1m just before Old Dungeon Ghyll Hotel

★ ⚕ £10.50

Open all year

Nestling in a green valley, sheltered by mature trees and surrounded by stunning fell views, this site is an ideal base for campers, climbers and fell walkers. The large grass tent area has some gravel parking for cars, and there is a separate area for groups and one for families with a children's play area. Attractive wooden cabins house the toilets, a shop, and drying rooms. A 9-acre site.

Leisure: /🖽

Facilities: 🖍 ⊙ ✳ 🔥 🖫

Disabled facilities: shower & toilet

Services: 🖾 🍴 ∅ → ♪

Notes: Quiet at 23.00 hrs

CUMBRIA

GREYSTOKE — NY43

Hopkinsons Whitbarrow Hall Caravan Park ►►► 62%

Berrier CA11 0XB
☎ 01768 483456

Dir: From M6 J40 take A66 to Keswick, after 8m turn R, follow tourist signs to Hopkinsons

🏕 🚐 👤

Open Mar-Oct Booking Advisable bank hols & for electric hook up Last arrival 21.00hrs Last departure 21.00hrs

A rural park in a peaceful location surrounded by trees and shrubs, on the fringe of the Lake District National Park. This family-run park offers plenty of amenities including a small bar and clubhouse, a games room and a tennis court. There is a good mix of grass pitches and hardstandings, and very clean toilet facilities. A 8-acre site with 81 touring pitches, 167 static.

Table tennis, pool table & video games

Leisure: 🎯 ⚲ ⚘

Facilities: 🛁 ⊙ 🔧 ※ ⚓ 🛒 🐕

Disabled facilities: disabled suite with toilet, shower, basin & handrails

Services: 🔌 🎱 ♿ 🛒 🔋 → ∪ ⌐18

▨▨ ▨▨ 🔊

KESWICK — NY22

Castlerigg Hall Caravan & Camping Park ►►►► 72%

Castlerigg Hall CA12 4TE
☎ 017687 74499 📠 017687 74499
📧 info@castlerigg.co.uk
🌐 www.castlerigg.co.uk

Dir: 1.5m SE of Keswick on A591, turn R at signpost and 200mtrs on R past Heights Hotel.

★ 🚐 £12.95-£14.95 🚐 £11.30-£13.50

👤 £9.30-£11.70

Open mid Mar-15 Nov Last arrival 21.00hrs Last departure 11.30hrs

Spectacular views over Derwentwater to the mountains beyond are among the many attractions at this lovely Lakeland park. Old farm buildings have been tastefully converted into excellent toilets with private washing and family bathroom, reception and a well-equipped shop, and there is a kitchen/dining area for campers with a courtyard tearoom which also serves breakfast. A 8-acre site with 48 touring pitches, 48 hardstandings.

Campers' kitchen, sitting room

Leisure: ⚲ 🖵

Facilities: 🚿 🛁 ⊙ 🔧 ※ 🛒 🐕

Disabled facilities: shower, toilet & washbasin

Services: 🔲 🔌 ⚖ 🛒 🔋 → ⌐9 🚬 🍴 🎯 ◎

△ **Notes:** No single sex groups

▨▨ ▨▨ 🔊

KESWICK NY22

Camping & Caravanning Club Site

►►► 73%

Crow Park Road CA12 5EP

☎ 01768 772392

[W] www.campingandcaravanningclub.co.uk

Dir: From Penrith on A5271, turn L into Main Street (Keswick), R to pass 'Lakes' bus stn, past rugby club, turn R, site on R

★ 🚐 £15.35-£18.35 🚙 £15.35-£18.35

⛺ £15.35-£18.35

Open Feb-Nov Booking Advisable BH's & peak periods Last arrival 21.00hrs Last departure noon

A well-situated lakeside site within walking distance of the town centre. Boat launching is available from the site onto Derwentwater, and this level grassy park also offers a number of all-weather pitches. A 14-acre site with 250 touring pitches, 96 hardstandings.

Leisure: /Λ\

Facilities: 🚿 ⊙ ☂ ✳ 📞 🛒 🏠 🐕

Disabled facilities: toilet, shower, washbasin & razor point

Services: [T] 🚐 ⚡ 🗑 🔒 ⛽ [≡] → 🎣 ⛵

💳 VISA Barclays CONNECT [S]

KIRKBY LONSDALE SD67

Woodclose Caravan Park

►►►► 75%

Casterton LA6 2SE

☎ 01524 271597 📠 01524 272301

[E] michaelhodgkins@woodclosecaravanpark.fsnet.co.uk

[W] www.woodclosepark.com

Dir: On A65, 0.25m beyond Kirkby Lonsdale, heading to Skipton

🚐 🚙 ⛺

Open Mar-Oct (rs Nov-Dec) Booking Advisable bank hols, Jul-Aug & Sep Last arrival 21.00hrs Last departure 13.00hrs

A peaceful park with excellent toilet facilities set in idyllic countryside in the beautiful Lune Valley. Ideal for those seeking quiet relaxation, and for visiting the Lakes and Dales. Devil's Bridge with its riverside walks, and historic Kirkby Lonsdale with shops, pubs and restaurants are an easy walk from the park. A 9-acre site with 50 touring pitches, 54 static.

Leisure: 🔍 /Λ\

Facilities: 🚿 ⊙ ☂ ✳ 📞 🛒

Disabled facilities: toilets

Services: 🚐 🗑 🔒 ⛽ → ⛳18 🎣

MILNTHORPE SD48

Hall More Caravan Park
►►► 70%

Hale LA7 7BP
☎ 01524 718695 📠 01524 784815
[E] enquiries@southlakeland-caravans.co.uk
[W] www.southlakeland-caravans.co.uk

Dir: Leave M6 J35 onto A6 towards Milnthorpe for 4m. Take L at Lakeland Wildlife Oasis and follow brown signs

★ 🚐 £10-£12 🚌 £10-£12 ⛺ £5-£6

Open Mar-Oct Booking Advisable bank/school holidays Last arrival 22.00hrs Last departure 10.00hrs

A mainly level grassy site in meadowland, adjacent to main road, with all hardstanding pitches and unsophisticated facilities. Close to farm and stables offering pony trekking, and there is trout fishing nearby. A 4-acre site with 38 touring pitches, 7 hardstandings and 60 static.

Facilities: 🚿 ⊙ 🔌 ✻ 📞 🐕
Services: 🚐 🧺 🔥 ♻ → ∪ ⛳18 🎣 🏪
Notes: No single sex groups

💳 💳 💳 💳 💳

PENRITH NY53

Lowther Holiday Park
►►►► 73%

Eamont Bridge CA10 2JB
☎ 01768 863631 📠 01768 868126
[E] sales@lowther-holidaypark.co.uk
[W] www.lowther-holidaypark.co.uk

Dir: 3m S of Penrith on A6

★ 🚐 £16-£18 🚌 £16-£18 ⛺ £16-£18

Open mid Mar-mid Nov Booking Advisable bank hols Last arrival 23.00hrs Last departure 22.00hrs

A secluded natural woodland site with lovely riverside walks and glorious surrounding countryside. The park is home to a rare colony of red squirrels, and trout fishing is available on the 2-mile stretch of the River Lowther which runs through it. A 50-acre site with 203 touring pitches, 43 hardstandings and 403 static.

Leisure: 🛝
Facilities: ➜ 🚿 ⊙ 🔌 ✻ 📞 🏪 🐕
Disabled facilities: toilets & shower
Services: [T] ✖ 🍺 🚐 🍴 🧺 🍷 🔥 ♻ ⊡ → ∪ ⛳18 🎦 🎣 ◎
Notes: No single sex groups (families only), no cats, no rollerblades, no skateboards, no commerical vehicles

💳 💳 💳 💳 💳 💳

POOLEY BRIDGE   NY42

Park Foot Caravan & Camping Park
▶▶▶ 71%

Howtown Road CA10 2NA
☎ 017684 86309 🖷 017684 86041
🅔 park.foot@talk21.com
🅦 www.parkfootullswater.co.uk

Dir: M6 J40 onto A66 towards Keswick, A592 to Ullswater. At jct L for Pooley Bridge, R at church, R at x-roads signed Howtown

★ 🚐 £17-£25 🚌 £11-£18 ▲ £11-£18

Open Mar-Oct (rs Mar-May, mid Sep-Oct Clubhouse open wknds only) Booking Advisable bank hols Last arrival 22.00hrs Last departure noon

A lively park with good outdoor sports facilities, and boat launching directly onto Lake Ullswater. The attractive mainly tenting park has many mature trees and lovely views across the lake. The Country Club bar and restaurant provides good meals, as well as late-night discos, live music and entertainment which may not appeal to those seeking a quiet holiday. A 18-acre site with 323 touring pitches, 131 static.
Pony trekking, pool table, table tennis

Leisure: ⚒ ◣ ⚏ ☖ ☐
Facilities: ⬔⊙⚏❅⚘☻☷⌕
Disabled facilities: toilet
Services: 🆃✕♿⚏☖♀🔒⊘➔ ∪↳⚓
⚠

Notes: No single sex groups

▮▮ ▬▬ ▦▦ ▧▧ 🅢

SILLOTH   NY15

Stanwix Park Holiday Centre 🏠
75%

Greenrow CA7 4HH
☎ 016973 32666 🖷 016973 32555
🅔 enquiries@stanwix.com
🅦 www.stanwix.com

Dir: 1m SW on B5300. From Wigton bypass (A596), follow signs to Silloth on B5302. In Silloth follow signs to Stanwix Park Holiday Centre, approx 1m on B5300.

★ 🚐 £15.25-£18.55 🚌 £15.25-£18.55
▲ £15.25-£18.55

Open all year (rs Nov-Feb (ex New Year) no entertainment/shop closed) Booking Advisable Etr, Spring bank hol, Jul-Aug & New Year Last arrival 22.00hrs Last departure 11.00hrs

A large well-run family park within easy reach of the Lake District. Attractively laid-out, with lots of amenities to ensure a lively holiday, including a 4-lane automatic 10-pin bowling alley. A 4-acre site with 121 touring pitches, 62 hardstandings and 212 static.
Amusement arcade, gym, kitchen

Leisure: ⚒ ◣ ⚏ ◣ ☖ ☐
Facilities: ⬔◖⊙⚏❅☻☷
Disabled facilities: ramps, lifts & toilets in leisure centre
Services: 🆃✕♿⚏☖♀🔒⊘➔ ⌐18 ⚓◎
Notes: No single sex groups

▮▮ ▬▬ ▦▦ ▧▧ 🅢

SILLOTH — NY15

Hylton Caravan Park ►►►► 71%

Eden Street CA7 4AY
☎ 016973 31707 📠 016973 32555
📧 enquiries@stanwix.com
🌐 www.stanwix.com

Dir: On entering Silloth on B5302 follow signs Hylton Caravan Park, approx 0.5m on L, (end of Eden St)

★ 🚐 £13.40-£16.26 🚙 £13.40-£16.26
🛖 £13.40-£16.26

Open Mar-15 Nov Booking Advisable school hols Last arrival 21.00hrs Last departure 11.00hrs

A smart, modern touring park with excellent toilet facilities including several bathrooms. This high quality park is a sister site to Stanwix Park, which is just a mile away and offers all the amenities of a holiday centre. A 18-acre site with 90 touring pitches, 213 static.

Use of facilities at Stanwix Park Holiday Centre

Leisure: 🅰
Facilities: ➡ �📷 ⊙ ⏾ ℂ 🏧
Disabled facilities: toilets & shower
Services: 🚭 ⅋ 🗑 🖬 🖋 ⌀ → ⏰18 🔧 ⅀ ⌾
Notes: Families only, no single sex groups

WASDALE HEAD — NY10

Wasdale Head National Trust Campsite ►►► 65%

CA20 1EX
☎ 019467 26220 📠
📧 wasdale.campsite@nationaltrust.org.uk
🌐 www.nationaltrust.org.uk/campsites /lakedistrict

Dir: From A595(N) turn L at Gosforth/ from A595(S) turn R at Holmrook for Santon Bridge & follow signs to Wasdale Head

★ 🚐 🚙 fr £10 🛖 £9-£10

Open all year Last arrival 23.00hrs Last departure noon

Set in a remote and beautiful spot at Wasdale Head, under the stunning Scafell peaks at the head of the deepest lake in England. Clean, well-kept facilities are set centrally amongst open grass pitches and trees. The renowned Wasdale Head Inn is close by. A 5-acre site with removespace touring pitches, 6 hardstandings.

Facilities: 📷 ⊙ ⏾ ✳ ℂ 🛒 📷
Disabled facilities: toilet/shower
Services: 🗑 🖬 ⌀ → 🔧 ⌂
Notes: No single sex groups of over 4, groups by arrangement, no cars by tents

---

The Quiet Site ▶▶▶ 69%

Ullswater CA11 0LS
☎ 01768 486337 📠 017684 486610
📧 info@thequietsite.co.uk
🌐 www.thequietsite.co.uk

Dir: Leave M6 at J40, turn W following signs to Ullswater (A592). Turn R at lake jct, then R at Brackenrigg Hotel. Site is 1.5m on R

★ 🚐 £14-£20 🚉 £14-£18 ▲ £10-£18

Open Mar-Nov Booking Advisable bank hols & Jul-Aug Last arrival 22.00hrs Last departure noon

A well-maintained site in a lovely, peaceful location, with very good facilities, including a family bathroom. A charming olde-worlde bar is another attraction. A 6-acre site with 60 touring pitches, 20 hardstandings and 23 static.

Pets' corner, pool/darts (for adults), caravan storage

Leisure: ♦ ⚠ 🖵
Facilities: 🚿 📵 ⊙ �€‹ ✳ 🔌 🚻 🐾
Disabled facilities: WC / washbasin / bathroom
Services: 🆃 🚽 🚐 ⑂ 🚰 🍴 🛒 ⌀ 🅿 → ∪ ⚓ 🔧

Cove Caravan & Camping Park ▶▶▶ 67%

Ullswater CA11 0LS
☎ 017684 86549 📠 017684 86549
📧 info@cove-park.co.uk
🌐 www.cove-park.co.uk

Dir: From M6 J40 follow signs for Ullswater (A592). Turn R at lake jct, then R at Brackenrigg Hotel. Site 1.5m on R

★ 🚐 £12-£15 🚉 £12-£15 ▲ £10-£12

Open Mar-Oct Booking Advisable bank & school hols Last arrival 21.00hrs Last departure noon

A peaceful family site in an attractive and elevated position with extensive fell views and glimpses of Ullswater Lake. The ground is gently sloping grass, but there are also hardstandings for motorhomes and caravans. A 3-acre site with 50 touring pitches, 14 hardstandings and 39 static.

Drinks machine

Leisure: ⚠
Facilities: 📵 ⊙ 🌶 ✳ 🔌 🚻 🛒 🛁 🐾
Disabled facilities: wide doors & handrails
Services: 🆃 🚐 🗄 ⌀ 🅿 → ∪ ⚓ 🔧
Notes: No single sex groups

CUMBRIA

WATERMILLOCK — NY42

Ullswater Caravan Camping Site & Marine Park ▶▶▶ 69%

High Longthwaite CA11 0LR
☎ 017684 86666 📠 017684 86095
📧 info@uccmp.co.uk
🌐 www.uccmp.co.uk

Dir: M6 J40, turn W for Ullswater (A592) for 5m. R alongside Ullswater for 2m, then R at telephone box. Site 0.5m on R

★ 🚐 £10-£15 🚛 £10-£15 ▲ £10-£15

Open Mar-Nov (rs bar open weekends only in low season) Booking Advisable public hols Last arrival 21.00hrs Last departure noon
A pleasant rural site with own nearby boat launching and marine storage facility making it ideal for sailors. The family-owned and run park enjoys fell and lake views, and there is a bar and café on site. A 12-acre site with 155 touring pitches, 34 hardstandings and 55 static.
Boat launching and moorings

Leisure: 🔦 🎢 🎱

Facilities: 🌧 ⊙ 🔧 ☀ 🧺 🖳 🏕

Disabled facilities: toilet, shower & washbasin

Services: 🔟 🕹 🖥 🌡 🧴 ⊡ → ∪ ↳ ➴ ⚓

Notes: No open fires, no single sex groups

WINDERMERE — SD49

Camping & Caravanning Club Site (Ashes Lane) ▶▶▶▶ 77%

Ashes Lane LA8 9JS
☎ 01539 821119
🌐 www.campingandcaravanningclub.co.uk

Dir: Signed off A591, 0.75m from rdbt with B5284 towards Windermere

★ 🚐 £15.45-£18.95 🚛 £15.45-£18.95
▲ £15.45-£18.95

AA CAMPSITE OF THE YEAR 2005

Open Mar-Jan Booking Advisable bank hols & peak periods Last arrival 21.00hrs Last departure noon
A top Club site in a beautifully landscaped setting bordered by bluebell woods. Many mature trees and shrubs add to the natural beauty, and there are rocky outcrops and lovely views to be enjoyed. First class toilet facilities, good security, a large adventure playground, and a bar (The Whistling Pig) serving breakfasts, snacks and hot meals all add to the popularity of this very well-redeveloped site. A 24-acre site with 300 touring pitches, 86 hardstandings.

Leisure: 🔦 🎢

Facilities: 🌧 ⊙ 🔧 ☀ 🧺 🖾 🏕 🏕

Disabled facilities: toilets, washbasin, shower & razor point

Services: 🔟 ✕ 🍴 🕹 ∀ 🖥 🌡 🧴 ⊡ → ∪ ↳
♨ ➴ ⚓ 🖳

Fallbarrow Park ►►►►► 77%

Rayrigg Road LA23 3DL
☎ 015394 44422 📠 015394 88736
📧 enquiries@southlakeland-caravans.co.uk
🌐 www.southlakeland-
caravans.co.uk/parks/1115/view

Dir: 0.5m N of Windermere on A591. At mini
rdbt take road to Bowness Bay & the Lake.
Fallbarrow 1.3m on the R

★ 🚐 £17-£24 🚙 £17-£24

Open Mar-14 Nov Booking Advisable bank
hols & Jul-Aug Last arrival 22.00hrs Last
departure 10.00hrs

*A very high quality park with excellent
facilities, a few minutes' walk from Bowness
on the shore of Lake Windermere. There is
direct access to the lake through the wooded
park. A restaurant with a specialist chef
proves popular. A 32-acre site with 38 touring
pitches, 269 static.*
Boat launching

Leisure: 🔸 ⚙ ☐
Facilities: 🅝 ⊙ 🎇 🔧 ℄ 🛒 🖻 🎄
Services: 🖥 ✕ 🛗 🚽 🚿 ↻ 🖥 🗑 ⓘ ∅ → ∪ ⌐18
⌐ ☎ 🗲 ◎ ♨

Notes: No tents ✗

🔲 🟦 🟫 🔳 ⑤

Park Cliffe Camping & Caravan
Estate ►►►► 70%

Birks Road Tower Wood LA23 3PG
☎ 01539 531344 📠 01539 531971
📧 info@parkcliffe.co.uk
🌐 www.parkcliffe.co.uk

Dir: M6 at J36 onto A590. R at Newby Bridge
onto A592. 4m turn R into site. (Due to difficult
access from main road this is the only advised
direction for approaching the site)

★ 🚐 £14-£17 🚙 £14-£17 ⚠ £12-£15.20

Open Mar-15 Nov Booking Advisable bank
hols & Aug Last arrival 22.00hrs Last
departure noon

*A lovely hillside park set in 25 secluded acres
of fell land. The camping areas is sloping and
uneven in places, but well drained and
sheltered; some pitches have spectacular
views of Lake Windermere. The park is very
well equipped for families, and there is an
attractive bar lounge. A 25-acre site with 250
touring pitches, 60 hardstandings and 50
static.* Off-licence

Leisure: 🔸 ⚙
Facilities: 🛒 🅝 ⊙ 🎇 ☀ ℄ 🛒 🖻 🎄 ♈
Disabled facilities: toilet, washbasin
& shower
Services: 🖥 ✕ 🛗 🚽 🚿 ↻ 🖥 🗑 ⓘ ∅ 🖾 → ∪
⌐18 ⌐ ☎ 🗲 ◎ ♨

Notes: No single sex groups, no noise
10.30pm -7.30am

🔲 🟦 🟫 🔳 ⑤

WINDERMERE SD49

Limefitt Park ▶▶▶▶▶ 74%

LA23 1PA
☎ 015394 32300
[E] enquiries@southlakeland-caravans.co.uk
[W] www.southlakeland-caravans.co.uk/parks/1117/view

Dir: From Windermere take A592 to Ullswater. Limefitt is 2.5m on R

★ 🚐 £13-£20 🚙 £13-£20 ⛺ £11-£17

Open Mar-Oct Booking Advisable bank hols & Jul-Aug Last arrival 22.00hrs Last departure 10.00hrs

An attractive family site with superb facilities in a lovely location in the Lake District National Park. Buildings are well-integrated into the landscape, and the River Troutbeck runs through the grounds. From its valley setting there are spectacular views of the surrounding hills, with direct access to the fells and plenty of walks. This is a family park and does not accept single sex groups. A 20-acre site with 72 touring pitches, 72 hardstandings and 59 static.

Leisure: 🔍 ⛺ 🖵

Facilities: 🚿 ⊙ 🧺 ✱ 📞 🏪 ⛩

Services: [T] ✕ 🏠 🚚 🚐 🗑 🍷 🔒 🍃 → Ư ⛳18 ✈ 📽 🎣 ◎ ⛵

Notes: 🐕

💳 💳 💳 💳 💳

ASHBOURNE SK14

Rivendale Touring Caravan & Leisure Park ▶▶▶ 70%

Buxton Road Alsop en le Dale DE6 1QU
☎ 01335 310311 📠 01335 310311
[E] rivendale@fsmail.net
[W] www.rivendalecaravanpark.co.uk

Dir: Off A515 (Ashbourne-Buxton) opposite turn for Biggin

🚐 🚙 ⛺

Open Mar-Jan (rs low & mid season bar & cafe opening hours restricted) Booking Advisable Jul & Aug Last arrival 21.00hrs Last departure 11.00hrs

A sheltered park centred around a long-closed quarry with all hardstandings. The site is well equipped with excellent facilities, and run by enthusiastic staff. It has a small country-style bar, and a restaurant serving food at busy holiday times. A 37-acre site with 105 touring pitches, 60 hardstandings and 20 static.
Nature walk, dog walking field

Leisure: 🔍 ⛺ 🖵

Facilities: 🚿 ⊙ ✱ 📞 🏪 🧺 ⛩ 🐕

Disabled facilities: toilets & showers

Services: [T] ✕ 🚐 🗑 🍷 🔒 🍃 [E] → Ư

💳 💳 💳 💳

BAKEWELL   SK26

Greenhills Holiday Park
▶▶▶ 69%

Crow Hill Lane DE45 1PX
☎ 01629 813052 📠 01629 815760
📧 info@greenhillsleisure.com
🌐 www.greenhillsleisure.com

> **Dir:** 1m NW of Bakewell on A6. Signed before Ashford in the Water, 50yds along unclass rd on R

★ 🚐 £13.50-£15 🚙 £12.50-£14 ▲ £10-£12

Open May-Sep (rs Oct, Mar & Apr bar & shop closed) Booking Advisable Etr-Sep Last arrival 21.00hrs Last departure noon
A well-established park set in lovely countryside on the slopes of the lower Wye Valley. Many pitches enjoy uninterrupted views, and there is easy accessibility to all facilities. A clubhouse, shop and children's playground are popular features. A 8-acre site with 172 touring pitches, 63 static.

Leisure: 🏬
Facilities: 🏕 ⊙ 🔍 ☀ 🌜 ⛽ 📷 🐕
Disabled facilities: toilets, access to shop
Services: 🚽 🚐 🚰 🔋 🔌 🍴 🗑 → ∪ ⅓ ⚡ ◎

BUXTON   SK07

Lime Tree Park ▶▶▶▶ 71%

Dukes Drive SK17 9RP
☎ 01298 22988 📠 01298 22988
📧 limetreebuxton@dukes50.fsnet.co.uk
🌐 www.ukparks.co.uk/limetree

> **Dir:** 1m S, between A515 & A6

🚐 £15-£16 🚙 £15-£16 ▲ fr £12
Open Mar-Oct Booking Advisable bank hols & Jul-Aug Last arrival 21.00hrs Last departure noon
A most attractive and well-designed site, set on the side of a narrow valley in an elevated location. Its backdrop of magnificent old railway viaduct and views over Buxton and the surrounding hills make this a sought-after destination. A 10.5-acre site with 99 touring pitches, 8 hardstandings and 43 static.

Leisure: 🔍 🏬 🖵
Facilities: 🏕 ⊙ 🔍 ☀ 🌜 🐕
Disabled facilities: toilets, shaver & wash basins
Services: 🚽 🚐 🔋 🔌 🗑 → ∪ ⅓ 18 ◎ ⚡
Notes: No single-sex groups

MATLOCK   SK35

Lickpenny Caravan Site
▶▶▶ 73%

Lickpenny Lane Tansley DE4 5GF
☎ 01629 583040 📠 01629 583040
📧 lickpenny@btinternet.com
🌐 www.lickpennycaravanpark.co.uk

Dir: From A615 between Alfreton and Matlock, approx 1m N of Tansley. Turn into Lickpenny lane at x-rds

★ 🚐 £12-£14 🚐 £12-£14

Open all year Last departure 12.00hrs
A picturesque site in the grounds of an old plant nursery with areas broken up and screened by rhododendrons. Pitches, several fully serviced, are spacious and well marked, and facilities are to a very good standard. An ideal base for touring the Peak District. A 16-acre site with 80 touring pitches, 80 hardstandings.
Child bath available

Leisure: 🏊
Facilities: 🏪 ⊙ ⊕ 🔌 🦽 🎍 🐾
Disabled facilities: shower, toilet & washbasin
Services: 🔧 🚐 🛒 🗑 🍴 → ∪ 🛐8 ↘ 🍴 🗑 🛱
◎

NEWHAVEN   SK16

Newhaven Holiday Camping & Caravan Park ▶▶▶ 70%

SK17 0DT
☎ 01298 84300 📠 01332 726027
🌐 www.newhavencaravanpark.co.uk

Dir: Halfway between Ashbourne & Buxton at jct with A515 & A5012

🚐 £8.25-£9.50 🚐 £8.25-£9.50
⛺ £8.25-£9.50
Open Mar-Oct Booking Advisable public hols Last arrival 23.00hrs Last departure anytime
Pleasantly situated within the Peak District National Park, with mature trees screening the three touring areas. Very good toilet facilities cater for touring vans and a large tent field, and there's a restaurant adjacent to the site. A 30-acre site with 125 touring pitches, 4 hardstandings and 73 static.

Leisure: 🔌 🏊
Facilities: 🏪 ⊙ ⊕ 🔌 ☀ 🦽 🦮 🎍 🐾
Services: 🖥 🚐 🛒 🗑 🍴 → ∪ ↘ 🍴 🗑 🛱 △

Parkers Farm Holidays
▶▶▶▶ 70%

Higher Mead Farm TQ13 7LJ
☎ 01364 652598 🖷 01364 654004
🖃 parkersfarm@btconnect.com
🆆 www.parkersfarm.co.uk

> **Dir:** From Exeter on A38, take 2nd L after
> Plymouth 26m sign, at Alston, signed
> Woodland-Denbury. From Plymouth on A38 take
> A383 Newton Abbot exit, turn R across bridge
> and rejoin A38, then as above.

★ 🚐 £7.50-£12.50 🚍 £7.50-£12.50

▲ £5.50-£11.50

Open Etr-end Oct Booking Advisable Whitsun
& school hols Last departure 10.00hrs
*A well-developed site terraced into rising
ground. Part of a working farm, this park
offers beautifully maintained, quality facilities.
Large family rooms with two shower cubicles,
a large sink and a toilet are especially
appreciated by families with small children.
There are regular farm walks when all the
family can meet and feed the various animals.
A 8-acre site with 100 touring pitches, 25
static.*

Leisure: ♦ ⋀

Facilities: ♠ ⊙ ✳ ℃ ⅄ 盍 ㅈ ⋔

Disabled facilities: toilet, washbasin
& shower

Services: ▯ ✕ ⬛ ⬤ ▣ ☡ ℓ ⊞ → ◢ ◪ ⬛

Notes: No single-sex groups

⬛ ⬛ ▩ 𝓈

River Dart Adventures
▶▶▶▶ 73%

Holne Park TQ13 7NP
☎ 01364 652511 🖷 01364 652020
🖃 enquiries@riverdart.co.uk
🆆 www.riverdart.co.uk

> **Dir:** From M5 take A38 towards Plymouth, exit
> at Ashburton follow signs to River Dart Country
> Park. Site 1m on L.

★ 🚐 £9.50-£16.50 🚍 £9.50-£16.50

▲ £9.50-£16.50

Open Jul-Aug, wknds& school hols Apr-Sep
(rs Etr & Sep no eve facilities & warden cover)
Booking Advisable spring BH & Jul-Aug Last
arrival 21.00hrs Last dep 11.00hrs
*Set in 90 acres of magnificent parkland with
many exotic trees, and in spring a blaze of
colour from the many azaleas and
rhododendrons. There are numerous outdoor
activities for all ages including abseiling,
caving and canoeing, plus high quality, well-
maintained facilities. Dartmoor is only a few
minutes away. A 7-acre site with 170 touring
pitches, 12 hardstandings. First aid room*

Leisure: ⋨ ९ ♦ ⋀ ▢

Facilities: ⬅ ♠ ⊙ ⅊ ✳ ℃ ⅄ 盍 ㅈ ⋔

Disabled facilities: toilet & washbasin,
shower

Services: ▯ ✕ ⬛ ⬅ ⬤ ▣ ☡ ℓ ⊞ → ∪ ⵏ18
◢ 𝓈 ⬛

⬛ ⬛ ▩ ▩ 𝓈

AXMINSTER   SY29

Andrewshayes Caravan Park ▶▶▶▶ 67%

Dalwood EX13 7DY
☎ 01404 831225 🖷 01404 831893
📧 enquiries@andrewshayes.co.uk
🌐 www.andrewshayes.co.uk

Dir: On A35 3m from Axminster. Turn N at Taunton Cross signed Stockland/Dalwood. Site 150mtrs on R

★ 🚐 £9-£15.50 🚐 £9-£15.50 ▲ £9-£15.50

Open Mar-Jan (rs Apr-21 May & Oct-Jan shop hrs limited, pool closed Sep-mid May) Booking Advisable Spring bank hol & Jul-Aug Last arrival 22.00hrs Last departure noon
A lively park within easy reach of Lyme Regis, Seaton, Branscombe and Sidmouth in an ideal touring location. This popular park boasts an attractive bistro beside the swimming pool, a bar, laundry and shop. A 12-acre site with 120 touring pitches, 97 hardstandings and 80 static.
Licenced Bistro May-Sep

Leisure: ⚡ ♠ ⚠ ▢
Facilities: ⚡ ⊙ ⚒ ⚹ ⚿ 🛢 🛉
Disabled facilities: toilet & shower room, static unit, access to pool & bar
Services: 🔲 ✖ 🛒 🚐 🖂 🛢 🖉 🖽 → ∪ ⤵
Notes: Dogs must be kept on leads, no teenage groups

▨▨ ▨▨ ▨▨ ▨▨ 🆂

BARNSTAPLE   SS53

Tarka Holiday Park ▶▶▶ 70%

Braunton Road Ashford EX31 4AU
☎ 01271 343691 🖷 01271 326355
📧 info@midlandpark.co.uk
🌐 www.midlandpark.co.uk

Dir: 2m from Barnstaple on A361 towards Chivenor. (This is a fast dual-carriageway & care should be taken)

★ 🚐 £6-£13 🚐 £6-£13 ▲ £6-£13

Open Mar-Nov Booking Advisable all year Last arrival 22.00hrs Last departure noon
A gently-sloping grass park divided into paddocks, and close to the Tarka cycle trail. It offers a licensed bar with occasional entertainment, pitch and putt, a bouncy castle and children's playground. The site is about 5m from sandy beaches. A 10-acre site with 35 touring pitches, 16 hardstandings and 82 static.
Eating area in clubhouse

Leisure: ♠ ⚠
Facilities: ⚡ ⊙ ⚹ ⚿ 🛢 🛉
Disabled facilities: toilets, ramps at entrances
Services: 🛢 🚐 🖂 ♀ 🛢 🖉 → ∪ 🖍 ☎ ⤵ ⊙ ◭
Notes: No single-sex groups

▨▨ ▨▨ ⑩ ▨▨ ▨▨ 🆂

BICKINGTON (NEAR ASHBURTON) SX87

The Dartmoor Halfway Caravan Park ►►►► 72%

TQ12 6JW
☎ 01626 821270 ▤ 01626 821820
🅔 BHUGG22430@aol.com

Dir: Direct access from A383, 1m from A38 Exeter-Plymouth road

🚐 🚐

Open all year Booking Advisable high season & bank hols Last departure 10.00hrs
A well-developed park tucked away on the edge of Dartmoor, beside the River Lemon and adjacent to the Halfway Inn. The neat and compact park has a small toilet block with immaculate facilities, and pitches separated by mature shrubs. An extensive menu at the inn offers reasonably-priced food all day and evening. A 2-acre site with 22 touring pitches.

Leisure: ⚙
Facilities: ⌂⊙❄⌇⛱⾢
Disabled facilities: toilet & shower
Services: ✕🕮🖳🗓→∪Ḿ18 ⚌🍴🗑🂫

⬛ ⬛ ⬛ ⦿ ⬛ ⬛ 🛈

BRAUNTON SS43

Lobb Fields Caravan & Camping Park ►►► 66%

Saunton Road EX33 1EB
☎ 01271 812090 ▤ 01271 812090
🅔 info@lobbfields.com
🅦 www.lobbfields.com

Dir: At x-rds in Braunton take B3231 to Croyde. Site signed on R leaving Braunton

★ 🚐 £7.50-£19 🚐 £7.50-£19 🛆 £6-£19

Open 18 Mar-30 Oct Booking Advisable Jul-Aug, Spring BH Last arrival 21.00hrs Last departure 10.30hrs
A bright, tree-lined park with the gently-sloping grass pitches divided into two open areas. Braunton is an easy walk away, and the golden beaches of Saunton Sands and Croyde are within easy reach. A 14-acre site with 180 touring pitches, 7 hardstandings.
Baby changing facilities

Leisure: ⚙
Facilities: ⌂⊙⛟❄⌇⾢
Disabled facilities: toilet, shower & wash basin
Services: 🕮🖳🛢🗓→∪Ḿ18 🍴🛆🂫
Notes: No under 18s unless accompanied by an adult

⬛ ⬛ ⬛ 🛈

BRIDGERULE SS20

Highfield House Camping & Caravanning ►► 76%

Holsworthy EX22 7EB
☎ 01288 381480
✉ nikki@highfieldholidays.freeserve.co.uk

Dir: Leave A3072 at Red Post x-rds onto B3254 towards Launceston. Direct access just over Devon border on R.

★ ⊞ fr £10 ⊞ fr £10 ▲ fr £8

Open all year
Set in a quiet and peaceful rural location, this park has extensive views over the valley to the sea at Bude, 5 miles away. The friendly young owners with small children of their own offer a relaxing holiday for families, with the simple facilities carefully looked after. A 4-acre site with 20 touring pitches.

Leisure: ⚏
Facilities: ↿ ⊙ ⁂ ⼞
Disabled facilities: showers
Services: ⬛ ▣ → ⼁18 ⼂ ⼃

BRIXHAM SX95

Galmpton Touring Park ►►► 67%

Greenway Road TQ5 0EP
☎ 01803 842066
✉ galmptontouringpark@hotmail.com
⊛ www.galmptontouringpark.co.uk

Dir: Signed from A3022 Torbay to Brixham road at Churston

★ ⊞ £7.90-£12.10 ⊞ £7.90-£12.10

▲ £7.90-£12.10
Open Etr-Sep Booking Advisable Jul-Aug & bank hols Last arrival 22.00hrs Last departure 11.00hrs
An excellent location on high ground overlooking the River Dart, with outstanding views of the creek and anchorage. Pitches are set on level terraces, and facilities are bright and clean. A 10-acre site with 120 touring pitches.
Under 5's bathroom (charged)

Leisure: ⚏
Facilities: ↿ ⊙ ⾆ ⁂ ⼋ ⼊ ⼞
Disabled facilities: toilet, shower & basin
Services: ⊺ ⼤ ⬛ ▣ ⽕ ⼕ → ⼁18 ⼖ ⼗ ⼂ ▣ ◎ ⼀ ⼃
Notes: Families and couples only, no dogs during peak season

BUDLEIGH SALTERTON   SY08

Pooh Cottage Holiday Park
►► 72%

Bear Lane EX9 7AQ
☎ 01395 442354
ⓔ info@poohcottage.co.uk
ⓦ www.poohcottage.co.uk

Dir: A3052 take B3178 to Knowle. Site on brow of hill before entering village

★ **⊕** £10-£18 **⊕** £10-£18 **Å** £10-£18

Open all year Booking Advisable Jul-Aug & bank hols Last arrival 23.00hrs Last departure 11.00hrs

A rural park with widespread views of the sea and peaceful countryside. Expect a friendly welcome to this attractive site, with its upgraded toilet facilities, lovely play area, and easy access to plenty of local walks, as well as the Buzzard Cycle Way. A 4-acre site with 42 touring pitches, 4 hardstandings and 3 static.

Leisure: ⚡ ⚐
Facilities: ⚡ ❋ ⚐ ⊢
Disabled facilities: toilet
Services: ⚡ ⊡ → ∪ ⊓18 ⚄ ⚄ ⊚

CHAPMANS WELL   SX39

Chapmanswell Caravan Park
►► 71%

PL15 9SG
☎ 01409 211382
Dir: Off A388 midway between Launceston and Holdsworthy

⚡ ⚐ Å

Open Mar-Oct Booking Advisable Jul & Aug Last arrival mdnt Last departure noon

Set on the borders of Devon and Cornwall in tranquil countryside, this park is just waiting to be discovered. It enjoys extensive views towards Dartmoor from level pitches, and is within easy driving distance of Launceston (7m) and the golden beaches at Bude (14m). New owners are currently upgrading the facilities to a good standard. A 4-acre site with 50 touring pitches, 30 static.

Leisure: ⚡ ⚐
Facilities: ⚡ ⊙ ❋ ⚄
Services: ✖ ⊡ ⚄ ⚄ ⊞ → ⚄ ⚄

Holmans Wood Holiday Park
▶▶▶ 70%

Harcombe Cross TQ13 0DZ
☎ 01626 853785 ▤ 01626 853792
📧 enquiries@holmanswood.co.uk
🌐 www.holmanswood.co.uk

Dir: Follow M5 past Exeter onto A38 after racecourse at top of Haldon Hill. L at BP station signed Chudleigh, park entrance on L of slip road.

★ ♣ £10-£15 ♣ £11 ▲ £11

Open mid Mar-end Oct Last arrival 22.00hrs Last departure 11.00hrs

Delightful small park set back from the A38 in a secluded wooded area, handy for touring Dartmoor National Park, and the lanes and beaches of South Devon. The facilities are bright and clean, and the grounds are attractively landscaped. A 12-acre site with 85 touring pitches, 71 hardstandings and 25 static.

Information room

Leisure: ⚠

Facilities: ⬤⊙◐⬤⬤⬤⬤

Disabled facilities: wide access to shower

Services: ⬤⬤⬤⬤→∪⬤

Notes: No single sex groups

▭ ▭ ▭ ▭ ⑤

Finlake Holiday Park 🏛 65%

TQ13 0EJ
☎ 01626 853833 ▤ 01626 854031
📧 info@finlake.co.uk
🌐 www.finlake.co.uk

Dir: Signposted off A38 at Chudleigh exit

★ ♣ £10-£22 ♣ £10-£22 ▲ £10-£22

Open all year (rs limited facilities during winter months) Booking Advisable bank hols & Jul-Aug Last arrival 21.00hrs Last departure 10.00hrs

A very well-appointed holiday centre set in a wooded valley surrounded by 130 acres of parkland. A wide range of leisure facilities and entertainment for adults and children is available, and the park has its own pitch & putt course and fishing lake. A 130-acre site with 275 touring pitches, 175 hardstandings and 41 static.

Fishing, horseriding, pitch & putt, health club

Leisure: ⬤⬤⬤⬤⚠

Facilities: ⬤⬤⊙⬤⬤⬤⬤⬤⬤

Disabled facilities: toilet facilities

Services: ⬤⬤⬤⬤⬤⬤→∪⬤⬤

Notes: No single-sex groups

COMBE MARTIN   SS54

Stowford Farm Meadows
▶▶▶▶ 75%

Berry Down EX34 0PW
☎ 01271 882476 📠 01271 883053
📧 enquiries@stowford.co.uk
🌐 www.stowford.co.uk

Dir: M5 J27 onto A361 to Barnstaple.
Take A39 for Lynton through Barnstaple town
centre & in 1m turn L onto B3230. R at garage
at Lynton Cross onto A3123 & site 1.5m on R

★ 🚐 £6.50-£17 🚛 £6.50-£17 ▲ £6.50-£20

Open Apr-Oct (rs Etr-Spring bank hol & Oct
some amenities available limited hrs) Booking
Advisable bank hols & Jul-Aug Last arrival
20.00hrs Last departure 10.00hrs
*Very gently sloping, grassy, sheltered and
south-facing site approached down a wide,
well-kept driveway. This large farm park is set
in 500 acres, and offers many quality
amenities, including a large swimming pool,
horse riding and crazy golf. A 60-acre wooded
nature trail is an added attraction, as is the
mini zoo with its stock of friendly animals. A
100-acre site with 700 touring pitches, 30
hardstandings.*
Horse rides, fun golf, cycle hire

Leisure: 🐾 ♦ 🎠 🎱
Facilities: 🛠 🔒 ⊙ 🔍 ✳ ✆ 🍴 🦺
Disabled facilities: toilet & shower room
Services: 📺 ✕ 🚿 🚐 🔘 🍺 🛢 🏧 → ∪ 🕐18 🎵
🛢 ◎

▬ ▬ 🗺 💷

CROYDE   SS43

Bay View Farm Caravan &
Camping Park ▶▶▶ 67%

EX33 1PN
☎ 01271 890501
🌐 www.bayviewfarm.co.uk

Dir: M5 J27 onto A361, through Barnstaple to
Braunton, turn L onto B3231. Site at entry to
Croyde village

🚐 🚛 ▲

Open Mar-Nov Booking Advisable high season
Last arrival 21.30hrs Last departure 11.00hrs
*A very busy and popular park close to surfing
beaches and rock pools, with a footpath
leading directly to the sea. Set in a stunning
location with views out over the Atlantic to
Lundy Island, it is just a short stroll from
Croyde's many pubs. Facilities are clean and
well maintained, and there is a fish and chip
shop on site. A 10-acre site with 70 touring
pitches, 30 hardstandings.*

Leisure: 🎱
Facilities: 🔒 ⊙ 🔍 ✳ ✆ 🦺
Services: 🚿 ✚ 🚐 🔘 🛢 🏧 → ∪ 🍴 🎵
Notes: No single sex groups

CROYDE BAY SS43

Ruda Holiday Park 🏅 674%

EX33 1NY
☎ 01271 890671, 890477 & 0870 420 2991
🖷 01271 890656
📧 enquiries@parkdeanholidays.co.uk
🌐 www.parkdeanholidays.co.uk

Dir: M5 J27, follow A361 to Braunton. L at main traffic lights and follow signs for Croyde

🚐 £10-£30 🚙 £7-£30 ▲ £7-£26
Open mid Mar-Nov Booking Advisable all times Last arrival 22.00hrs Last departure 10.00hrs
A spacious, well-managed park with its own glorious blue flag sandy beach, a surfer's paradise. Set in well-landscaped grounds, and with a full leisure programme plus daytime and evening entertainment for all the family. Cascades tropical adventure pool and a nightclub are very popular features. A 220-acre site with 313 touring pitches, 280 static. Children's Club.

Leisure: 🏊 🎣 🎯 🎪 🖵
Facilities: 🖕 📵 ⊙ 🖳 ✸ 🔧 🛒 🎠
Disabled facilities: toilet, ramped access to Club Ruda
Services: ✖ 🖕 🖳 🖲 🖵 🖊 🖉 🖽 → ∪ ⋔18 🎵 ♨
Notes: 🗙 No single sexed groups under 25yrs/mixed groups under 21yrs

DARTMOUTH SX85

Woodlands Leisure Park
▶▶▶▶ 77%

Blackawton TQ9 7DQ
☎ 01803 712598 🖷 01803 712680
📧 fun@woodlandspark.com
🌐 www.woodlandspark.com

Dir: 4m from Dartmouth on A3122. From A38 take turn for Totnes & follow brown tourist signs

★ 🚐 £10.50-£16.50 🚙 £10.50-£16.50
▲ £10.50-£16.50
Open Etr-6 Nov Booking Advisable anytime Last departure 11.00hrs
An extensive woodland park with a terraced grass camping area, and quality facilities which are maintained to a very high standard. The park caters for all the family in a relaxed atmosphere under the supervision of the owner's family, and boasts the UK's biggest indoor venture zone, several water-coasters and rides, and a wildlife park. A 16-acre site with 225 touring pitches, 16 hardstandings. Watercoasters, toboggan run, gliders, falconry centre

Leisure: 🎯 🎪 🖵
Facilities: 🖕 📵 ⊙ 🖳 ✸ 🔧 🛒 🎣 🎠
Disabled facilities: toilet & bathroom
Services: 🆔 ✖ 🖕 🖳 🖲 🖊 🖉 🖽 → ∪ ⋔27 ♨ 🎵
Notes: 🗙

Cofton Country Holiday Park
▶▶▶▶ 69%

Starcross EX6 8RP

☎ 01626 890111 📄 01626 891572

📧 info@coftonholidays.co.uk

🌐 www.coftonholidays.co.uk

Dir: On A379 Exeter/Dawlish road 3m from Dawlish

★ 🚐 £7.50-£18.50 🚙 £7.50-£18.50

🛖 £7.50-£18.50

Open Etr-Oct (rs Etr-Spring bank hol & mid Sep-Oct swimming pool closed) Booking Advisable bank hols & Jul-Aug Last arrival 20.00hrs Last departure 11.00hrs
Set in a rural location surrounded by spacious open grassland, with plenty of well-kept flower beds throughout the park. Most pitches overlook either the swimming pool complex or the fishing lakes and woodlands. An on-site pub serves drinks, and meals or snacks, for all the family, and a mini-market caters for most shopping needs. A 16-acre site with 450 touring pitches, 20 hardstandings and 66 static.
Coarse fishing, pub with family room

Leisure: 🏊 ♦ ⚓

Facilities: 🅁 ⊙ 🍴 ※ ↳ 🐕 🛠

Disabled facilities: toilet & shower

Services: 🆃 🗙 🍴 🚐 📡 ♀ 🛒 ⊡ → 📶18 ↳ ♪

◎ Notes: No pets in accommodation, mainly non-smoking

🔲 ▭ ▭ 🔳 5️⃣

Golden Sands Holiday Park 🏠
68%

Week Lane EX7 0LZ

☎ 01626 863099 📄 01626 867149

📧 info@goldensands.co.uk

🌐 www.goldensands.co.uk

Dir: Signed off A379 Exeter/Dawlish road. 1m from Dawlish

★ 🚐 £9-£16.50 🚙 £9-£16.50 🛖 £9-£16.50

Open Etr-Oct Booking Advisable May-Sep Last arrival 22.00hrs Last departure 10.00hrs
A holiday centre for all the family, offering a wide range of entertainment. The small touring area is surrounded by mature trees and hedges in a pleasant area, and visitors enjoy free use of the licensed club, and heated swimming pools. Organised children's activities are a popular feature. A 2.5-acre site with 60 touring pitches, 188 static.

Leisure: 🏊 🏊 ♦ ⚓

Facilities: 🅁 ⊙ 🍴 ↳ 🛠

Disabled facilities: toilet, shower & ramps to all buildings

Services: 🆃 🗙 🍴 🚐 📡 ♀ 🛒 → 📶18 ♪ ◎

Notes: ✈ No single sex groups

🔲 ▭ ▭ 🔳 5️⃣

DAWLISH — SX97

Peppermint Park 69%

Warren Road EX7 0PQ
☎ 01626 863436 ▤ 01626 866482
✉ info@peppermintpark.co.uk
Ⓦ www.peppermintpark.co.uk

> **Dir:** From A379 at Dawlish follow signs for Dawlish Warren. Site 1m on L

★ ⛟ £10-£16 ⛟ £10-£16 ▲ £8-£14

Open Etr-Oct (rs early/late season shop, pool, club closed) Booking Advisable Spring bank hol & Jul-Aug Last arrival 20.00hrs Last departure 11.00hrs

Well managed attractive park close to the coast, with excellent facilities including club and bar which are well away from pitches. Nestling close to sandy beaches, the park offers individually marked pitches on level terraces in pleasant, sheltered grassland. The many amenities include a heated swimming pool and water chute, coarse fishing and launderette. A 26-acre site with 250 touring pitches.

Licensed club, entertainment, coarse fishing lake

Leisure: 🎣 ⚓ ♨

Facilities: 🛈 ⊙ ✳ ⚲ 🛒 🛉

Disabled facilities: toilet facilities

Services: 🛆 ⛟ ⓘ 🍴 🛈 ⌀ ⊞ → �🅟18 ❄ 🗡

Notes: No single sex groups of young people

EAST WORLINGTON — SS71

Yeatheridge Farm Caravan Park
▶▶▶▶ 66%

EX17 4TN
☎ 01884 860330
✉ yeatheridge@talk21.com
Ⓦ www.yeatheridge.co.uk

> **Dir:** On B3042 1.5m W of Thelbridge Cross Inn. Site is NOT in East Worlington village which is unsuitable for caravans

★ ⛟ £7-£11.50 ⛟ £7-£11.50 ▲ £7-£11.50

Open Etr-Sep Booking Advisable Etr, Spring bank hol & school hols Last arrival 22.00hrs Last departure 22.00hrs

Gently sloping grass site with mature trees, set in meadowland in rural Devon. There are good views of distant Dartmoor, and the site is of great appeal to families with its farm animals, horse riding, and two indoor swimming pools, one with flume. There are many attractive villages in this area. A 9-acre site with 85 touring pitches, 13 static.

Horse riding, fishing & pool table

Leisure: ♨ ⚓ ♨ 🏓

Facilities: 🛒 📞 ⊙ ⚲ ✳ 🛒 🐎 🛉

Disabled facilities: toilets, shower, access to facilities

Services: 🛈 ✕ ♨ ⛟ ⓘ ⓠ ⓘ ⌀ ⊞ → ∪ 🗡

Webbers Farm Caravan & Camping Park ►►►► 76%

Castle Lane Woodbury EX5 1EA
☎ 01395 232276 📠 01395 233389
📧 reception@webberspark.co.uk
🌐 www.webberspark.co.uk

Dir: 4m from M5 J30. Take A376, then B3179 to Woodbury. Site is 500yds E of village

★ 🚐 £11-£15 🚐 £11-£15 ▲ £11-£15

Open Etr-Oct Booking Advisable peak season & BH's Last arrival 20.00hrs Last departure 11.00hrs

An unspoilt family park set in three areas, offering a quiet and relaxing touring location. A high quality toilet block provides en suite family rooms and plenty of smart private facilities. The park has good views towards the Haldon Hills, and plenty to explore including 3, acres of Woodbury Common and nearby beaches. A 8-acre site with 115 touring pitches, 2 static.
Pets' corner, caravan storage facilities

Leisure: 🅰

Facilities: 🚾 📶 ⊙ 🕑 ⚒ ☽ 📞 🔧 🏃

Disabled facilities: toilet, shower & washbasin

Services: 🚐 🚐 ∨ 🗑 🗑 ∅ → ∪ ⌐18 ♪

▨ ▨ 🔜 🅢

Devon Cliffs Holiday Park 🏅 74%

Sandy Bay EX8 5BT
☎ 01395 226226
🌐 www.havenholidays.com

Dir: M5 J30/A376 towards Exmouth, follow brown signs to Sandy Bay

🚐 🚐 ▲

Open Mar-Oct Last arrival 22.00hrs Last departure noon

A large and exciting holiday park on a hillside setting close to Exmouth, with spectacular views across Sandy Bay. The all-action park offers a superb entertainment programme for all ages throughout the day, with very modern sports and leisure facilities available for everyone. An internet café is just one of the quality amenities, and though some visitors may enjoy relaxing and watching others play, the temptation to join in is overpowering. A 163-acre site with 144 touring pitches, 2 static.

Leisure: 🏊 ⚲ 🎾 🎣 🅰 🖳

Facilities: 🚾 📶

Services: ✕ 🗑 🝙 📞 🔧

ILFRACOMBE SS54

Watermouth Cove Holiday Park ▶▶▶ 66%

Berrynarbor EX34 9SJ
☎ 01271 862504
🅴 info@watermouthcoveholidays.co.uk
🆆 www.watermouthcoveholidays.co.uk

Dir: From M5 J27, take A361 to 2nd rdbt at South Molton, then A399 through Coombe Martin. Turn L at seafront & site 2m on R

★ 🚐 £8-£23.50 🚋 £8-£23.50 ▲ £8-£23.50

Open Etr-Oct (rs Etr-Whit & Sep-Nov pool, takeaway, club & shop limited) Booking Advisable Whit & Jul-Aug Last arrival anytime Last departure 11.00hrs

A popular site in very attractive surroundings, set amidst trees and bushes in meadowland with access to sea, beach and main road. This beautiful cove has a private sandy beach, and offers launching for boats and other water craft, as well as swimming. The site is two miles from both Combe Martin and Ilfracombe. A 6-acre site with 90 touring pitches, 10 hardstandings.
Coastal headland fishing

Leisure: ⚲ ⚫ Ⓜ ▢
Facilities: ⋔ ⊙ ⚒ ✻ ⚸ ⛢ ⏚ ⊓ ⟊
Services: 🅃 ✗ 🖳 🚰 🖩 ⚇ ⛟ ⊘ 🖽 → ∪ Ⱶ18 ⚁
⚳ ♪ ◎ ⊿
Notes: No motorcycles, no single sex groups
▨ ▧ ▨ ⑤

KENNFORD SX98

Kennford International Caravan Park ▶▶▶ 76%

EX6 7YN
☎ 01392 833046 🖷 01392 833046
🅴 ian@kennfordint.fsbusiness.co.uk
🆆 www.kennfordint.co.uk

Dir: At end of M5, take A38, site signed at Kennford slip road

🚐 £10-£12.70 🚋 £10-£12.70 ▲ £10-£12.70
Open all year

Screened by trees and shrubs from the A38, this park offers many pitches divided by hedging for privacy. A high quality toilet block complements the park's facilities. A good, centrally-located base for touring the coast and countryside of Devon, and Exeter is easily accessible via a nearby bus stop. A 15-acre site with 127 touring pitches, 15 static.

Leisure: ⚫ Ⓜ
Facilities: ⇥ ⋔ ⊙ ⚒ ✻ ⚸ ⛢ ⏚ ⊓ ⟊
Services: ✗ 🖳 ⚇ ⚁ 🖩 🖽 → ∪ Ⱶ18 ⚁ ⚳ ♪
⑤ ▨ ▧ ⑤

KENTISBEARE ST00

Forest Glade Holiday Park ►►►►
68%

Cullompton EX15 2DT
☎ 01404 841381 📠 01404 841593
📧 enquiries@forest-glade.co.uk
🌐 www.forest-glade.co.uk

Dir: Tent traffic from A373, signed at Keepers Cottage Inn, 2.5m E of M5 J28. Touring caravans via Honiton/Dunkeswell road, telephone for details of access

🚐 £11-£14.50 🚐 £11-£14.50 ▲ £9-£11
Open 2 wks before Etr-end Oct (rs low season limit shop hours) Booking Advisable school hols Last arrival 21.00hrs
A quiet, attractive park in a forest clearing with well-kept gardens and beech hedge screening. One of the main attractions is the immediate proximity of the forest, which offers magnificent hillside walks with surprising views over the valleys. Please telephone for route details. A 15-acre site with 80 touring pitches, 40 hardstandings and 57 static.
Adventure play area & paddling/ball pools

Leisure: 🏊 🎱 🎯 🎢
Facilities: 🌡️⊙🧺☼🧼🛒🎍🏪
Disabled facilities: toilet, handbasin & shower
Services: 🔲🚿💧♨️🔄🔌🚽➔🔄🔧
Notes: Couples & families only

LADRAM BAY SY08

Ladram Bay Holiday Centre
71%

EX9 7BX ☎ 01395 568398 📠 01395 568338
📧 welcome@ladrambay.co.uk
🌐 www.ladrambay.co.uk

Dir: M5 J30 onto A3052 signed Sidmouth. At Newton Poppleford take B3178 to Budleigh Salterton, through Colaton Raleigh, 1m L at brick monument, signed Otterton. Fork R at Otterton, follow signs

★ 🚐 £18-£22 🚐 £12-£16 ▲ £10-£12
Open Spring BH-Sep (rs Etr-Spring BH no boat hire & entertainment) Booking Advisable for caravans, school & spring BH Last arrival 18.00hrs Last dep 10.00hrs
A country holiday centre beside the sea, offering a variety of free family entertainment, and with its own private beach with sand and rock pools at low tide. Most pitches are set on tiered grassy banks to take advantage of the views. The park also boasts a superb indoor swimming pool. A 50-acre site with 305 touring pitches, 469 static.
Boat hire, doctor's surgery (in season)

Leisure: 🏊 🎯 🎢
Facilities: 🌡️⊙☼🧼🛒🎍🏪
Disabled facilities: static. caravan, shower, toilets
Services: 🔲✕🚿🚐🔌♨️💧🔄➔🔄🏪18🔧🎪
🔧🔲🎱 Notes: No under 25s, dogs on leads

LYNTON   SS74

Camping & Caravanning Club Site ►►► 66%

Caffyns Cross EX35 6JS
☎ 01598 752379
🕸 www.campingandcaravanningclub.co.uk

Dir: From M5 J27 onto A361 to Barnstable. Turn R to Blackmoor Gate signed Lynmouth & Lynton. Follow road for approx 5m to Caffyns Cross, immediately R to site in 1m

★ ⊞ £11.75-£15.35 ⊞ £11.75-£15.35
▲ £11.75-£15.35

Open Mar-Oct Booking Advisable bank hols & peak periods Last arrival 21.00hrs Last departure noon
Set on high ground with excellent views over the Bristol Channel, and close to the twin resorts of Lynton & Lynmouth. This area is known as Little Switzerland because of its wooded hills, and the park is ideal for walking, and cycling on the nearby National Cycle Network. A 5.5-acre site with 105 touring pitches, 10 hardstandings.

Leisure: ⚏
Facilities: 🝔☉🝴☀️🝭🛁
Disabled facilities: WC & shower
Services: 🎱⊞⬚🚽🚿➔⊍🛒
▨▨▨▨▨

LYNTON   SS74

Channel View Caravan and Camping Park ►►►► 65%

Manor Farm EX35 6LD
☎ 01598 753349 🖨 01598 752777
🅔 relax@channel-view.co.uk
🕸 www.channel-view.co.uk

Dir: A39 E for 0.5m on L past Barbrook

★ ⊞ £8.50-£12 ⊞ £8-£12 ▲ £8-£12

Open 15 Mar-15 Nov Booking Advisable Jul-Aug Last arrival 22.00hrs Last departure noon
On the top of the cliffs overlooking the Bristol Channel, a well-maintained park on the edge of Exmoor, and close to both Lynton and Lynmouth. Pitches can be selected from a hidden hedged area, or with panoramic views over the coast. A 6-acre site with 76 touring pitches, 15 hardstandings and 36 static.
Parent & baby room

Leisure: ⚏
Facilities: 🝢🝔☉🝴☀️🝭🛁🛒🝰
Disabled facilities: toilet & shower
Services: 🎱✖️⊞⬚🚽🛢🚿➔⊍🛒🚽◎
⚠ Notes: Groups by prior arrangement only

MODBURY SX65

Pennymoor Camping & Caravan Park ▶▶▶ 66%

PL21 0SB
☎ 01548 830542 📠 01548 830542
[E] enquiries@pennymoor-camping.co.uk
[W] www.pennymoor-camping.co.uk

Dir: Leave A38 at Wrangaton Cross. Turn L & straight over x-roads. Continue for 4m, pass petrol station & take 2nd left. Site 1.5m on R

★ 🚐 £6-£12 🚌 £5-£9 ⛺ £6-£12

Open 15 Mar-15 Nov (rs 15 Mar-mid May 1 toilet & shower block only open) Booking Advisable Jul-Aug Last arrival 20.00hrs Last departure noon

A well-established rural park on gently sloping grass with good views over distant Dartmoor and the countryside in between. The park is very carefully tended, and has a relaxing atmosphere. A 12.5-acre site with 145 touring pitches, 76 static.

Leisure: 🛝

Facilities: 🚿 ⊙ ✱ 📞 🏪 🐕

Disabled facilities: toilet, shower & washbasin

Services: [T] 🍽 🗑 🧯 🍃 ⬚ → ∪ 🧪

Notes: No single sex groups

MODBURY SX65

Camping & Caravanning Club Site ▶▶▶ 71%

PL21 0SG
☎ 01548 821297
[W] www.campingandcaravanningclub.co.uk

Dir: Leave A38 at Wrangton Cross onto A3121, continue to x-rds. Cross over onto B3196, L after California Cross sign before petrol station, site on R

★ 🚐 £11.75-£15.35 🚌 £11.75-£15.35
⛺ £11.75-£15.35

Open Apr-Nov Booking Advisable bank hols & peak periods Last arrival 21.00hrs Last departure noon

A gently-sloping site with some terracing, set in a rural location midway between Ivybridge and Kingsbridge. This well-ordered site is protected by high hedging, and is an ideal base for exploring the lovely South Devon countryside. A 3.66-acre site with 80 touring pitches, 11 hardstandings.

Leisure: 🛝

Facilities: 🚿 ⊙ 🔌 ✱ 📞 👪

Disabled facilities: toilet, handbasin, razor point & shower

Services: [T] 👍 🦆 🍽 ⛽ 🗑 🧯 🍃 ⬚ → ∪ 🧪 🏪 ⛵ AMERICAN EXPRESS VISA Barclays CONNECT DELTA [S]

DEVON

MODBURY SX65

Moor View Touring Park
▶▶▶ 76%

California Cross PL21 0SG
☎ 01548 821485 📠 01548 821485
🅴 info@moorviewtouringpark.co.uk
🆆 www.moorviewtouringpark.co.uk

Dir: Leave A38 at Wrangaton Cross & turn L at top of slip road onto B3121. Continue over x-rds for 4m past petrol station & park in 0.5m

★ 🚐 £6.50-£12.90 🚍 £6.50-£12.90
▲ £6.50-£12.90

Open 15 Mar-15 Nov Booking Advisable All the time Last arrival 18.00hrs Last departure 11.00hrs

A compact terraced park in picturesque South Hams, with wide views of Dartmoor. Many pitches are divided by low mature hedging, and there is a good mix of hardstandings and grass. The excellent facilities include a bright, modern toilet block, and a games room/TV lounge. The park is for adults only. A 3.5-acre site with 68 touring pitches, 32 hardstandings.

Leisure: ◉ 🎪 ⛱
Facilities: 🅁 ⊙ ⏱ ☀ ⚲ 🖧 🏛 ♜
Services: 🖽 🚿 🚽 🚐 🛢 🛇 ⌷ → ∪ ⋔18 🥄
Notes: No single sex groups, adults only

▦ ▦ ▨ 🆂

MOLLAND SS82

Yeo Valley Holiday Park
▶▶▶ 66%

EX36 3NW
☎ 01769 550297 📠 01769 550101
🅴 info@yeovalleyholidays.com
🆆 www.yeovalleyholidays.com

Dir: off A361 onto B3227 towards Bampton. Follow brown signs for Blackcock Inn. Site is opposite

★ 🚐 £9-£12.50 🚍 £9-£12.50 ▲ £9-£12.50

Open all year (rs Sep-Mar swimming pool closed) Booking Advisable Jul-Aug Last arrival 22.30hrs Last departure 10.00hrs

Set in a beautiful secluded valley on the edge of Exmoor National Park, this family-run park has easy access to both the moors and the North Devon coastline. The park is adjacent to the Blackcock Inn (under the same ownership), and has a very good heated indoor pool. A 7-acre site with 65 touring pitches, 15 hardstandings.

Fishing lake & bike hire

Leisure: 🏊 ◉ 🎪 ⛱
Facilities: 🅁 ⊙ ⏱ ☀ ⚲ 🖧 ♜
Services: ✕ 🚐 🛢 🚽 🛢 🛇 → ∪ 🥄

▦ ▦ ▨ ▨ 🆂

MORTEHOE SS44

Warcombe Farm Caravan & Camping Park ▶▶▶ 72%

Station Road EX34 7EJ
☎ 01271 870690 📠 01271 871070
[E] info@warcombefarm.co.uk
[W] www.warcombefarm.co.uk

Dir: N towards Mortehoe from Mullacot Cross rdbt at A361 jct with B3343. Site 2m on R

★ 🚐 £8-£17 🚌 £7-£17 ⛺ £7-£15

Open 15 Mar-Oct Booking Advisable Jul & Aug Last arrival 10.00hrs Last departure noon

Extensive views over the Bristol Channel can be enjoyed from the open areas of this attractive park, while other pitches are sheltered in paddocks with maturing trees. The superb sandy beach with Blue Flag award at Woolacombe Bay is only 1.5m away, and there is a fishing lake with direct access from some pitches. A 19-acre site with 100 touring pitches, 5 hardstandings.

Private fishing

Leisure: 🛝

Facilities: 🛁 🚿 ⊙ 🧺 ✳ 📞 🛒 🍽 ⛱ 🐕

Disabled facilities:

toilet/shower/pitches/access to reception & shop

Services: [T] ✖ 🧯 🚐 🍽 🗑 🍷 🔥 🍃 ⊡ → ∪ ⛳18 🎦 🎣 ◎

Notes: No groups unless booked in advance

💳 💳 💳 💳 💳

MORTEHOE SS44

Easewell Farm Holiday Parc & Golf Club ▶▶▶ 65%

EX34 7EH
☎ 01271 870343 📠 01271 870089
[E] goodtimes@woolacombe.com
[W] www.woolacombe.com

Dir: From Mullacott Cross take B3343 to Mortehoe. Turn R at unclass road & site is 2m on R

★ 🚐 £15-£42 🚌 £15-£42 ⛺ £4.50-£26

Open Etr-Oct (rs Etr no shop) Booking Advisable Jul-Aug Last arrival 22.00hrs Last departure 10.00hrs

A peaceful clifftop park with full facility pitches for caravans and motorhomes, and superb views. The park offers a range of activities including indoor bowling and a golf course, and all the facilities of the three other nearby holiday centres within this group are open to everyone. A 17-acre site with 311 touring pitches, 30 hardstandings.

9-hole golf on site

Leisure: 🏊 🎱 🛝

Facilities: 🚿 ⊙ 🧺 ✳ 📞 🛒 🐕

Services: [T] ✖ 🧯 🚐 🗑 🍷 🔥 🍃 ⊡ → ∪ ⛳9 ✈ 🎦 🎣 ◎ ⛵

💳 💳 💳 💳 💳

DEVON

MORTEHOE SS44

North Morte Farm Caravan & Camping Park ▶▶▶ 70%

North Morte Road EX34 7EG
☎ 01271 870381 📠 01271 870115
📧 info@northmortefarm.co.uk
🌐 www.northmortefarm.co.uk

Dir: Turn off B3343 into Mortehoe Village, then R at post office. Park 500yds on L

★ ⬜ £9-£14.50 ⬜ £9-£14.50 ▲ £9-£13

Open Etr-Sep (rs Oct Caravan owners only) Last arrival 23.30hrs Last departure noon
Set in spectacular coastal countryside close to National Trust land and 500yds from Rockham Beach. This attractive park is very well run and maintained by friendly family owners, and the quaint village of Mortehoe with its cafés, shops and pubs is just a 5 minute walk away. A 22-acre site with 180 touring pitches, 6 hardstandings and 73 static.

Leisure: ⚲
Facilities: 🛏☉🍴※💺🛒🏧
Disabled facilities: toilets & shower
Services: 🔌🔋🚰🚿🗑🚽→☌🅿🛒🔧🗑🛢
Notes: No large groups, no single sex groups & dogs must be on lead at all times

MORTEHOE SS44

Twitchen Parc 🏆 68%

Station Road EX34 7ES
☎ 01271 870343 📠 01271 870089
📧 goodtimes@woolacombe.com
🌐 www.woolacombe.com

Dir: From Mullacott Cross rdbt take B3343 Woolacombe Rd to Turnpike Cross jct. Take the R fork & site is 1.5m on the L

★ ⬜ £15-£40 ⬜ £15-£40 ▲ £4.50-£26

Open Mar-Oct Booking Advisable Etr/Whit & Jul-Aug Last arrival 24.00hrs Last departure 10.00hrs
A very attractive park with good leisure facilities. Visitors can use the facilities at all three of Woolacombe Bay holiday parks, and a bus service connects them all with the beach. The touring features pitches offering either sea views or a country and woodland outlook. A 45-acre site with 334 touring pitches, 110 hardstandings and 282 static. Table tennis, sauna, bus to beach, kids' club

Leisure: 🏊 🎯 🏐 ⚲ 🎱
Facilities: 🛏☉🍴※💺🛒🏧🎢🏧
Services: 📺✖🛁🔌🔋🚰🚿🗑🚽→☌🅿🔧
🎱🔧🗑🛢☉♨

NEWTON ABBOT SX87

Twelve Oaks Farm Caravan Park ▶▶▶ 71%

Teigngrace TQ12 6QT
☎ 01626 352769 Fax 01626 352769
E info@twelveoaksfarm.co.uk
W www.twelveoaksfarm.co.uk

Dir: From Exeter on A38 turn L signed Teigngrace (only), 0.25m before Drumbridges rdbt. Continue 1.5m through village, site on L. From Plymouth pass Drumbridges rdbt, take slip road for Chudleigh Knighton. R over bridge, rejoin A38 towards Plymouth. L for Teigngrace (only), then as above

★ £6.50-£10 £6.50-£10 £6.50-£10

Open all year Last arrival 21.00hrs Last departure 11.00hrs

An attractive small park on a working farm close to Dartmoor National Park, and bordered by the River Teign. The tidy pitches are located amongst trees and shrubs, and the modern facilities are very well maintained. Children will enjoy all the farm animals, and nearby is the Templar Way walking route. A 2-acre site with 35 touring pitches, 17 hardstandings.

Leisure:
Facilities:
Services: → 18

NEWTON ABBOT SX87

Dornafield ▶▶▶▶▶ 75%

Dornafield Farm Two Mile Oak TQ12 6DD
☎ 01803 812732 Fax 01803 812032
E enquiries@dornafield.com
W www.dornafield.com

Dir: Take A381 (Newton Abbot-Totnes) for 2m. At Two Mile Oak Inn turn R, then L at x-roads in 0.5m to site on R

★ £10.50-£17 £10.50-£17 £10-£15

Open Mar-Oct Booking Advisable bank hols & Jul-Aug Last arrival 22.00hrs Last departure 11.00hrs

An excellent park in a secluded wooded valley setting, with well laid out pitches and a peaceful atmosphere. A lovely 15th-century farmhouse sits at the entrance, and reception and the shop are housed in converted barns around a courtyard. The park is divided into three separate areas, served by two modern, heated toilet blocks, and the friendly family owners are always available. A 30-acre site with 135 touring pitches, 75 hardstandings.
Caravan storage (all year)

Leisure:
Facilities:
Disabled facilities: toilet, shower & ramps
Services: T → 18
Notes: No single sex groups

NEWTON ABBOT   SX87

Ross Park ▶▶▶▶▶ 80%

Park Hill Farm Ipplepen TQ12 5TT
☎ 01803 812983 📄 01803 812983
📧 enquiries@rossparkcaravanpark.co.uk
🌐 www.rossparkcaravanpark.co.uk

Dir: Off A381, 3m from Newton Abbot towards Totnes, signed opposite Jet garage towards 'Woodland'

★ 🚐 £10.75-£16.75 🚐 £10.75-£16.75
▲ £9.75-£15.75

Open end Feb-1 Jan (rs Nov-Feb & 1st 3wks of Mar Restaurant/bar closed (ex Xmas/New Year) Booking Advisable Jul, Aug & BH's Last arrival 21.00hrs Last departure 10.00hrs
A top-class park in every way, with large secluded pitches, high quality toilet facilities and floral displays throughout the 26 acres. The beautiful tropical conservatory also offers a breathtaking show of colour. This very rural park enjoys superb views of Dartmoor, and good quality meals to suit all tastes and pockets are served in the restaurant. A 26-acre site with 110 touring pitches, 82 hardstandings.
Snooker, table tennis, badminton, croquet

Leisure: ◀ ⚑ ☐
Facilities: ⌂ ⊙ ☜ ❄ ☪ ⅊ ⊡ 🎄 ⚲ 🐾
Disabled facilities: toilet & shower, ramps to restaurant & shop
Services: 🎫 ✕ 🍺 🚐 ⌱ 🗑 ☿ 🗞 ⌀ ⊞ → ∪ ⍬18 ⚏ ⏀

PAIGNTON   SX86

Paignton Holiday Park ▶▶▶ 65%

Totnes Road TQ4 7PY
☎ 01803 550504 📄 01803 521684

Dir: 1.5m W of Paignton on A385, near entry to town from Totnes direction.

🚐 🚐 ▲
Open Etr-Oct
A large park set in a beautiful valley, close to the beaches of Paignton and Goodrington and with all the attractions of Torbay within easy reach. A major upgrading has so far resulted in a new swimming pool, gym and leisure suite, though toilets are still fairly basic and clean. The park has its own 'inn on the park', a 16th-century thatched pub and restaurant. Contact the park for details of facilities. A 18-acre site with 204 touring pitches, 96 static.

Leisure: ⍩ ⚑
Facilities: ⌂ ☜ ⚲
Services: ✕ 🚐 🗞

Byslades International Touring & Camping Park ▶▶▶ 73%

Totnes Road TQ4 7PY
☎ 01803 555669 🖷 01803 555072
🅴 info@byslades.co.uk
🆆 www.byslades.co.uk

Dir: on A385, halfway between Paignton & Totnes

★ 🚐 £6-£11.50 🚐 £6-£11.50 ▲ £6-£11.50

Open Whit-mid Sep (rs May & Oct bar & swimming pool closed) Booking Advisable Jul-Aug Last arrival 22.00hrs Last departure 10.00hrs

A well-kept terraced park in beautiful countryside, only 2m from Paignton. It offers a good mix of amenities, and a licensed club with high season entertainment, plus a children's playground, and large heated outdoor swimming pool with special area for toddlers. A 23-acre site with 190 touring pitches, 40 hardstandings.
Crazy golf

Leisure: ⚅ ⚈ ⚁ /∆

Facilities: 🅝 ⊙ ⚅ ⚄ ⚌ 🖳 🛒 ᴨ ⍦

Disabled facilities: toilets, washbasin & shower

Services: 🔲 ✕ 💧 ♨ 🚐 🔳 🔳 🖵 ⚊ ⌀ 🔲 → ∪ ⋔18 ⚄ 😊 🎵 ◬

Notes: No single sex groups, no commercial vehicles, no dogs mid Jul-Aug

🔲 🔲 🔲 🔲 🆂

Widend Touring Park ▶▶▶▶ 68%

Berry Pomeroy Road Marldon TQ3 1RT
☎ 01803 550116 🖷 01803 550116

Dir: Signed off the Torbay ring road

★ 🚐 £6-£13 🚐 £6-£13 ▲ £6-£13

Open Apr-end Sep (rs Apr-mid May & mid Sep swimmimg pool & club house closed) Booking Advisable Jul-Aug & Whit Last arrival 21.00hrs Last departure 10.00hrs

A terraced grass park paddocked and screened on high ground overlooking Torbay with views of Dartmoor. This attractive park is well laid out, divided up by mature trees and bushes but with plenty of open grassy areas. Facilities are of a high standard and offer a heated outdoor swimming pool with sunbathing area, a small lounge bar and a well-stocked shop. A 22-acre site with 207 touring pitches, 6 hardstandings.

Leisure: ⚅ ⚈ /∆

Facilities: 🅝 ⊙ ⚌ 🖳 🛒 ⍦

Disabled facilities: toilet, washbasin, shower

Services: 🔲 💧 🚐 🔳 🔳 ⚊ ⌀ 🔲 → ∪ ⋔18 ⚄ 😊 🎵 ◎ ◬

Notes: No single sex/mixed groups, no dogs mid Jul-Aug

🔲 🔲 🔲 🔲 🆂

PAIGNTON SX86

Hoburne Torbay 66%

Grange Road TQ4 7JP
☎ 01803 558010 📠 01803 696286
✉ enquiries@hoburne.com
🌐 www.hoburne.com

Dir: S on A380 past jct A385, L at traffic lights into Goodrington Road, 0.75m turn L into Grange Road, site in 500yds

★ 🚐 £10-£25 🚍 £10-£25

Open Mar-Oct Booking Advisable public hols & Jul-Aug Last arrival 21.00hrs Last departure 10.00hrs

A large grass park set amongst woodland with spectacular views across Torbay town to the sea about 0.5m away. The leisure and entertainment complex has been refurbished, and offers something for all ages. The touring pitches are divided into two areas, and three separate toilet blocks are kept in very good condition. A 65-acre site with 146 touring pitches, 492 static.

Crazy golf, sauna, steam room, snooker, bowling

Leisure: 🎱 🏊 ♥ ⚲

Facilities: ➔ 🕭 ⊙ 🚿 ⚲ ↻ 🛁

Services: 🄣 ✕ 🍴 🛒 🚲 ⚡ 🖫 ♀ 🛢 ⌀ → ∪ ⌐18 ⚡ 🍽 ✦ ◎ △

Notes: ✖ No commercial vehicles, no single sex groups

PAIGNTON SX86

Beverley Parks Caravan & Camping Park 72%

Goodrington Road TQ4 7JE
☎ 01803 661979 📠 01803 845427
✉ info@beverley-holidays.co.uk
🌐 www.beverley-holidays.co.uk

Dir: Along A380/A3022, 2m S of Paignton turn L into Goodrington Road

★ 🚐 £11-£23.50 🚍 £11-£23.50

⛺ £7-£19.50

Open Feb-Nov Booking Advisable Jun-Sep Last arrival 22.00hrs Last departure 10.00hrs

A high quality family-run park with extensive views of the bay, and plenty of on-site amenities. The park boasts indoor and outdoor heated swimming pools, and the toilet facilities are very modern and clean. The park complex is attractively laid out. A 12-acre site with 189 touring pitches, 30 hardstandings and 195 static.

Table tennis, pool, spa bath, crazy golf, sauna

Leisure: 🎱 🏊 ♥ ⚲ ⚲

Facilities: ➔ 🕭 ⊙ 🚿 ⚲ ↻ 🛁 🛒

Disabled facilities: toilet & shower room, level access/lift to facilities

Services: 🄣 ✕ 🍴 🚲 🛒 ♀ 🛢 ⌀ → ∪ ⌐18 ✦ 🍽 ♪ 🖫 ♀ ◎ △

Notes: ✖

PLYMOUTH SX45

Riverside Caravan Park
▶▶▶▶ 73%

Leigham Manor Drive PL6 8LL
☎ 01752 344122 🖷 01752 344122
📧 info@riversidecaravanpark.com
🌐 www.riversidecaravanpark.com

Dir: A38 follow signs at Marsh Mills rdbt, take 3rd exit, then L. In 400yds turn R & keep River Plym on R to park

★ 🏕 🚐 Å

Open all year (rs Oct-Etr Bar, Restaurant & Take-away closed) Booking Advisable Jun-Aug Last arrival 22.00hrs Last departure 10.00hrs

A well-groomed site on the outskirts of Plymouth on the banks of the River Plym, in a quiet location surrounded by woodland. The toilet facilities are to a very good standard, and include private cubicles. This park is an ideal stopover for the ferries to France, and makes an excellent base for touring Dartmoor and the coast. A 11-acre site with 293 touring pitches.

Leisure: 🎣 ♦ 🎱 ▢
Facilities: 🌣 ⊙ 🍽 ✻ 🛒 🐕 🛉
Services: 🔌 ✗ 🖶 🍺 🗊 🛢 🍴 ⊞ → ∪ ♪ 18 ⅄
🚑 🎵 🗊 🛒 ◎ ♨
▭ ▭ VISA 🆂

SALCOMBE SX73

Higher Rew Caravan & Camping Park ▶▶▶ 66%

Higher Rew Malborough TQ7 3DW
☎ 01548 842681 & 843681 🖷 01548 843681
📧 enquiries@higherrew.co.uk
🌐 www.higherrew.co.uk

Dir: Follow A381 to Salcombe. Turn R at Townsend Cross & follow signs to Soar for 1m. L at Rew Cross

🚐 £8-£13 🚐 £8-£13 Å £7-£11

Open Etr-Oct Booking Advisable Spring bank hol & mid Jul-Aug Last arrival 22.00hrs Last departure noon

A long-established park in a remote location in sight of the sea. The spacious, open touring field has some tiered pitches in the sloping grass, and there are lovely countryside or sea views from every pitch. Friendly family owners are continually improving the facilities. A 5-acre site with 85 touring pitches.
Play barn

Leisure: ♦ ♦
Facilities: 🌣 ⊙ 🍽 ✻ 🛒 🛒 🛉
Services: 🖶 🗊 🛢 🍴 ⊞ → ⅄ 🍴 ♨
Notes: No groups of young people in peak season

SALCOMBE   SX73

Karrageen Caravan & Camping Park ►►► 71%

Bolberry Malborough TQ7 3EN
☎ 01548 561230 🖷 01548 560192
🅔 phil@karrageen.co.uk
🅦 www.karrageen.co.uk

Dir: At Malborough on A381, turn sharp R through village, after 0.6m R again, after 0.9m site on R.

🚐 £8-£14 🚍 £8-£14 ▲ £8-£14

Open 15 Mar-Sep Booking Advisable bank & school hols Last arrival 21.00hrs Last departure 11.30hrs

A small friendly, family-run park with terraced grass pitches giving extensive sea and country views. There is a varied takeaway menu available every evening, and a well-stocked shop. This park is just 1m from the beach and pretty hamlet of Hope Cove. A 7.5-acre site with 70 touring pitches, 25 static.

Baby room, licensed shop, 2 play areas, family shower

Facilities: 🝙⊙🦡❄️🌜🅴🞲

Disabled facilities: toilet, shower & handbasin in room

Services: 🆃🝙🅿🖀🝙⌀🖽→🦑🗡️⌀

SALCOMBE   SX73

Sun Park Caravan & Camping Site ►►► 67%

Soar Mill Cove TQ7 3DS
☎ 01548 561378 🖷 01548 561378
🅔 bj.sweetman@talk21.com
🅦 www.sun-park.co.uk

Dir: On entering village of Malborough on A381, turn sharp R signed Soar. Follow signs on this road to Soar Mill Cove. Site situated 1.5m on R

★ 🚐 £7-£11 🚍 £7-£11 ▲ £6-£11

Open Etr-Sep (rs Oct Statics only) Booking Advisable Jul-Aug Last arrival 21.00hrs Last departure 11.00hrs

An open park in a peaceful rural location, with extensive country views and glimpses of the sea. The safe sandy beach at Soar Cove is approx 0.75m from this well-managed park run by keen and friendly owners. A 4.5-acre site with 65 touring pitches, 34 static.

Leisure: 🝙🝙🗔

Facilities: 🝙⊙🦡❄️🌜

Services: 🅿🝙⌀🖽→🦑🗡️🝙⌀

Notes: No groups of young people

Kings Down Tail Caravan & Camping Park ▶▶▶ 67%

Salcombe Regis EX10 0PD
☎ 01297 680313 📠 01297 680313
📧 info@kingsdowntail.co.uk
🌐 www.kingsdowntail.co.uk

Dir: Off A3052 3m E of jct with A375

★ 🏕 £8.80-£13.30 🚐 £8.80-£13.30

🅰 £8.80-£13.30

Open 15 Mar-15 Nov Booking Advisable Whit, bank hols & mid Jul-Sep Last arrival 22.00hrs Last departure noon

A well-kept site on level ground in a tree-sheltered spot on the side of the Sid Valley. This neat family-run park makes a good base for exploring the East Devon coast. A 5-acre site with 100 touring pitches, 41 hardstandings and 2 static.

Off licence

Leisure: 🟢 🛝
Facilities: 🏪 ⊙ 🔧 ※ 🛒 🐕 🌳
Services: 🗊 🏧 🛢 🛎 🗑 🖃 → ∪ ⋔18 ⅄ 🛒 🥤 🖲

Salcombe Regis Caravan & Camping Park ▶▶▶ 69%

Salcombe Regis EX10 0JH
☎ 01395 514303 📠 01395 514314
📧 info@salcombe-regis.co.uk
🌐 www.salcombe-regis.co.uk

Dir: Off A3052 1m E of jct with A375. Or from other direction take L past Donkey Sanctuary

★ 🏕 £7.85-£12.85 🚐 £7.85-£12.85

🅰 £7.85-£12.85

Open Etr-Oct Booking Advisable bank hols & Jul-Aug Last arrival 20.00hrs Last departure 10.00hrs

Set in quiet countryside with glorious views, this spacious park has well-maintained facilities, and a good mix of grass and hardstanding pitches. A footpath runs from the park to the coastal path and the beach. A 16-acre site with 100 touring pitches, 40 hardstandings and 10 static.

Off licence, bike hire & putting

Leisure: 🛝
Facilities: 🚻 🏪 ⊙ 🔧 ※ 🛒 🏢 🐕
Disabled facilities: bathroom
Services: 🗊 🏧 🛢 🛎 🗑 🖃 → ∪ ⋔18 ⅄ 🛒 🥤
◎ ♨ Notes: No single sex groups

DEVON

SIDMOUTH SY18

Oakdown Touring & Holiday Home Park ►►►► 76%

Weston EX10 0PH
☎ 01297 680387 📠 01297 680541
🅔 enquiries@oakdown.co.uk
🆆 www.oakdown.co.uk

Dir: Off A3052, 2.5m E of jct with A375

★ 🚐 £8.90-£21.30 🚏 £8.90-£21.30
🅰 £8.90-£21.30

Open Apr-Oct Booking Advisable Spring bank hol & Jul-Aug Last arrival 22.00hrs Last departure 10.30hrs

Friendly, well-maintained park with good landscaping and plenty of maturing trees. Pitches are grouped in paddocks surrounded by shrubs, and the park is well screened from the A3502. The park's conservation areas offer attractive walks, and there is a hide by the Victorian reed bed for bird watchers. A 13-acre site with 100 touring pitches, 90 hardstandings and 62 static.

Free use of microwave

Leisure: 🏊 🎱

Facilities: 🛏 🕯 ⊙ ⊙ 🔍 ※ 🌜 🚗 📮 🐾 🐕

Disabled facilities: bathroom with bath, shower, handbasin & toilet

Services: 🔟 🚐 🗪 ᶄ 🚐 🛢 🖊 🖥 → ∪ ↑9 🧺 🚌 🥣 🎱 ◎ ◊

Notes: Dogs must be kept on leads & exercised off park, no bikes, no skateboards

▨▨ ▨▨ ▨▨ ▨ S

STOKENHAM SX84

Old Cotmore Farm ►►► 68%

TQ7 2LR
☎ 01548 580240 📠 01548 580875
🅔 graham.bowsher@btinternet.com
🆆 www.oldcotmorefarm.co.uk

Dir: Leave Kingsbridge on A379 Dartmouth rd, passing through Frogmore & Chillington to mini rdbt at Stokenham. R towards Beesands, site 1m on R

★ 🚐 £8.25-£12.50 🚏 £8.25-£12.50
🅰 £8.25-£12.50

Open mid Mar-Oct Booking Advisable Jul & Aug Last arrival 20.00hrs Last departure 11.00hrs

A quiet park with some gentle slopes and mainly flat pitches set in an Area of Outstanding Natural Beauty. The family-run park enjoys fine views of the picturesque countryside of the South Hams. Facilities are modern and well maintained, and pebble and sandy beaches with cliff walks through woods and fields are within walking distance. A 3-acre site with 30 touring pitches, 11 hardstandings.

Leisure: ♦ 🏊

Facilities: 🕯 ⊙ 🔍 ※ 🌜 🚗 📮 🐕

Disabled facilities: toilet & shower

Services: 🔟 🗪 🛢 🖊 🖥 → ∪ 🧺 🥣

Notes: Dogs must be kept on leads

▨▨ ▨▨ ▨▨ ▨ S

Harford Bridge Holiday Park
▶▶▶ 69%

Peter Tavy PL19 9LS
☎ 01822 810349 ▤ 01822 810028
🄴 enquiry@harfordbridge.co.uk
🅦 www.harfordbridge.co.uk

Dir: 2m N of Tavistock, off A386 Okehampton
Rd, take Peter Tavy turn, entrance 200yds on R.

★ 🚐 £10.25-£16 🚍 £10.25-£16

🅐 £7.25-£12.50

Open all year end Mar-mid Nov (rs Nov-Mar
Statics only & 5 hardstanding pitches)
Booking Advisable Aug Last arrival 21.00hrs
Last departure noon
*This beautiful spacious park is set beside the
River Tavy in the Dartmoor National Park.
Pitches are located beside the river and
around the copses, and the park is very well
equipped for the holidaymaker. An adventure
playground and games room entertain
children, and there is fly-fishing and a free
tennis court. A 16-acre site with 120 touring
pitches, 5 hardstandings and 80 static.
Fly fishing*

Leisure: 🔍 🔍 🅰 ▯
Facilities: 🅝 ⊙ 🜚 ✕ 🌣 🦽 🎏 🕇
Disabled facilities: ramps, shower & toilet
Services: 🚐 ⑂ 🖥 🗑 🛢 ⊿ ⊞ → ∪ ⋔18 ♨ 🍴 🛒
◎ 🔥 Notes: No single sex groups

■■ ■■ ▨ 🔄 𝓢

Langstone Manor Camping &
Caravan Park ▶▶▶ 71%

Moortown PL19 9JZ
☎ 01822 613371 ▤ 01822 613371
🄴 jane@langstone-manor.co.uk
🅦 www.langstone-manor.co.uk

Dir: Take B3357 from Tavistock to Princetown,
after 1.5m turn R at x-rds, follow signs

★ 🚐 £7-£9 🚍 £7-£9 🅐 £7-£9

Open 15 Mar-15 Nov Booking Advisable bank
hols & Jul-Aug Last arrival 22.00hrs Last
departure 11.00hrs
*A secluded site set in the well-maintained
grounds of a manor house in Dartmoor
National Park. Many attractive mature trees
provide a screen within the park, and there is
a popular lounge bar with an excellent menu
of reasonably priced evening meals. Plenty of
activities and places of interest can be found
within the surrounding moorland. A 5.5-acre
site with 40 touring pitches, 5 hardstandings
and 25 static.*

Leisure: 🔍 🅰
Facilities: 🅝 ⊙ 🜚 ✕ 🌣 🦽 🎏 🕇
Services: ▯ ✕ 🚐 🖥 🛢 🍴 ⊿ ⊞ → ∪ ⋔18 ♨ 🍴
◎ 🔥 🔥 Notes: No single sex groups

■■ ■■ ▨ 🔄 𝓢

TAVISTOCK SX47

Woodovis Park ▶▶▶▶ 69%

Gulworthy PL19 8NY
☎ 01822 832968 📠 01822 832948
[E] info@woodovis.com
[W] www.woodovis.com

Dir: From Tavistock take A390 signposted to Liskeard. At top of hill turn R at x-roads signed Lamerton & Chipshop. Park 1m on L.

★ 🚐 £16-£18 🚌 £16-£18 ⛺ £14-£16

Open Apr-Oct Booking Advisable Jun-Aug Last arrival 22.00hrs Last departure noon

A well-kept park in a remote woodland setting on the edge of the Tamar Valley. This peacefully-located park is set at the end of a half-mile private tree-lined road, and has lots of on-site facilities. The toilets are excellent, and there is an indoor swimming pool, all in a friendly atmosphere. A 14.5-acre site with 50 touring pitches, 18 hardstandings and 35 static.

Mini-golf, sauna, jacuzzi

Leisure: 🏊 🎾 ⛹

Facilities: 🚿 ⊙ 🧺 ✱ 📞 🛒 ⛱ 🐕

Disabled facilities: toilet & washand basin

Services: [T] 🍴 🗑 🧯 ♻ → ∪ ⛳18 🎣 ◎

Notes: Dogs must be kept on leads

💳 VISA Barclays CONNECT DELTA Switch

TAVISTOCK SX47

Higher Longford Caravan & Camping Park ▶▶▶▶ 76%

Moorshop PL19 9LQ
☎ 01822 613360 📠 01822 618722
[E] stay@higherlongford.co.uk
[W] www.higherlongford.co.uk

Dir: From A30 to Tavistock take B3357 on L towards Princetown. 2m on R before hill onto moors

★ 🚐 £9-£13 🚌 £9-£13 ⛺ £9-£13

Open all year (rs Nov-Mar take-away closed) Booking Advisable Etr, Jun-Aug Last arrival 22.30hrs Last departure noon

A very pleasant park in Dartmoor National Park, with panoramic views of the moors. The mainly grassy pitches are sheltered, and some are secluded for extra peace and quiet. Higher Longford is surrounded by moorland parks, lanes and pretty rivers, yet Tavistock is only 2.5m away. The park is open all year round, and is well served with a shop. A 7-acre site with 82 touring pitches, 10 hardstandings and 24 static.

Pool table, campers' lounge

Leisure: 🎾 ⛹ 📺

Facilities: 🚿 ⊙ 🧺 ✱ 📞 🛒 🏪 ⛱ 🐕

Disabled facilities: contact for details

Services: [T] 🍺 🍴 🗑 🧯 ♻ 🗄 → ∪ ⛳18 🎬 🎣

Notes: Dogs must be kept on leads

💳 VISA 💳 Barclays CONNECT DELTA Switch

TORQUAY   SX96

Widdicombe Farm Tourist Park
►►►► 70%

Marldon TQ3 1ST
☎ 01803 558325 🖷 01803 559526
🄴 g.glynn@farmersweekly.net
🆆 www.widdicombefarm.co.uk

Dir: On A380 midway between Torquay & Paignton

★ 🚐 £6.50-£14 🚛 £6.50-£14 ▲ £6.50-£12

Open mid Mar-Oct Booking Advisable Whit & Jul-Aug Last arrival 21.30hrs Last departure 11.00hrs

A friendly family-owned and run park on a working farm, with good quality facilities and extensive views. The level pitches are terraced to take advantage of the views towards the coast and Dartmoor. A quiet but happy atmosphere pervades this park, encouraged by a large children's play area. Other amenities include a well-stocked shop, a restaurant, and a lounge bar. A 8-acre site with 200 touring pitches, 180 hardstandings and 3 static.

Family bathrooms, BBQ patio

Leisure: 🎣 ⚲

Facilities: ➔ 🄿 ⊙ 🝆 ✻ 🌢 🛢 �· ⚘ 🎠 🛉

Disabled facilities: toilet, bathroom & shop, bar, restaurant & reception access

Services: 🔲 ✕ 🛒 ➔ 🝆 ⅄ 🄿 🛒 🔊 ⚘ 🗓 → ∪ 🕗18 ⚽ ⚘ ◎

Notes: Families & couples only

UMBERLEIGH   SS62

Camping & Caravanning Club Site
►►► 66%

Over Weir EX37 9DU
☎ 01769 560009
🆆 www.campingandcaravanningclub.co.uk

Dir: On A377 from Barnstaple turn R at Umberleigh sign.

★ 🚐 £11.75-£15.35 🚛 £11.75-£15.35

▲ £11.75-£15.35

Open Apr-Oct Booking Advisable bank hols & peak periods Last arrival 21.00hrs Last departure noon

There are fine country views from this compact site set on high ground. The site has the advantage of a games room with table tennis and skittle alley, and two quality tennis courts, with an adjacent wooded area for walks, and a nearby fishing pond. A 3-acre site with 60 touring pitches, 12 hardstandings.

Leisure: ⚲ 🎣 ⚲

Facilities: 🄿 ⊙ 🝆 ✻ 🝆 🛢 🎠 🛉

Services: 🔲 🝆 🛢 🛱 ⚘ 🗓 → ∪ ⚽ 🛒

WEST DOWN SS54

Hidden Valley Park ▶▶▶▶ 75%

EX34 8NU
☎ 01271 813837 📠 01271 814041
[E] relax@hiddenvalleypark.com
[W] www.hiddenvalleypark.com

Dir: Direct access off A361, 8m from Barnstaple & 2m from Mullacott Cross

🚐 🚌 ⛺

Open all year (rs 15 Nov-15 Mar All weather pitches only) Booking Advisable peak season Last arrival 21.30hrs Last departure 11.00hrs
A delightful, well-appointed family site set in a wooded valley, with superb facilities and a restaurant. The park is set in a very rural, natural position not far from the beautiful coastline around Ilfracombe. A 25-acre site with 135 touring pitches, 74 hardstandings.
Gardens, woodland walks & lake

Leisure: 🔍 ⛓

Facilities: 🛁 🚿 ⊙ 🧺 ✻ 📞 🛒 🍖 🪑 🐕

Disabled facilities: toilet & shower, access to restaurant & bar

Services: [T] 🍴 👍 🎮 🗑 🍷 🔥 🌿 ⊞ → U ⛳18 ✈ 🎬 🎣 ⛵

💳 💳 💳 💳 💳 💳

WHIDDON DOWN SX69

Dartmoor View Holiday Park ▶▶▶▶ 70%

EX20 2QL
☎ 01647 231545 📠 01647 231654
[E] jo@dartmoorview.co.uk
[W] www.dartmoorview.co.uk

Dir: From M5 J31, take A30 towards Okehampton. Turn L at 1st rdbt towards Whiddon. Site is 1m on R

★ 🚐 £10.75-£14 🚌 £10.75-£14
⛺ £8.50-£11.75

Open Mar-Oct Booking Advisable Etr, Whitsun & Jul-Aug Last arrival 22.30hrs Last departure noon
Located on high ground on the northern edge of Dartmoor National Park, this family-run park is well presented throughout. A pleasant, informal site with all facilities maintained to a high standard. A 10-acre site with 52 touring pitches, 28 hardstandings and 79 static.
Off licence, putting

Leisure: 🏊 🔍 ⛓ 📺

Facilities: 🚿 ⊙ 🧺 ✻ 📞 🛒 🐕

Services: [T] 🎮 🗑 🍷 🔥 🌿 ⊞ → U 🎣

💳 💳 💳 💳

DEVON

Woolacombe Sands Holiday Park
68%

Beach Road EX34 7AF
☎ 01271 870569 📠 01271 870606
📧 lifesabeach@woolacombe-sands.co.uk
🌐 www.woolacombe-sands.co.uk

Dir: From M5 J27 take A361 to Barnstaple. Follow signs to Ilfracombe, until Mullacott Cross. Turn L onto B3343 to Woolacombe. Site on L

★ 🚐 £12.50-£32.50 🚗 £12.50-£32.50 ▲ £12.50-£32.50

Open Apr-Oct Booking Advisable 24-31 May & 19 Jul-30 Aug Last arrival 22.00hrs Last departure 10.00hrs

Set in rolling countryside with grassy terraced pitches, most with spectacular views overlooking the sea at Woolacombe. The lovely blue flag beach can be accessed directly by footpath in 10-15 minutes, and there is a full entertainment programme for all the family in high season. A 20-acre site with 200 touring pitches, 80 static.

Leisure: 🏊 🎾 🎱 Ⓜ
Facilities: 🌂 ⊙ 🍴 ❄ 🛒 🐕 🌳
Services: 🖭 ✕ 🏪 🏧 🗑 🍽 🍺 🛢 🛁 🔌 → ∪ ⋒18 🎵
◎ 💳 💳 💳 🍴 §

Golden Coast Holiday Village
70%

Station Road EX34 7HW
☎ 01271 870343 📠 01271 870089
📧 goodtimes@woolacombe.com
🌐 www.woolacombe.com

Dir: Follow road to Woolacombe Bay from Mullacott & site is 1.5m on L

★ 🚐 £14-£40 🚗 £14-£40 ▲ £7.50-£26

Open Feb-Dec Booking Advisable bank hols & mid Jul-end Aug Last arrival 24.00hrs Last departure 10.00hrs

A holiday village offering excellent leisure facilities as well as the amenities of the other Woolacombe Bay holiday parks. There is a neat touring area with a unisex toilet block, maintained to a high standard. Bowling alleys, a number of bars and plenty of activities add to the holiday experience. A 10-acre site with 93 touring pitches, 53 hardstandings and 80 static.

Sauna, solarium, jacuzzi, tennis, golf, fishing, snooker

Leisure: 🏊 🎾 🎱 ⊛ Ⓜ □
Facilities: 🌂 ⊙ 🍴 ❄ 🛒 🐕 🏪 🎏
Services: 🖭 ✕ 🏪 🛒 🏧 🗑 🍽 🍺 🛢 🛁 🔌 → ∪ ⋒9 ⛄ 🎿 🎵 🛢 🐕 ◎ ⌂

Notes: 🐾
💳 💳 💳 🍴 §

WOOLACOMBE SS44

Woolacombe Bay Holiday Village
🏕 71%

Sandy Lane EX34 7AH
☎ 01271 870343 📄 01271 870089
📧 goodtimes@woolacombe.com
🌐 www.woolacombe.com

Dir: From Mullacott Cross rdbt take B3343 Woolacombe rd to Turnpike Cross jct. Turn R to Morthoe, site approx 1m L

★ ▲ £9-£26

Open Mar-Oct Booking Advisable Whit & summer holidays Last arrival mdnt Last departure 10.00hrs
A well-developed touring section in a holiday complex with a full entertainment and leisure programme. This tents-only park offers excellent facilities including a steam room and sauna. For a small charge a bus takes holidaymakers to the other two Woolacombe Bay holiday centres where they can take part in any of the activities offered, and there is also a bus to the beach. A 8.5-acre site with 143 touring pitches, 237 static.
Entertainment, children's club, health suite, bowls

Leisure: 🏊 🎾 🎯 🏐 🛖 🎮
Facilities: 🚿 ⊙ 🍴 ✳ 🔥 🛒 🏪 🛗 🐕
Disabled facilities: toilets & showers
Services: ✖ 🏧 🔌 🛢 🍴 🍽 🛢 🥤 🔄 → ∪ 🛶 🛥 ⚭
🍴 ◎ ⬡ ▨ ▨ ▨ ▨ 🏧 ⑤

BERE REGIS SY89

Rowlands Wait Touring Park
▶▶▶ 67%

Rye Hill BH20 7LP
☎ 01929 472727 📄 01929 472727
📧 aa@rowlandswait.co.uk
🌐 www.rowlandswait.co.uk

Dir: Approaching Bere Regis follow signs to Bovington Tank Museum. At top of Rye Hill, 0.75m from village turn R for 200yds to site

★ 🚐 £9.50-£12.50 🚙 £9.50-£12.50
▲ £7.50-£10.50

Open mid Mar-Oct (winter by arrangement) Booking Advisable bank hols & Jul-Aug Last arrival 21.30hrs Last departure noon
This park lies in a really attractive setting overlooking Bere and the Dorset countryside, set amongst undulating areas of trees and shrubs. Within a few miles of the Tank Museum, the mock tank battles are an attraction of the area. A 8-acre site with 71 touring pitches.

Leisure: 🎯 🛖
Facilities: 🔌 🚿 ⊙ 🍴 ✳ 🛒 🏪 🛗 🐕
Services: 🔌 🔌 🛢 🛢 🍴 🔄 → ∪ 🛶 18 🥤 ◎
▨ ▨ ▨ ▨ ▨ 🏧 ⑤

BLANDFORD FORUM ST80

The Inside Park ►►►► 65%

Down House Estate DT11 9AD
☎ 01258 453719 🖹 01258 459921
📧 inspark@aol.com
🌐 members.aol.com/inspark/inspark

Dir: From town cross River Stour and follow signs for Winterborne Stickland. Site in 1.5m

★ ⊕ £9.65-£15.35 ⊕ £9.65-£15.35

▲ £9.65-£15.35

Open Etr-Oct Booking Advisable bank hols & Jul-Aug Last arrival 22.00hrs Last departure noon

An attractive, well-sheltered and quiet park, 0.5m off a country lane in a wooded valley. Spacious pitches are divided by mature trees and shrubs, and amenities are housed in an 18th-century coach house and stables. There are some lovely woodland walks within the park. A 12-acre site with 125 touring pitches. Farm trips (main season), kennels for hire

Leisure: ◣ ⚲

Facilities: 🏪 ⊙ 🗟 ☼ ⚄ ⛨ 🐾

Disabled facilities: toilet & shower

Services: 🔳 🛒 ⊕ ⊟ ⓘ ⊘ ⊞ → ∪ ⊢18 ⤵

▓▓ ▓▓ ▓▓ ▓▓ 𝄢

BRIDPORT SY49

Highlands End Farm Holiday Park ►►►►► 75%

Eype DT6 6AR
☎ 01308 422139 🖹 01308 425672
📧 holidays@wdlh.co.uk
🌐 www.wdlh.co.uk

Dir: 1m W of Bridport on A35, turn S for Eype. Park signed

★ ⊕ £10.75-£16.50 ⊕ £10.75-£16.50

▲ £8.25-£14.50

Open mid Mar-early Nov Booking Advisable public hols & Jul-Aug Last arrival 22.00hrs Last departure 11.00hrs

A well-screened site with magnificent clifftop views over the Channel and Dorset coast, adjacent to National Trust land and overlooking Lyme Bay. Pitches are mostly sheltered by hedging and well spaced on hardstandings. There is a mixture of statics and tourers, but the tourers enjoy the best clifftop positions. A 9-acre site with 195 touring pitches, 45 hardstandings and 160 static.

Gym, steam room, sauna, pitch & putt

Leisure: ⚲ ⚲ ◣ ⚲

Facilities: 🏪 ⊙ 🗟 ☼ ⚄ ⛨ 🐾

Disabled facilities: toilet & shower

Services: 🔳 ✕ 🍴 ⊕ ⩊ 🗟 ⚑ ⓘ ⊘ ⊞ → ∪ ⊢18

⤵ ⤵ ▓▓ ▓▓ 𝄢

DORSET

BRIDPORT — SY49

West Bay Holiday Park 68%

West Bay DT6 4HB
☎ 01308 422424 & 459491 & 0870 420 2991
📠 01308 421371
📧 enquiries@parkdeanholidays.co.uk
🌐 www.parkdeanholidays.co.uk

Dir: From A35 Dorchester road, W towards Bridport, take 1st exit at 1st rdbt, 2nd exit at 2nd rdbt into West Bay, park on R

🚐 £9-£27 🚐 £7-£27 ▲ £7-£24

Open 23 Mar-2 Nov (rs 6 Apr-25 May & 14-19 Sep Entertainment restricted) Booking advisable. Last arrival 21.00hrs Last departure 10.00hrs
Overlooking the pretty little harbour at West Bay, and close to the shingle beach, this park offers a full entertainment programme for all ages. There are children's clubs and sports activities for all the family, and plenty of evening fun with talent shows and cabaret etc. The grassy touring area is terraced to enjoy the seaward views. A large adventure playground is very popular. A 6-acre site with 131 touring pitches, 285 static.
Entertainment & children's clubs

Leisure: ⌇ ◣ ⌂
Facilities: ♄ ⊙ ℗ ✳ 🐾 ⊞ 戸
Disabled facilities: toilet facilities and ramp access
Services: ✕ 🛁 🚽 🖳 🖳 ♀ 🚰 ∅ 🖃 → ∪ ⌂18 ⅄ ♪

BRIDPORT — SY49

Freshwater Beach Holiday Park 68%

Burton Bradstock DT6 4PT
☎ 01308 897317 📠 01308 897336
📧 enquiries@freshwaterbeach.co.uk
🌐 www.freshwaterbeach.co.uk

Dir: Take B3157 from Bridport towards Burton Bradstock. Located 1.5m on R from Crown rdbt

🚐 🚐 ▲

Open 15 Mar-10 Nov Booking Advisable Jul-Aug Last arrival 23.30hrs Last departure 10.00hrs
A family holiday centre sheltered by a sandbank and enjoying its own private beach. The park offers a wide variety of leisure and entertainment programmes for all the family. It is well placed at one end of the Weymouth/Bridport coast with spectacular views of Chesil Beach. There are three immaculate toilet blocks. A 40-acre site with 500 touring pitches, 250 static.
Entertainment, amusement arcade, horse riding

Leisure: ⌇ ◣ ⌂
Facilities: ♄ ⊙ ℗ ✳ 🐾 ⌂
Disabled facilities: toilet & showers
Services: 🖳 ✕ 🛁 🖳 🖳 ♀ 🚰 ∅ 🖃 → ∪ ⌂18 ⅄ ♪ ◎
Notes: No single sex groups or unaccompanied teenagers

CHARMOUTH SY39

Camping & Caravanning Club Site

►►►► 70%

Monkton Wylde Farm DT6 6DB

☎ 01297 32965

🌐 www.campingandcaravanningclub.co.uk

Dir: on A35 from Dorchester, turn R onto B3165, signed Hawkchurch, site on L within 0.25m

★ 🚐 £15.35-£18.35 🚚 £15.35-£18.35

⛺ £15.35-£18.35

Open Mar-Nov Booking Advisable bank hols & peak periods Last arrival 21.00hrs Last departure noon

Located in a rural setting almost on the Devon/Dorset border, this attractively terraced park with high quality toilet facilities is ideally placed for visiting the resorts of Charmouth, Lyme Regis and the Jurassic Coast. Friendly managers keep the whole park in tiptop condition. A 12-acre site with 80 touring pitches, 34 hardstandings.

Leisure:

Facilities:

Disabled facilities: WC, shower

Services:

VISA Barclays CONNECT

CHARMOUTH SY39

Monkton Wyld Farm Caravan Park

►►►► 72%

DT6 6DB

☎ 01297 34525 📠 01297 33594

✉ holidays@monktonwyld.co.uk

🌐 www.monktonwyld.co.uk

Dir: A35, 200mtrs inside Dorset turn inland (brown signs), 2nd site on L

★ 🚐 £9.75-£15.40 🚚 £9.75-£15.40

⛺ £9.75-£15.40

Open Etr-Oct Booking Advisable school hols Last arrival 22.00hrs Last departure 11.00hrs

A pleasant family park in a secluded location yet central for Charmouth, Lyme and the coast. Owned and run by working farmers, it has been tastefully designed with maturing landscaping. The slightly sloping pitches face south, and trees bordering the perimeter shield them from the lane. Opposite the entrance is the mainly sheep farm which children enjoy visiting. A 6-acre site with 60 touring pitches, 45 hardstandings.

Family shower room

Leisure:

Facilities:

Disabled facilities: wheelchair access to shower block

Services: → U 18

VISA Barclays CONNECT

DORSET

Wood Farm Caravan & Camping Park ▶▶▶▶ 74%

Axminster Road DT6 6BT
☎ 01297 560697 🖹 01297 561243
🖲 holidays@woodfarm.co.uk
🌐 www.woodfarm.co.uk

Dir: Park entered directly off A35 rdbt on Axminster side of Charmouth.

★ 🚐 £10.50-£18 🚐 £10.50-£18

▲ £8.50-£15

Open Etr-Oct Booking Advisable school hols Last arrival 19.00hrs Last departure noon
A pleasant, well-established and mature park overlooking Charmouth, the sea and the Dorset hills and valleys. It stands on a high spot, and the four camping fields are terraced, each with its own impressive toilet block. Convenient for Lyme Regis, Axminster, and this famous fossil coastline. A 13-acre site with 216 touring pitches, 175 hardstandings and 83 static.
Coarse fishing lake

Leisure: 🐟 🔍 🎯 🕎 🖵
Facilities: 🚽 🅿 🛆 ⊙ 🕎 ❋ 🗜 🛒 🕇
Disabled facilities: toilet & shower
Services: 🆃 🖒 🖾 ⅋ ⬗ 🖾 🏧 🗑 → 🖯 ⊓18 🗲 🍴
🎵 ◎ 🛆

Notes: No skate boards, scooters or roller skates

▦ ▦ ▦ 🔀 🄢

Manor Farm Holiday Centre ▶▶▶ 66%

DT6 6QL
☎ 01297 560226
🖲 enquiries@manorfarmholidaycentre.co.uk
🌐 www.manorfarmholidaycentre.co.uk

Dir: Travelling W on A35, enter Charmouth, Manor Farm 0.75m on R

🚐 £9-£14 🚐 £9-£14 ▲ £9-£14

Open all year (rs End Oct-mid Mar Statics only) Booking Advisable high season Last arrival 20.00hrs Last departure 10.00hrs.
Set just a short walk from the safe sand and shingle beach at Charmouth, this popular family park offers a good range of facilities. Children enjoy the activity area and outdoor swimming pool (so do their parents!), and the park is well placed for touring this beautiful area. A 15-acre site with 250 touring pitches, 80 hardstandings and 29 static.

Leisure: 🐟 🔍 🎯 🕎
Facilities: 🅿 ⊙ 🕎 ❋ 🗜 🛒 � 🕇
Disabled facilities: toilet, shower, washbasin
Services: 🗙 🖒 🅿 ⅋ ⬗ 🖾 🏧 🗑 → 🖯 ⊓18 🗲 🍴
🎵 ◎ 🛆

Notes: No single sex groups

▦ ▦ ▦ 🔀 🄢

DORSET

CHARMOUTH — SY39

Newlands Caravan & Camping Park ▶▶▶ 73%

DT6 6RB
☎ 01297 560259 📠 01297 560787
📧 enq@newlandsholidays.co.uk
🌐 www.newlandsholidays.co.uk

Dir: 4m W of Bridport on A35

🚐 🚙 Å

Open all year (rs Nov-Mar restaurant, bar & shop closed) Booking Advisable school hols Last arrival 22.30hrs Last departure 10.00hrs
A very smart site with excellent touring facilities, including five 'millennium' pitches complete with water, electricity, chemical disposal point, washing machine and tumble dryer. The park offers a full cabaret and entertainment programme for all ages, and boasts an indoor swimming pool with spa and an outdoor pool with water slide. Set on gently sloping ground in hilly countryside near the sea. A 23-acre site with 240 touring pitches, 52 hardstandings and 86 static.

Leisure: 🥏 🎣 🏊 🎱 ⛳ 🎮 ☐
Facilities: 🛋 ⊙ 🔌 ✻ 🚿 ⚷ 🔥 🎀
Services: ▨ ✕ 🛒 🚽 🚐 ⚺ 🍴 🚰 🌀 → ∪ ↑18 🏊 ❄ 🍴
Notes: ✂ No single sex groups

▨ ▨ VISA ▨ ▨ 🔩 ⑤

CHRISTCHURCH — SZ19

Grove Farm Meadow Holiday Caravan Park ▶▶▶▶ 76%

Stour Way BH23 2PQ
☎ 01202 483597 📠 01202 483878
📧 enquiries@meadowbank-holidays.co.uk

Dir: Take Christchurch/Airport exit off A338, turn L for Christchurch and follow signs

★ 🚐 £7-£25 🚙 £7-£25

Open Mar-Oct Booking Advisable at all times Last arrival 21.00hrs Last departure noon
A very smart park on the banks of the River Stour, with a colourful display of hanging baskets and flower-filled tubs around the superb reception area. Toilet facilities are modern and spotless, and there is excellent play equipment for children. Visitors can choose between pitch sizes, including some luxury fully-serviced ones. A 2-acre site with 41 touring pitches, 22 hardstandings and 180 static.
Fishing on site, 21 fully serviced pitches

Leisure: 🥏 ⛳
Facilities: 🚻 🛋 ⊙ 🔌 ⚷ 🚿 🔥
Disabled facilities: toilet
Services: ▨ 🚽 🚐 🛒 🚰 🌀 ▣ → ∪ ↑18 🏊 ❄ 🍴 🌀 ◎ △
Notes: ✂ No single sex groups

▨ ▨ VISA ▨ ▨ 🔩 ⑤

HOLTON HEATH   SY99

Sandford Holiday Park 🏛 68%

BH16 6JZ
☎ 0870 0667793 📠 01202 625678
📧 bookings@weststarholidays.co.uk
🌐 www.weststarholidays.co.uk

Dir: From Poole take A35 towards Dorchester, at lights turn onto A351 towards Wareham. Turn R at Holton Heath. Park 100yds on L

★ 🚐 £12.50-£28.50 🚙 £12.50-£28.50

🚃 £12.50-£28.50

Open Mar-Nov Booking Advisable Jul-Aug & bank hols Last arrival 22.00hrs Last departure 10.00hrs

With touring pitches set individually in 20 acres surrounded by woodland, this park offers a full range of leisure activities and entertainment for the whole family. The touring area is neat and well maintained, and there are children's clubs in the daytime and nightly entertainment. A 64-acre site with 500 touring pitches, 284 static.

Fun factory, bowling, entertainment, crazy golf

Leisure: 🏊 🎾 🎯 🎣 🏛 🎱

Facilities: 🚿 🔥 ⊙ ⊛ 🕯 🛒 🖬 🚲 🎏 🏕

Disabled facilities: purpose built 'Fern Lodge' for disabled

Services: ✗ 🛒 🚐 🗑 🔄 🗑 🔧 → ∪ 🏮 ◎ 🌳 ⚌

🔧 **Notes:** No single sex groups or unaccompanied persons under 21

🚗 🚙 🛻 🚐 🄂

LYME REGIS   SY39

Shrubbery Touring Park
▶▶▶ 67%

Rousdon DT7 3XW
☎ 01297 442227 📠 01297 442227
🌐 www.ukparks.co.uk/shrubbery

Dir: 3m W of Lyme Regis on A3052 coast road

★ 🚐 £7.50-£11.50 🚙 £7-£10.75

🚃 £7-£10.75

Open Mar-Oct Booking Advisable BH's & Jul-Aug Last arrival 23.00hrs Last departure 11.00hrs

Mature trees enclose this peaceful park which has distant views of the lovely countryside. The modern facilities are well kept, and there is plenty of space for children to play. Located on the Devon/Dorset border, just 3 miles from Lyme Regis. A 10-acre site with 120 touring pitches.

Leisure: 🏛

Facilities: 🔥 ⊙ ⊛ 🕯 🛒 🏕

Disabled facilities: toilet, shower & washbasin

Services: 🚐 🗑 🗑 🔄 🄂 → 🏮18 🌳 ⚌ 🔧 ◎ ⚊

MORETON SY88

Camping & Caravanning Club Site
►►► 71%

Station Road DT2 8BB
☎ 01305 853801
[W] www.campingandcaravanningclub.co.uk

Dir: From Poole on A35, continue past Bere Regis, turn L onto B3390 signposted Alfpuddle. After 2m site on L before Moreton Station and next to public house

★ 🚐 £12.95-£18.35 🚐 £12.95-£18.35
⛺ £12.95-£18.35

Open Mar-Nov Booking Advisable bank hols & peak periods Last arrival 21.00hrs Last departure noon

Modern purpose-built site on level ground with good amenities. This tidy, well-maintained park offers electric hook-ups to most pitches, and there is a first class play area for children. A 7-acre site with 130 touring pitches.

Leisure:
Facilities:
Disabled facilities: toilet, washbasin, shower & hand dryer
Services:

OWERMOIGNE SY78

Sandyholme Caravan Park
►►► 72%

Moreton Road DT2 8HZ
☎ 01305 852677 📠 01305 854677
[E] smeatons@sandyholme.co.uk
[W] www.sandyholme.co.uk

Dir: From A352 (Wareham to Dorchester road) turn R to Owermoigne for 1m. Site on L.

★ 🚐 £10.50-£15 🚐 £10.50-£15
⛺ £8-£12.75

Open 20 Mar-31 Oct Booking Advisable peak periods Last arrival 21.30hrs Last departure 10.30hrs

A quiet family-run site in a tree-lined rural setting within easy reach of the coast at Lulworth Cove, and handy for several seaside resorts. The facilities are very good, including a superb toilet block, and good food is available in the lounge/bar. A 6-acre site with 50 touring pitches, 55 static.

Table tennis

Leisure:
Facilities:
Disabled facilities: toilet & shower
Services:
Notes: Dogs must be kept on leads, no single sex groups

POOLE SZ09

Beacon Hill Touring Park ►►► 69%

Blandford Road North BH16 6AB
☎ 01202 631631 🖷 01202 625749
bookings@beaconhilltouringpark.co.uk
www.beaconhilltouringpark.co.uk

Dir: On A350, 0.25m N of jct with A35, 4m N of Poole

Open Etr-Sep (rs low & mid season some services closed/restricted opening) Booking Advisable Etr, Whit & Jul-Aug Last arrival 23.00hrs Last departure 11.00hrs
Set in attractive, wooded area with conservation very much in mind. Two large ponds are within the grounds and the terraced pitches offer some fine views. A 30-acre site with 170 touring pitches, 10 hardstandings.
Fishing & view point

Leisure:
Facilities:
Disabled facilities: toilet & shower room
Services: 18
Notes: Groups of young people accepted at management's discretion

POOLE SZ09

Rockley Park 68%

Hamworthy BH15 4LZ
☎ 01202 679393 🖷 01202 683159
www.british-holidays.co.uk

Dir: Take A31 off M27 to Poole centre, then follow signs to park

Open Mar-Oct Booking Advisable Jul-Aug & bank hols Last arrival 20.00hrs Last departure noon
A complete holiday experience including a wide range of day and night entertainment, and plenty of sports and leisure activities. Water sports are comprehensively covered, and there is also mooring and launching from the park. The touring area has been upgraded to provide good quality facilities. A 4.25-acre site with 71 touring pitches, 1,077 static.

Leisure:
Facilities:
Disabled facilities: toilet
Services: 9

DORSET

Forest Edge Touring Park
▶▶▶ 65%

229 Ringwood Road BH24 2SD
☎ 01590 648331 📠 01590 645610
📧 holidays@shorefield.co.uk
🌐 www.shorefield.co.uk

Dir: 3m W of Ringwood off A31, turn L at rdbt into Boundary Lane

★ 🚐 £8-£24 🚐 £8-£24 ▲ £8-£24

Open Feb-Dec (rs mid Jul-Aug pool only open school & summer holidays) Booking Advisable at all times Last arrival 21.00hrs Last departure 10.00hrs
A tree-lined park set in grassland with plenty of excellent amenities for all the family, including an outdoor heated swimming pool and toddlers' pool, an adventure playground, and two launderettes. Visitors are invited to use the superb leisure club plus all amenities and entertainment at the sister site of Oakdene Forest Park less than a mile away. Some pitches may experience traffic noise from the nearby A31. A 9-acre site with 202 touring pitches.

Leisure: ⚡ ◆ /🄰
Facilities: ⬛ ⊙ ⚛ ✷ ✆ 🕿
Services: 🆃 🚐 🗑 🆘 🍴 🅰 ⇥ ∪ ⌂ ◎

Notes: 1 dog & car per pitch, no under 25s unless in family unit

Oakdene Forest Park 🏞 68%

BH24 2RZ
☎ 01590 648331 📠 01590 645610
📧 holidays@shorefield.co.uk
🌐 www.shorefield.co.uk

Dir: 3m W of Ringwood off A31, turn L after foot bridge over A31

★ 🚐 fr £22 ▲

Open Feb-2 Jan Booking Advisable all times Last arrival 22.00hrs Last departure 10.00hrs
Set in 55 acres of parkland beside the beautiful Avon Forest, this full-entertainment park offers 'fun and games' for the whole family, and there are both indoor and outdoor pools, and a riding stable on site. A special children's programme is offered during high season. A 55-acre site with 81 touring pitches, 105 static.
Woodland walks & crazy golf

Leisure: ⚡ ⚡ ◆ /🄰
Facilities: ⬛ ⊙ ⚛ ✷ ✆ 🕿 🎣 🕿
Services: 🆃 ✗ 🍴 🚐 🗑 🆘 🅰 ⇥ ∪ ⌂18 ♪

Notes: No single sex groups, no under 25s unless in a family group

DORSET

SWANAGE   SZ07

Ulwell Cottage Caravan Park
▶▶▶ 70%

Ulwell Cottage Ulwell BH19 3DG
☎ 01929 422823 📠 01929 421500
📧 enq@ulwellcottagepark.co.uk
🌐 www.ulwellcottagepark.co.uk

Dir: From Swanage travel N for 2m on unclass road towards Studland

★ ⚏ £12.25-£28 ⚏ £10-£28 ⚏ £10-£17

Open Mar-7 Jan (rs Mar-spring bank hol & mid Sep-early Jan takeaway closed,shop open variable hours) Booking Advisable bank hols & Jul-Aug Last arrival 22.00hrs Last departure 11.00hrs
Nestling under the Purbeck Hills surrounded by scenic walks and only 2 miles from the beach. This park caters well for families and couples, offering high quality facilities including an indoor heated swimming pool and village inn. A 13-acre site with 77 touring pitches, 12 hardstandings and 140 static.

Leisure: 🏊 🎱

Facilities: 🌂 ⊙ ✳ 🏪 🍴

Disabled facilities: toilet & shower

Services: ✕ 🔌 📶 🗜 🎱 🛢 → ∪ ↑36 ⚓ ✈ ◎ ⚠

THREE LEGGED CROSS   SU00

Woolsbridge Manor Farm Caravan Park ▶▶▶ 67%

BH21 6RA
☎ 01202 826369 📠 01202 820603
📧 woolsbridge@btconnect.com
🌐 www.woolsbridgemanorfarmcaravanpark.co.uk

Dir: 2m off A31, 3m W of Ringwood. From Three Legged Cross continue S to Woolsbridge. Site 1.75m on L

★ ⚏ £10-£15 ⚏ £10-£15 ⚏ £10-£15

Open Etr-Oct Booking Advisable bank hols & Aug Last arrival 20.00hrs Last departure 10.30hrs
A small farm site with spacious pitches on a level field. This quiet site is an excellent central base for touring the New Forest, Salisbury and the south coast, and is close to Moors Valley Country Park for outdoor family activities. A 6.75-acre site with 60 touring pitches.

Leisure: 🎱

Facilities: 🌂 ⊙ 🗜 ✳ 🏪 🍴 🐾

Disabled facilities: toilet, shower

Services: 🔌 🔌 🗜 🛢 → ∪ ↑18 ✈ 🛢

DORSET

VERWOOD SU00

Camping & Caravanning Club Site ►►► 66%

Sutton Hill Woodlands BH21 8NQ
☎ 01202 822763
[W] www.campingandcaravanningclub.co.uk

Dir: Turn L on A354 13m from Salisbury onto B3081, site is 1.5m W of Verwood

★ 🚐 £12.95-£16.35 🚚 £12.95-£16.35
⛺ £12.95-£16.35

Open Mar-Nov Booking Advisable bank hols & peak periods Last arrival 21.00hrs Last departure noon

Set on rising ground between the woodland of the New Forest and the rolling downs of Cranborne Chase and Salisbury Plains. This comfortable site is well kept by very keen wardens. A 12.75-acre site with 150 touring pitches, 12 hardstandings.

Leisure: 🔍 ⛹

Facilities: 🚿 ⊙ ✂ ✱ 📞 🏠 🐕

Disabled facilities: toilet, washbasin, razor point & shower

Services: [T] 🍴 🧺 🔋 🌿 ▣ → ⛳ ✈ 🚜 ⛵

💳 💳 💳 💳 💳

WAREHAM SY98

Lookout Holiday Park ►►► 71%

Stoborough BH20 5AZ
☎ 01929 552546 📠 01929 556662
[E] enquiries@caravan-sites.co.uk
[W] www.caravan-sites.co.uk

Dir: Off A351

★ 🚐 £10-£21 🚚 £10-£21 ⛺ £8-£15.50

Open all year Booking Advisable bank hols & Jul-Aug Last arrival 22.00hrs Last departure noon

Divided into two paddocks and set well back from the Swanage road, this touring park is separated from the static. part of the operation. A superb children's playground and plenty of other attractions make this an ideal centre for families. A 5-acre site with 150 touring pitches, 94 hardstandings and 90 static.

Leisure: 🔍 ⛹

Facilities: 🚿 ⊙ ✂ ✱ 📞 🚜

Disabled facilities: static caravan with disabled facilities

Services: [T] 🛒 🍴 🧺 🔋 🌿 ▣ → ∪ ⛳18 ✈ 🎥 🎣

Notes: 🐕 No single sex groups

💳 💳 💳 💳 💳

WAREHAM SY98

Birchwood Tourist Park ►►► 73%

Bere Road North Trigon BH20 7PA
☎ 01929 554763 📠 01929 556635
[W] www.birchwoodtouristpark.co.uk

Dir: From Poole (A351) or Dorchester (A352) on N side of railway line at Wareham, follow road signed Bere Regis (unclassified). 2nd tourist park after 2.25m

🚐 🚙 ⛺

Open Mar-Oct (rs Nov-Feb Some restrictions) Booking Advisable bank hols & Jul-Aug Last arrival 21.00hrs Last departure 11.30hrs

Set in 50 acres of parkland located within Wareham Forest, this site offers direct access into ideal areas for walking, mountain biking, and horse and pony riding. The modern facilities are centrally located and well-organised. A 25-acre site with 175 touring pitches, 8 hardstandings.

Games field, bike hire, pitch & putt, paddling pool

Leisure: 🔍 ⛬

Facilities: 🚿 ⊙ 🪒 ✱ 📞 🏪 ⛩ 🐕

Services: [T] 🧺 🔌 🗑 🔒 🌿 ⬍ → ↺ ⛳18 ✈ 🎬 🎣

Notes: No generators, no groups at Bank Hols

💳 💳 💳 💳 💳

WAREHAM SY98

Wareham Forest Tourist Park ►►►► 76%

North Trigon BH20 7NZ
☎ 01929 551393 📠 01929 558321
[E] holiday@wareham-forest.co.uk
[W] www.wareham-forest.co.uk

Dir: On unclass road between Bere Regis & Wareham, approx 3m from Bere Regis

★ 🚐 £8.50-£16 🚙 £8.50-£16 ⛺ £8.50-£16

Open all year (rs Some services only in high season) Booking Advisable Spring bank hol & Jul-Aug Last arrival 21.00hrs Last departure 10.30hrs

A friendly woodland park ideally located within the tranquil Wareham Forest, with its many walks and proximity to Poole, Dorchester and the Purbeck coast. It offers two luxury blocks, with combined washbasin/WCs for total privacy, and a high standard of cleanliness. A heated outdoor swimming pool, off licence, snack bar, shop and games room are among the amenities. A 42-acre site with 200 touring pitches, 54 hardstandings.

Leisure: 🏊 🔍 ⛬

Facilities: 🚿 🪒 ✱ 📞 🏪 🏠 ⛩ 🐕

Disabled facilities: disabled bathrooms

Services: [T] 🔌 🍷 🗑 🔒 🌿 ⬍ → ↺ ⛳18 ✈ 🎬 🎣

Notes: Couples & families only

💳 💳 💳 💳 💳

Bagwell Farm Touring Park ▶▶▶ 65%

Knights in the Bottom Chickerell DT3 4EA
☎ 01305 782575 📠 01305 780554
[E] aaenquiries@bagwellfarm.co.uk
[W] www.bagwellfarm.co.uk

Dir: 4m W of Weymouth on B3157 (Weymouth-Bridport),from Weymouth 500yds past Victoria Inn pub

🚐 £8-£25 🚌 £8-£25 ⛺ £8-£17
Open all year Booking Advisable Bank & school hols Last arrival 21.00hrs Last departure 11.00hrs
An idyllically-placed terraced site on a hillside and a valley overlooking Chesil Beach. The park is well equipped with mini-supermarket, children's play area and pets corner, and a bar and grill serving food in high season. A 14-acre site with 320 touring pitches, 10 hardstandings.
Wet suit shower, campers' shelter

Leisure: 🔍 ⛩
Facilities: 🛁 🚿 ⊙ 💇 ❄ 📞 🛒 🏠 🪑 🐕
Disabled facilities: toilets & shower
Services: [T] 🍴 🍟 🔥 ⬇ 🧊 🍷 🔒 🌿 [÷] → U ⛳18 🎣
American Express Visa Barclays CONNECT Switch Solo

East Fleet Farm Touring Park ▶▶▶▶ 71%

Chickerell DT3 4DW
☎ 01305 785768
[E] enquiries@eastfleet.co.uk
[W] www.eastfleet.co.uk

Dir: On B3157 Weymouth-Bridport road, 3m from Weymouth

★ 🚐 £5.50-£13.50 🚌 £5.50-£13.50
⛺ £5.50-£13.50
Open 16 Mar-15 Jan Booking Advisable Peak season Last arrival 23.00hrs Last departure 10.30hrs
Set on a working organic farm overlooking Fleet Lagoon and Chesil Beach, with a wide range of amenities and quality toilet facilities. The friendly owners are welcoming and helpful, and their family bar serving meals and take-away food is open from Easter, with glorious views from the patio area. A 21-acre site with 270 touring pitches, 26 hardstandings.

Leisure: 🔍 ⛩
Facilities: 🛁 🚿 ⊙ 💇 ❄ 📞 🛒 🏠 🪑 🐕
Disabled facilities: shower/private washroom
Services: [T] 🍴 🍟 🐦 🔥 ⬇ 🧊 🍷 🔒 🌿 [÷] → U 🎥 🎣 ◎ ⛵
Notes: No single sex groups
American Express Visa Barclays CONNECT Switch Solo

WEYMOUTH SY67

Seaview Holiday Park 🏖 67%

Preston DT3 6DZ
☎ 01305 833037
🌐 www.havenholidays.com

Dir: A354 to Weymouth & signs for Preston/Wareham. Park 3m on R just after Weymouth Bay Park

★ ⊕ ⊕ Å

Open Mar-Oct Last arrival 22.00hrs Last departure noon
A fun-packed holiday centre for all the family, with plenty of activities and entertainment during the day and evening. Terraced pitches are provided for caravans, and there is a separate field for tents. The park is close to Weymouth and other coastal attractions. A 20-acre site with 96 touring pitches, 259 static.

Leisure: 🏊 🎣 🎱 🎯 🎡 ▢
Facilities: 🛁
Services: ✗ 🚿 🗑 🍽 🛢

WEYMOUTH SY67

Littlesea 🏖 68%

Lynch Lane DT4 9DT
☎ 01305 774414
🌐 www.havenholidays.com

Dir: A354/B3157. At 3rd rdbt L towards Chickerell & Portland. R immediately after traffic lights R into Lynch Land Trading Estate. Park at end of road on L

⊕ ⊕ Å

Open Mar-Oct Last arrival 22.00hrs Last departure noon
Just 3 miles from Weymouth with its lovely beaches and many attractions, Littlesea has a cheerful family atmosphere and fantastic facilities. Indoor and outdoor entertainment and activities are on offer for all the family, and the toilet facilities on the touring park are of a good quality. A 75-acre site with 220 touring pitches, 720 static.

Leisure: 🏊 🎣 🎱 🎯 🎡 ▢
Facilities: 🛁
Services: ✗ 🚿 🗑 🍽

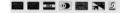

WEYMOUTH   SY67

Waterside Holiday Park 🏆 73%

Bowleaze Cove DT3 6PP
☎ 01305 833103 🖷 01305 832830
📧 info@watersideholidays.co.uk
🌐 www.watersideholidays.co.uk

Dir: From Weymouth take A353 E for 2m, then R fork to park in 0.5m

★ 🚐 £17-£28 🚛 £17-£28

Open Apr-Oct Booking Advisable peak holidays Last arrival 21.30hrs Last departure 10.00hrs

A top quality leisure park with a full range of activities and entertainment. The touring area of this large complex is ideal for families of all ages, offering individual grass pitches divided by hedging. The beach is a short distance away, and a frequent bus service connects this holiday centre with Weymouth. The private owners maintain very high standards in all areas. A 35-acre site with 70 touring pitches, 540 static.

Leisure: 🏊 🏄 ♦ 🎣 ⚲
Facilities: 🛉 ⊙ 🦺 ⚒ ✕ 🕻 🗜 🞿 🞱

Disabled facilities: shower, toilet & entrance ramps

Services: ✕ 🖶 🖳 🗑 🞹 → ∪ 🛈 18 ⚓ 🞤 🞥 ◎

⚠ Notes: No pets, no commercial vehicles

🞐 🞑 🞒 🞓 🞔 𝒮

WIMBORNE MINSTER   SZ09

Merley Court Touring Park
▶▶▶▶▶ 70%

Merley BH21 3AA
☎ 01202 881488 🖷 01202 881484
📧 holidays@merley-court.co.uk
🌐 www.merley-court.co.uk

Dir: Merley Court is clearly signed on A31 Wimborne by-pass & Poole jct rdbt

★ 🚐 £10.50-£15.50 🚛 £10.50-£15.50

▲ £10.50-£15.50

Open Mar-7 Jan (rs low season pool closed & bar, shop open limited hrs) Booking Advisable bank hols & Jun-Sep Last arrival 21.00hrs Last departure 11.00hrs

A superb site in a quiet rural position on the edge of Wimborne, with woodland on two sides and good access roads. The park is well landscaped, and offers generous individual pitches in sheltered grassland. There are plenty of amenities, including heated pool and adventure playground. A 20-acre site with 160 touring pitches, 50 hardstandings. Badminton, mini football, table tennis, crazy golf.

Leisure: 🏄 ♦ 🎣 ⚲ 🞣
Facilities: 🞵 🛉 ⊙ 🦺 ✕ 🕻 🗜 🞱 🞰

Disabled facilities: toilet facilities, ramps & shower

Services: 🞿 ✕ 🖶 🖳 🞷 🗑 🞹 🞤 🞲 🞳 → ∪ 🛈 18 ⚓ 🞥 🞤 ◎

Notes: Couples and families only,
🞗 17 Jul-3 Sep

🞐 🞑 🞒 🞓 𝒮

WIMBORNE MINSTER   SZ09

Wilksworth Farm Caravan Park
►►►►► 76%

Cranborne Road BH21 4HW
☎ 01202 885467 ▤ 01202 885467
ⓔ rayandwendy@
   wilksworthfarmcaravanpark.co.uk
ⓦ www.wilksworthfarmcaravanpark.co.uk

Dir: 1m N of Wimborne on B3078

★ ⊞ £8-£18 ⊞ £8-£18 ▲ £8-£18

Open Mar-Oct (rs Mar & Oct no shop or coffee shop) Booking Advisable Spring bank hol & Jul-Aug Last arrival 20.00hrs Last departure 11.00hrs
A popular and attractive park set in the grounds of a listed house, tranquilly placed in the heart of rural Dorset. The spacious site has much to offer visitors, including a heated swimming pool, take-away and café, and games room. The ultra-modern toilet facilities contain en suite rooms. A 11-acre site with 85 touring pitches, 20 hardstandings and 77 static.
Paddling pool, volley ball, mini football pitch

Leisure: ⚡ ⚲ ⚫ ⑭
Facilities: ⋔ ⊙ � ✳ ⚸ ⚹ ➤ ⍑
Disabled facilities: toilet, washbasin & shower
Services: ▣ ✕ ⚙ ⚡ ▣ ⚙ ⌀ ⊞ → ∪ ⅄18 ⚌ ⚘
◎

WOOL   SY88

Whitemead Caravan Park
►►► 66%

East Burton Road BH20 6HG
☎ 01929 462241 ▤ 01929 462241
ⓔ whitemeadcp@aol.com
ⓦ www.whitemeadcaravanpark.co.uk

Dir: Signed from A352 at level crossing on Wareham side of Wool

★ ⊞ £7.20-£11.50 ⊞ £7.20-£11.50
▲ £7.20-£11.50
Open mid Mar-Oct Booking Advisable public hols & mid Jul-Aug Last arrival 22.00hrs Last departure noon
A well laid-out site in the valley of the River Frome, close to the village and surrounded by woodland. A shop and games room enhance the facilities here, and the toilet block, though dated, is clean and well maintained.
A 5-acre site with 95 touring pitches.

Leisure: ⚫ ⑭
Facilities: ⋔ ⊙ ⍑ ✳ ⚸ ⚹ ➤ ⍑
Services: ▣ ⚡ ⚙ ▣ ⚙ ⌀ ⊞ → ∪ ⅄18 ⚘

BARNARD CASTLE   NZ01

Camping & Caravanning Club Site
▶▶▶▶ 70%

Dockenflatts Lane Lartington DL12 9DG
☎ 01833 630228
ⓦ www.campingandcaravanningclub.co.uk

Dir: Take B6277 to Middleton-in-Teesdale. After 1m turn L signed Raygill Riding Stables. Site 500mtrs on L

★ ⊞ £12.95-£16.35 ⊞ £12.95-£16.35

▲ £12.95-£16.35

Open Mar-Nov Booking Advisable bank hols & peak periods Last arrival 21.00hrs Last departure noon

A peaceful site surrounded by mature woodland and meadowland, with first class facilities. This immaculately-maintained park is set in the heart of the countryside. Pitches are well laid out and generous, on mainly level grass with some hardstandings. A 10-acre site with 90 touring pitches, 12 hardstandings.

Leisure: ⚏
Facilities: ⋒ ⊙ ⊄ ✳ ⚘ 丙 ☛
Disabled facilities: toilet, shower & washbasin
Services: ⚏ ⚘ ⚏ ⚏ ⚏ ⚏ → ∪ ⚮ ⚿ ⚿

⬛ ⬛ ⬛ ⬛ ⚿

BRENTWOOD   TQ59

Camping & Caravanning Club Site
▶▶▶ 66%

Warren Lane Doddington, Kelvedon Hatch CM15 0JG
☎ 01277 372773
ⓦ www.campingandcaravanningclub.co.uk

Dir: M25 J28. Brentwood 2m L on A128 signed Ongar. After 3m turn R and site signposted

★ ⊞ £11.75-£15.35 ⊞ £11.75-£15.35

▲ £11.75-£15.35

Open Mar-Nov Booking Advisable bank hols & peak periods Last arrival 21.00hrs Last departure noon

A very pretty rural site with many separate areas amongst the trees, and a secluded field for campers. This peaceful site has older-style toilet facilities which are kept very clean, and smart laundry equipment. A 12-acre site with 90 touring pitches, 23 hardstandings.

Leisure: ⚏
Facilities: ⋒ ⊙ ⊄ ✳ ⚘ 丙 ☛
Disabled facilities: toilet, shower, washbasin & razor point
Services: ⚏ ⚘ ⚏ ⚏ ⚏ ⚏ → ∪ ⚮ ⚿ ⚿

⬛ ⬛ ⬛ ⬛ ⚿

CLACTON-ON-SEA TM11

Valley Farm Holiday Park 68%

Valley Road CO15 6LY
☎ 01255 422484 📠 01255 687599
📧 Rebecca.Gibb@park-resorts.com
🌐 www.park-resorts.com

Dir: From A12 onto A120 signposted Clacton. Onto A133, follow brown tourist signs

★ 🚐 £5-£23 🚙 £5-£23

Open Mar-Oct & wknds in winter Booking Advisable all season Last arrival 23.30hrs Last departure 10.00hrs

A well-managed holiday park with a landscaped touring site sheltered behind high hedging, and a small brook running through the camping area. Access is well lit, and the toilet facilities are clean. The central leisure area includes an impressive swimming complex with both indoor and outdoor pools around a large sun terrace, amusement arcade, adventure playground, restaurant and show bar. A 50-acre site with 35 touring pitches, 520 static.

Leisure: 🏊 🎣 🎱 �
Facilities: 🖚 ⊙ 🐕 💺 🛒 🛁
Services: ✖ 🛒 🚐 🔲 🛢 💡 → ∪ ⌂18 🎾 🎣 ◎
⚠ **Notes:** No cars by caravans. No single sex parties, minimum age 25

COLCHESTER TL92

Colchester Camping Caravan Park ▶▶▶▶ 72%

Cymbeline Way Lexden CO3 4AG
☎ 01206 545551 📠 01206 710443
📧 enquiries@colchestercamping.co.uk
🌐 www.colchestercamping.co.uk

Dir: Follow tourist signs from A12, then A133 Colchester Central slip road

★ 🚐 £10.50-£16.10 🚙 £10.50-£16.10
▲ £10-£14.10

Open all year Booking Advisable public hols Last arrival 20.00hrs Last departure noon

A well-designed campsite on level grassland, on the west side of Colchester near the town centre. Close to main routes to London (A12) and east coast. There is good provision for hardstandings, and the owner's attention to detail is reflected in the neatly trimmed grass and well-cut hedges. Toilet facilities are housed in three buildings, two of which are modern and well equipped. A 12-acre site with 168 touring pitches, 38 hardstandings. Badminton court

Leisure: ⚘
Facilities: 🖚 ⊙ 🐕 ☀ 💺 🛒 🐕
Disabled facilities: toilet, shower & washbasin
Services: 📶 🚐 🔲 🛢 🖋 → ∪ ⌂18 🎾 🎣 ⚠
Notes: No commercial vehicles, no single sex groups

MERSEA ISLAND

Waldegraves Holiday Park
65%

CO5 8SE
☎ 01206 382898 📠 01206 385359
📧 holidays@waldegraves.co.uk
🌐 www.waldegraves.co.uk

> **Dir:** B1025 to Mersea Island across the
> Strood. L to East Mersea, 2nd turn on R,
> follow tourist signs to park

★ 🚐 £14-£20 🚐 £14-£20 ▲ £14-£20

Open Mar-Nov Booking Advisable all times
Last arrival 22.00hrs Last departure noon
*A spacious and pleasant site, located between
farmland and its own private beach on the
Blackwater Estuary. Facilities include two
freshwater fishing lakes, heated swimming
pool, club, amusements, café and golf, and
there is generally good provision for families.
A 25-acre site with 60 touring pitches, 250
static.*
Boating and fishing on site

Leisure: 🏃 🌊 🛝 ⌂
Facilities: 🅿 ⊙ 🍳 ⚡ ⚘ 🚿 🛒 🎋 🐾
Disabled facilities: toilets & showers,
accessible caravan
Services: 🔲 ✗ 🎂 🚐 ⚕ 🔥 🛢 ⛽ ⊘ → ⌱18 🖋
◎ ⚠

Notes: No under 21s or single sex groups

GLOUCESTER

Red Lion Camping & Caravan Park
▶▶▶ 67%

Wainlode Hill Norton GL2 9LW
☎ 01452 730251 📠 01452 730251
🌐 www.redlioninn-caravancampingpark.co.uk

> **Dir:** Turn off A38 at Norton and follow road
> to river

🚐 £9-£11.50 🚐 £9-£11.50 ▲ £8-£11
Open all year Booking Advisable Spring bank
hol Last arrival 22.00hrs Last departure
11.00hrs
*An attractive meadowland park, adjacent to a
traditional pub, with the River Severn just
across a country lane. This is an ideal touring
and fishing base. A 13-acre site with 60
touring pitches, 20 static.*
Freshwater fishing & private lake

Leisure: 🛝
Facilities: 🅿 ⊙ 🍳 ⚡ ⚡ 🛒 🎋 🐾
Disabled facilities: toilet & shower
Services: 🔲 ✗ 🚐 🔥 🛢 ⚕ 🛢 ⊘ → ∪ ⌱18 🖋

SOUTH CERNEY · SU09

Hoburne Cotswold 🏠 72%

Broadway Lane GL7 5UQ
☎ 01285 860216 📠 01285 868010
📧 enquiries@hoburne.com
🌐 www.hoburne.com

Dir: From Cirencester take A419 for 3m. Turn R at sign for Cotswold Water Park and R again in 1m. Site on L

★ 🚐 £11.50-£28 🚕 £11.50-£28
⛺ £11.50-£28

Open Mar-Oct Booking Advisable public hols & high season Last arrival 21.00hrs Last departure 10.00hrs

A large holiday centre set out on level grassy ground adjoining the Cotswold Water Park. This well-equipped park is close to several lakes, each one adapted for either sailing, water skiing, fishing or a nature reserve. There is also a lake on site with a good stock of tench. Excellent menu and bar facilities at the Prickly Pike pub/restaurant. A 70-acre site with 294 touring pitches, 285 static.
Crazy golf, fishing, pedal-boat hire, mini bowling

Leisure: 🐟 ⚡ 🎱 🔍 🎿
Facilities: 🏪 ☉ 🍽 🔧 🛒
Disabled facilities: toilets & ramps
Services: 🅃 ✕ 🚿 🚐 ∿ 🔌 🛢 🗑 → ∪ 🅿 18 ⚡
🍴 🎿 ⚠
Notes: ✈

◼ 💳 ◼ 🔄 ⑤

WINCHCOMBE · SP02

Camping & Caravanning Club Site ▶▶▶ 70%

Brooklands Farm Alderton GL20 8NX
☎ 01242 620259
🌐 www.campingandcaravanningclub.co.uk

Dir: Leave M5 J9 onto A46, keep straight on at rdbt and onto B4077 signed Stow-on-the-Wold. Site 3m on R

★ 🚐 £12.95-£16.35 🚕 £12.95-£16.35
⛺ £12.95-£16.35

Open Mar-Jan Booking Advisable BHs & peak periods Last arrival 21.00hrs Last departure noon

A pleasant rural park with pitches spaced around two attractive lakes offering good fishing, and the benefit of a long season. This flower-filled park is in an area of historic buildings and picturesque villages between Cheltenham and Tewkesbury. A 20-acre site with 80 touring pitches, 44 hardstandings.
Fishing, pool table, table tennis

Leisure: 🐟 🎿
Facilities: 🏪 ☉ 🍽 ❄ 🔧 🛒 🎣 🐕
Disabled facilities: washbasin, toilet, razor point & shower
Services: 🅃 🚿 🚐 🗑 🛢 🔌 🗑 → ∪ 🅿 🎿 ⚠
◼ 💳 ◼ 🔄 ⑤

GLOUCESTERSHIRE

FORDINGBRIDGE   SU11

Sandy Balls Holiday Centre 🏛
74%

Sandy Balls Estate Ltd Godshill SP6 2JY
☎ 01425 653042 📠 01425 653067
📧 post@sandy-balls.co.uk
🌐 www.sandy-balls.co.uk

Dir: M27 J1 & take B3078/B3079, W 8m to Godshill. Park 0.25m after cattle grid

★ 🚐 £12.75-£28.50 🚍 ▲ £12.75-£28.50

Open all year (rs Nov-Feb Activities & pitches reduced) Booking Advisable BH school hols, wknds Last arr 21.00hrs Last dep 11.00hrs
A large, mostly wooded holiday complex with good touring facilities on terraced, well laid-out fields. Pitches are fully serviced with shingle bases, and groups can be sited away from the main site. Excellent sport, leisure and entertainment for the whole family. A 120-acre site with 200 touring pitches, 233 hardstandings and 133 static.
Jacuzzi, steam room, sauna, gym, riding

Leisure: 🏊 ⚲ ♦ �
Facilities: ➡ ♠ ⊙ 🌂 ✳ ⚘ 🛒 👌 🎋 ⛌
Disabled facilities: toilet, shower, ramps & pool facilities
Services: 🅣 ✕ 🍺 ➡ ⚡ ⋁ 🖾 ⚲ 🍴 🗑 🔲 → ∪ ♪ △
Notes: No single sex or under 25 groups, other groups by arrangement

▨▨ ▨▨ ▨▨ 📶 💲

MILFORD ON SEA   SZ29

Lytton Lawn Touring Park
▶▶▶ **70%**

Lymore Lane SO41 0TX
☎ 01590 648331 📠 01590 645610
📧 holidays@shorefield.co.uk
🌐 www.shorefield.co.uk

Dir: From Lymington A337 to Christchurch for 2.5m to Everton. L onto B3058 to Milford-on-Sea. After 0.25m L onto Lymore Lane

🚐 🚍 ▲

Open Feb-2 Jan (rs Xmas/New Year no grass pitches available) Booking Advisable at all times Last arrival 22.00hrs Last departure 10.00hrs
A pleasant well-run park with good facilities, located near the coast. The park is peaceful and quiet, but the facilities of a sister park 2.5 miles away are available to campers, including swimming pool, tennis courts, bistro and bar/carvery, and large club with family entertainment. Fully-serviced pitches provide good screening, and standard pitches are on gently-sloping grass. A 5-acre site with 136 touring pitches, 48 hardstandings.

Leisure: ♦ ♦credit
Facilities: ♠ ⊙ 🌂 ✳ ⚘ 🛒 🎋
Disabled facilities: toilet & shower
Services: 🅣 🚐 🖾 🗑 ⚘ → ∪ 🍴18 ♪ △
Notes: Family park only, no single sex groups, no under 25s unless in family group

▨▨ ▨▨ ▨▨ 📶 💲

HAMPSHIRE

NEW MILTON — SZ29

Hoburne Bashley 74%

Sway Road BH25 5QR
☎ 01425 612340 📠 01425 632732
📧 enquiries@hoburne.com
🌐 www.hoburne.com

Dir: 1m N of New Milton on B3055

★ 🚐 £11-£34.50 🚐 £11-£34.50

Open Mar-Oct Last arrival 22.00hrs Last departure 10.00hrs

A large, well-organised park bordered by woodland and a shrubbery and set in 100 acres with indoor and outdoor swimming pools, clubhouse and entertainment. There is plenty to occupy the whole family. The multi-service pitches are an excellent feature of touring area, and these are well screened by discreet planting. A 100-acre site with 307 touring pitches, 425 static.

Crazy golf, 9-hole par 3, petanque, indoor play area

Leisure: ⚽ ⚲ ⚘ ⚘ ⚑
Facilities: ⚑ ⊙ ⚑ ⚑ ⚑ ⚑
Disabled facilities: toilet & shower
Services: ⚑ ⚑ ⚑ ⚑ ⚑ ⚑ → ∪ Γ18 ⚑ ⚑ ⚑ ◎
Notes: No single sex groups, or unaccompannied teenagers

🔲 🔲 🔲 🔲

ROMSEY — SU32

Hill Farm Caravan Park
▶▶▶▶ 74%

Branches Lane Sherfield English SO51 6FH
☎ 01794 340402 📠 01794 342358
📧 gjb@hillfarmpark.com
🌐 www.hillfarmpark.com

Dir: Signed off A27 Salisbury to Romsey road in Sherfield English, 4m NW of Romsey and M27 J2

★ 🚐 £15-£24 🚐 £1-£24 ⚑ £11-£16

Open Mar-Oct Booking Advisable bank & school hols Last arrival 20.00hrs Last departure noon

A small, well-sheltered park peacefully located amidst mature trees and meadows. The two toilet blocks offer smart unisex showers as well as a fully en-suite family/disabled room and plenty of privacy in the wash rooms. The owners are continuing to develop this attractive park, and with its proximity to Salisbury and the New Forest, it makes an appealing holiday location. A 10.5-acre site with 70 touring pitches, 16 hardstandings and 6 static.

9-hole, par 3, pitch 'n' putt, goal posts, badminton

Leisure: ⚑
Facilities: ⚑ ⊙ ⚑ ⚘ ⚑ ⚑ ⚑ ⚑
Disabled facilities: toilet, shower & washbasin
Services: ⚑ ✗ ⚑ ⚑ ⚑ ⚑ ⚑ ⚑ ⚑ → ∪ Γ18 ⚑
Notes: Minimal noise after 11pm, one unit per pitch

PETERCHURCH   SO33

Poston Mill Caravan & Camping Park ▶▶▶▶ 76%

HR2 0SF

☎ 01981 550225 🖷 01981 550885

🅴 enquiries@poston-mill.co.uk

🆆 www.bestparks.co.uk

Dir: 11m SW of Hereford on B4348

★ 🚐 £12-£16 🚑 £12-£16 ▲ £12-£16

Open all year (rs Nov-Mar Limited toilet facilities) Booking Advisable bank & summer hols Last departure noon

Delightfully set in the Golden Valley surrounded by hills, and with beautiful views. This quality park has excellent facilities including sporting amenities which are to one side of the site. There is also an adjoining restaurant, The Mill, and a pleasant walk alongside the River Dore. A 33-acre site with 93 touring pitches, 63 hardstandings and 95 static.

Leisure: 🔍 🐾 🛝 ▭

Facilities: ℝ ⊙ 🖐 ❄ 🌡 🎇 🖃 🎇 🛒 🌲 🌴

Disabled facilities: toilet & washbasin

Services: 🔟 ✖ 🖿 🛒 🖴 ⅋ 🗓 🅿 🍝 🗑 ∅ 🖳 → ⁁9 🍷 ◎

▦ ▦ ▦ ▧ 🛒 🆂

HERTFORD   TL31

Camping & Caravanning Club Site ▶▶▶▶ 71%

Mangrove Road SG13 8QF

☎ 01992 586696

🆆 www.campingandcaravanningclub.co.uk

Dir: From A10 follow A414 Hertford signs straight over next rdbt. After 200yds L signed Balls Park & Hertford Uni. L at T-jct into Mangrove Rd. Site on L

★ 🚐 £15.35-£16.35 🚑 £15.35-£16.35

▲ £15.35-£16.35

Open all year Booking Advisable BHs and peak periods Last arrival 21.00hrs Last departure noon

A spacious, well-landscaped club site in a rural setting one mile south of Hertford, with immaculate modern toilet facilities. There are several hedged areas with good provision of hardstandings, and a cosy camping section in an old orchard. All kinds of wildlife flourish around the lake. A 32-acre site with 250 touring pitches, 54 hardstandings.

Leisure: 🛝

Facilities: ℝ ⊙ 🖐 ❄ 🌡 🎇 🛒

Disabled facilities: toilet, washbasin, razor point and hand dryer

Services: 🔟 🛒 ⅋ 🗑 🖴 ∅ 🖳 → ∪ ⁁18 🍷 🐾

△ ▦ ▦ ▦ ▧ 🛒 🆂

ASHFORD — TR04

Broad Hembury Holiday Park
▶▶▶ 76%

Steeds Lane Kingsnorth TN26 1NQ
☎ 01233 620859 🖷 01233 620918
🅔 holidays@broadhembury.co.uk
🅦 www.broadhembury.co.uk

Dir: From M20 J10 take A2070 for 3m. L at 2nd rdbt signed Kingsnorth, then L at 2nd x-roads in village

★ 🛖 £10-£20 🚐 £10-£20 ▲ £10-£14

Open all year Booking Advisable Jul-Aug, BH's Last arrival 23.00hrs Last departure noon
Well-run and maintained small family park surrounded by open pasture and neatly landscaped, with pitches sheltered by mature hedges. Some super pitches have proved a popular addition, and there is a well-equipped campers' kitchen. A 7-acre site with 60 touring pitches, 14 hardstandings and 25 static.
Football, volleyball & kitchen appliances

Leisure: ♦ ⚲ ▢
Facilities: ♘ ⊙ ⚲ ✳ 🝙 ⼖
Services: ▯ ▣ ⍋ 🗇 🕯 ⊞ → ∪ ⌂18 🚲 ⌁

▆▆ ▆▆ ▆▆ ⑤

BIRCHINGTON — TR36

Two Chimneys Caravan Park
▶▶▶ 68%

Shottendane Road CT7 0HD
☎ 01843 841068 & 843157 🖷 01843 848099
🅔 info@twochimneys.co.uk
🅦 www.twochimneys.co.uk

Dir: From A28 to Birchington Sq, turn R into Park Lane (B2048). Turn L at Manston Rd (B2050) then 1st L

★ 🛖 £11-£18 🚐 £1-£18 ▲ £11-£18

Open Mar-Oct (rs Mar-May & Sep-Oct shop, bar, pool & takeaway restricted) Booking Advisable bank & school hols Last arrival 23.00hrs Last departure noon
A good, well-managed site with two swimming pools and a fully-licensed clubhouse. Other attractions include a tennis court and children's play area. A 30-acre site with 200 touring pitches, 5 hardstandings and 100 static.
Amusement arcade

Leisure: ⚲ ⚲ ⚲
Facilities: ♘ ⊙ ⚲ ✳ ⚲ 🝙
Disabled facilities: toilets & ramps
Services: ▯ ⧆ ▣ ▣ ⚲ 🕯 🗇 ⊞ → ∪ ⌂18 ⊁ 🚲
⌁ ▆▆ ▆▆ ▆▆ ▨ ⑤

CANTERBURY TR15

Camping & Caravanning Club Site
▶▶▶ 72%

Bekesbourne Lane CT3 4AB
☎ 01227 463216
ⓦ www.campingandcaravanningclub.co.uk

Dir: From Canterbury follow A257 signs (Sandwich), turn R opposite golf course

★ ⊕ £12.95-16.35 ⊕ £12.95-16.35
Å £12.95-16.35

Open all year Booking Advisable bank hols & peak periods Last arrival 21.00hrs Last departure noon

An attractive tree-screened site in pleasant rural surroundings yet within walking distance of the city centre. The park is well landscaped, and offers very smart toilet facilities in one block, with another older but well-kept building housing further facilities. A 20-acre site with 200 touring pitches, 21 hardstandings.

Leisure: ⋔
Facilities: ⋈ ⊙ ℚ ✳ ☏ ⋧ 🖚 ⋔
Disabled facilities: toilet, handbasin & shower
Services: 🖵 ♨ ⋎ 🖥 ▮ ⊘ ⊞ → ∪ Ո18 ⊿ ⚠

▦ ▦ ▦ ▦ 𝒮

FOLKESTONE TR23

Little Satmar Holiday Park
▶▶▶ 68%

Winehouse Lane Capel Le Ferne CT18 7JF
☎ 01303 251188 📄 01303 251188
ⓔ info@keatfarm.co.uk
ⓦ www.keatfarm.co.uk/touringparks/littlesatmar.htm

Dir: Signposted off B2011

★ ⊕ £10-£15 ⊕ £10-£15 Å £10-£15

Open Mar-Oct Booking Advisable bank hols & Jul-Aug Last arrival 23.00hrs Last departure 14.00hrs

A quiet, well-screened site well away from the road and statics, with clean and tidy facilities. A useful base for visiting Dover and Folkestone, and just a short walk from cliff paths with their views of the Channel, and sandy beaches below. A 5-acre site with 60 touring pitches, 80 static.

Leisure: ◕ ⋔
Facilities: ⋈ ⊙ ℚ ✳ ☏ ⋧
Services: 🖵 ♨ 🖥 ▮ ⊘ ⊞ → ∪ Ո18 ⚏ ⊿

▦ ▦ 𝒮

MANSTON — TR36

Manston Caravan & Camping Park
▶▶▶ 69%

Manston Court Road CT12 5AU
☎ 01843 823442
🅔 enquiries@manston-park.co.uk
🅦 www.manston-park.co.uk

Dir: From B2050, N of Manston Airport, take minor road (Manston Court Rd) to site in 0.24m on R

🚐 🚐 🅰

Open Apr/Etr-Oct (rs Apr shop open weekends only (off-peak)) Booking Advisable bank hols & Jul-Aug Last arrival 23.55hrs Last departure 11.00hrs

A neatly-kept grassy park broken up by mature trees, handy for Manston Airport and the seaside resorts on the Isle of Thanet. The older-style toilet facilities are well maintained, and there is an excellent children's play area. A 5-acre site with 100 touring pitches, 46 static.

Leisure: ⚏

Facilities: 🅡 ⊙ ⚒ 🝋 🅛 🖳 🎣 🕇

Services: 🔟 🖾 🅘 🖉 → ∪ ⴖ18 ⚓ 😇 🥢 🗇 🖲 🖳
◎ ⚴

Notes: No single sex groups

▭▭ ▭▭ ▧ 🆂

WHITSTABLE — TR16

Seaview Holiday Village
▶▶▶ 68%

St John's Road CT5 2RY
☎ 01227 792246 📠 01227 792247
🅔 seaviewpark@fsnet.co.uk

Dir: From A299 take A2990 then B2205 to Swalecliffe, site between Herne Bay & Whitstable

★ 🚐 £12-£14 🚐 £12-£14 🅰 £12

Open Mar-Oct (rs Feb & Nov limited facilities) Booking Advisable all times Last arrival 21.30hrs Last departure noon

A pleasant open site on the edge of Whitstable, set well away from the static area, with a smart, modern toilet block and both super and hardstanding pitches. A 12-acre site with 171 touring pitches, 32 hardstandings and 452 static.

Amusements in games room & adventure trail

Leisure: ⚉ ⚏ ☐

Facilities: 🅡 ⊙ 🝋 ⚒ 🅛 🖳 🎣 🕇

Disabled facilities: toilet, shower, access to cafe & clubhouse

Services: 🔟 🗙 🖳 🛒 🖇 🝋 🖾 🖲 🅛 🅘 🖉 → ∪ ⴖ18
🥢 😇 🥢 🗇 ◎ ⚴

▭▭ ▭▭ ▭▭ ▧ 🆂

BLACKPOOL   SD33

Marton Mere Holiday Village 70%

Mythop Road FY4 4XN

☎ 01253 760771 📠 01253 767544

> **Dir:** From M55 J4 onto A583 towards Blackpool. Turn R past windmill at 1st traffic lights into Mythop Rd. Park 150yds on L

Open Mar-Oct Last arrival 22.00hrs Last departure noon

A very attractive holiday centre in an unusual setting on the edge of the mere, with plenty of birdlife to be spotted. The on-site entertainment is directed at all ages, and includes a superb show bar. There's a regular bus service into Blackpool for those who want to explore further afield. The separate touring area is well equipped with hardstandings and electric pitches, and there are good quality facilities. A 30-acre site with 431 touring pitches, 921 static.

Leisure: 🎣 ♦ ♦ ⚲ 🖵
Facilities: ⚡ ⊙ ⏲ ☀ ❄ ✆ ⚘ 🛒 🍴
Services: 🔲 ✕ ♨ ♨ 💂 🛢 💧 🖬 → ∪ ⏏ 18 ⚡
♨♨ ♪ ◎

🟦 🟦 🟥 📇 🟩

CAPERNWRAY   SD57

Old Hall Caravan Park ▶▶▶ 78%

LA6 1AD

☎ 01524 733276 📠 01524 734488

🅔 oldhall@charis.co.uk

🆆 www.oldhall.uk.com

> **Dir:** M6 J35 follow signs to Over Kellet, L onto B6254, L at village green signed Capernwray. Site 1.5m on R

★ ♨ £15.50-£17.50 ♨ £15.50-£17.50

Open Mar-10 Jan (rs Nov-10 Jan only for seasonal tourers & static. vans) Booking Advisable wknds, bank hols & Jul-Aug

A lovely secluded park set in a clearing amongst trees at the end of a half-mile long drive. This peaceful park is home to a wide variety of wildlife, and there are marked walks in the woods. Facilities are well maintained by friendly owners. A 3-acre site with 38 touring pitches, 38 hardstandings and 220 static.

Leisure: ⚲
Facilities: ⚡ ⊙ ⏲ ✆ 🖬 🍴
Disabled facilities: toilet & shower
Services: ♨ 🖬 🛢 ⊘ 🖬 → ∪ ⏏ ♪ ♨ ⚡

GARSTANG SD44

Bridge House Marina & Caravan Park ▶▶▶ 66%

Nateby Crossing Lane Nateby PR3 0JJ
☎ 01995 603207 🖷 01995 601612
📧 edwin@bridgehousemarina.co.uk
🌐 www.bridgehousemarina.co.uk

Dir: Off A6 at pub and sign for Knott End, immediately R into Nateby Crossing Lane, over canal bridge to site on L

🚐 🚐

Open Mar-4 Jan Booking Advisable bank hols Last arrival 22.00hrs Last departure 13.00hrs
A well-maintained site in attractive countryside by the Lancaster Canal, with good views towards the Trough of Bowland. The boatyard atmosphere is interesting, and there is a super children's playground. A 4-acre site with 50 touring pitches, 20 static.

Leisure: ⚙
Facilities: 🛁 ⊙ 🔧 ✳ 🔥 🛒 🛖
Services: 🆃 🚽 🖭 🔋 🝙 ⊘ 🖽 → ⊢18 ⤫ 🅹
▨ ▨ ▨ 🔰 🗊

GARSTANG SD44

Claylands Caravan Park ▶▶▶▶ 75%

Cabus PR3 1AJ
☎ 01524 791242 🖷 01524 792406
📧 alan@claylands.com
🌐 www.claylands.com

Dir: Turn off M6 J33 S to Garstang, approx 6m pass Little Chef, signed off A6 into private road on Lancaster side of Garstang

🚐 🚐 🅰

Open Mar-4 Jan (rs Jan & Feb Holiday park only) Booking Advisable bank hols & Jul-Aug Last arrival 23.00hrs Last departure 14.00hrs
A well-maintained site with lovely river and woodland walks and good views over the River Wyre towards the village of Scorton. This friendly park is set in delightful countryside. Guests can enjoy fishing, and the atmosphere is very relaxed. The quality facilities and amenities are of a high standard, and everything is immaculately maintained. A 14-acre site with 30 touring pitches, 30 hardstandings and 68 static.

Leisure: ⚙
Facilities: 🛁 ⊙ ✳ 🔥 🛒 🕳 🆁 🛖
Disabled facilities: toilet & shower
Services: 🆃 ✗ 🧹 🚽 🚽 🖭 🔋 🅿 🝙 ⊘ 🖽 → ∪ ⊢18 ⤫ 🅹 Notes: No single sex groups
▨ ▨ 🔰 🗊

LONGRIDGE SD63

Beacon Fell View Caravan Park ►►► 66%

110 Higher Road PR3 2TF
☎ 01772 785434 🖷 01772 784204

Dir: Leave A6 at Broughton on B5269 into Longridge & follow B6243 out of town centre. Take L fork signed Jeffrey Hill. Site 0.75m on R

★ 🚐 £4.50-£21.50 🚙 £4.50-£21.50

▲ £4.50-£21.50

Open 2 Mar-16 Nov (rs after Etr-end May entertainment weekends only) Booking Advisable bank hols, school hols & wknds Last arrival 21.00hrs Last departure noon
An elevated park with views over Beacon Fell. This tiered park with level pitches has an indoor swimming pool, and an extensive free evening entertainment programme in the clubhouse. A new country club will be ready for the 2005 season. A 7-acre site with 90 touring pitches, 397 static.
Free evening entertainment, pool tables, darts

Leisure: ♨ ♣ ⋔
Facilities: ⋔ ⊙ ℗ ℄ 🛂 ⊬
Disabled facilities: toilet, 1 fitted caravan
Services: 🖾 🖸 🖳 🗄 ∅ → ∪ ⅂18 ♪

▨ ▨ ▨ ▨ ⑤

MORECAMBE SD46

Venture Caravan Park ►►► 66%

Langridge Way Westgate LA4 4TQ
☎ 01524 412986 🖷 01524 422029
🅱 mark@venturecaravanpark.co.uk
🆆 www.venturecaravanpark.co.uk

Dir: From M6 J34 take follow Morecambe signs. At rdbt take road towards Westgate & follow park signs. 1st R after fire stn.

★ 🚐 £9-£11 🚙 £9-£11 ▲ £7-£11

Open all year Feb-Dec (rs 6 Jan-22 Feb touring vans only, one toilet block open) Booking Advisable bank hols & peak periods Last arrival 22.00hrs Last departure noon
A large park with good modern facilities, including a small indoor heated pool, a licensed clubhouse and a family room with children's entertainment. The site has many statics, and is close to the town centre. A 17.5-acre site with 56 touring pitches, 304 static.
Amusement arcade & off licence

Leisure: ♨ ♣ ⋔ ▢
Facilities: ⇥ ⋔ ⊙ ℗ ☀ ℄ 🛂
Disabled facilities: toilets, shower & caravans for disabled
Services: 🗍 🚽 🖳 🗄 ⬙ 🖸 🖳 🖃 → ⅂18 ♨ ♪

▨ ▨ ▨ ▨ ⑤

ORMSKIRK SD40

Abbey Farm Caravan Park
▶▶▶▶ 76%

Dark Lane L40 5TX
☎ 01695 572686 ▤ 01695 572686
📧 abbeyfarm@yahoo.com
🌐 www.abbeyfarmcaravanpark.co.uk

Dir: M6 J27 onto A5209 to Burscough. 4m L onto B5240. Immediate R into Hobcross Ln. Park 1.5m on R

★ 🏕 £9.60-£14.50 🚐 £9.60-£14.50
⛺ £5-£12

Open all year Booking Advisable public hols & Jul-Aug Last arrival 22.00hrs Last dep 13.00hrs
Delightful hanging baskets and flower beds brighten this garden-like rural park which is sheltered by hedging and mature trees. Modern, very clean facilities include a family bathroom, and there are special pitches for disabled visitors near the toilets. A superb recreation field caters for children of all ages, and there is an indoor games room, large library, fishing lake and dog walk. Tents have their own area with BBQ and picnic tables. A 6-acre site with 56 touring pitches, 44 static.
Off-licence, farm walk

Leisure: ♦ ⚲

Facilities: ➤ �📷 ⊙ ⚲ ☀ 🎕 🛒 🖳 🎢 🚻 🐾

Disabled facilities: washing & toilet facilities (separate block)

Services: 🔲 🎮 🗖 🖺 ∅ 🔁 → ∪ 🉆18 🎵

Notes: No single sex groups

⬜ 🔳 🔳 📶 🔗

SILVERDALE SD47

Holgate's Caravan Park
▶▶▶▶▶ 78%

Middlebarrow Plain Cove Road LA5 0SH
☎ 01524 701508 ▤ 01524 701580
📧 caravan@holgates.co.uk
🌐 www.holgates.co.uk

Dir: M6 J35. 5m NW of Carnforth. From Carnforth centre take unclass Silverdale road & follow tourist signs after Warton

★ 🏕 £25.75-£27.75 🚐 £25.75-£27.75
⛺ £23-£25

Open 22 Dec-7 Nov Booking Advisable school hols, public hols & wknds Last arrival 22.00hrs Last departure 14.00hrs
A superb family holiday park set in wooded countryside next to the sea. This park demonstrates high quality in all areas, and offers a wide range of leisure amenities. Its relaxing position overlooking Morecambe Bay combined with excellent touring facilities mark this park out as special. A 10-acre site with 70 touring pitches, 70 hardstandings and 350 static.
Sauna, spa bath, steam room, mini-golf, gym

Leisure: ⚲ ♦ ⚲

Facilities: 📷 ⊙ ⚲ ☀ 🛒 🖳 🐾

Disabled facilities: toilet, shower & ramps

Services: 🔲 🗙 🛒 🎮 🗖 🖺 🛒 ∅ → ∪ 🉆18 🎵

Notes: No single sex groups or unaccompanied children

⬜ 🔳 🔳 📶 🔗

ANCASTER   SK94

Woodland Waters ▶▶▶ 69%

Willoughby Road NG32 3RT
☎ 01400 230888 ≜ 01400 230888
🖂 info@woodlandwaters.co.uk
🌐 www.woodlandwaters.co.uk

Dir: On A153 W of x-roads with B6403

★ 🚐 £7.75-£9.75 🚍 £7.75-£9.75

▲ £5.50-£9.50

Open all year Booking Advisable BHs
*Peacefully set around impressive fishing lakes,
with a few log cabins in a separate area, a
pleasant open park. The access road is
through mature woodland, and there is a very
good heated toilet block, and a pub/club
house with restaurant. A 5-acre site with 62
touring pitches.*
4 fishing lakes

Leisure: 🐟 🗚

Facilities: 🖍 ⊙ 🕄 🕻 🖫 🖦 🖂 🖮

Disabled facilities: toilets & lodges

Services: ✗ 🖶 🚐 🖳 🕱 🔄 → ∪ ⋏ 🎝

Notes: Dogs must be kept on leads at all times

BOSTON   TF24

Orchard Park ▶▶▶▶ 65%

Frampton Lane PE20 3QU
☎ 01205 290328 ≜ 01205 290247
🌐 www.orchardpark.co.uk

Dir: On B1192, between A52 (Boston-
Grantham) & A1121 (Boston-Sleaford)

★ 🚐 £12-£12 🚍 £12-£12 ▲ £6-£12

Open Tourers Mar-Nov, Statics Mar-Jan (rs
end Oct-Etr shop/rest may close/bar also mid
Dec-Feb) Booking Advisable bank hols Last
arrival 10.30hrs Last departure 11.00hrs
*Ideally located for exploring the unique
fenlands, this rapidly-improving park has two
lakes - one for fishing and the other set aside
for conservation. A very attractive restaurant
and bar are popular with visitors. A 36-acre
site with 87 touring pitches, 3 hardstandings
and 128 static.*
Angling lake

Leisure: 🖎 🐟 🗚

Facilities: ➡ 🖍 ⊙ 🕄 ✳ 🕻 🖫 🖦 🖂 🖮

Disabled facilities: shower/toilet cubicle

Services: 🆃 ✗ 🚐 🖳 🕱 🕯 🔄 🖂 → ∪ ⋏18 🎝

CLEETHORPES TA30

Thorpe Park Holiday Centre 69%

DN35 0PW

📞 01472 813395 📠 01472 813395

Dir: Take unclass road off A180 at Cleethorpes, signed Humberstone and Holiday Park

🏕 🚐 ⚲

Open Mar-Oct Booking Advisable bank & school hols Last departure noon

A large static site with touring facilities, including fully-serviced pitches, adjacent to the beach. This holiday centre offers excellent recreational and leisure activities, including an indoor pool with bar, bowling greens, crazy golf, tennis courts, and a games area. Parts of the site overlook the sea. A 100-acre site with 95 touring pitches, 2,500 static.

Crazy golf & pets' corner

Leisure: ⚲ ⚲ ⚲ ⚲

Facilities: ⚲ ⚲ ⚲ ⚲ ⚲ ⚲

Disabled facilities: toilets

Services: ✕ ⚲ ⚲ ⚲ ⚲ ⚲ ⚲ ⚲ → ∪ ⌐18 ⚲ ⚲ ⚲ 🅿 🅿 🅿 🅿 🅿 🅿

MABLETHORPE TF58

Camping & Caravanning Club Site ▶▶▶ 67%

Highfield 120 Church Lane LN12 2NU

📞 01507 472374

🌐 www.campingandcaravanningclub.co.uk

Dir: On outskirts of Mablethorpe, on A1104, just after the 'Welcome to Mablethorpe' sign turn R into Church Ln. Continue 800yds to end of lane. Site on R

★ 🚐 £11.75-£15.35 🚐 £11.75-£15.35

⚲ £11.75-£15.35

Open Mar-Nov Booking Advisable bank hol & peak periods Last arrival 21.00hrs Last departure noon

Located next to flat agricultural land 1m from the sea, and well away from the road. The camping area is in two hedged fields with rural views, and the modern toilet facilities and laundry are centrally sited. A 6-acre site with 105 touring pitches.

Leisure: ⚲

Facilities: ⚲ ⚲ ⚲ ⚲ ⚲ ⚲

Disabled facilities: toilet, shower, handbasin & hand dryer

Services: ⚲ ⚲ ⚲ ⚲ ⚲ ⚲ → ∪ ⌐18 ⚲ ⚲ ⚲ 🅿 🅿 🅿 🅿 🅿

MABLETHORPE   TF58

Kirkstead Holiday Park ▶▶▶ 70%

North Road Trusthorpe LN12 2QD
☎ 01507 441483 🖷 01507 443447
🅔 mark@kirkstead.co.uk
🆆 www.kirkstead.co.uk

Dir: From Mablethorpe town centre take
A52 S towards Sutton on Sea, after 1m turn
sharp R at 2 telephone boxes into North Rd,
site signed in 300yds

★ ⊞ £14-£20 ⊞ £14-£20 ⚊ £8-£16

Open Mar-Nov Booking Advisable bank hols &
Jul-Aug Last arrival mdnthrs Last departure
15.00hrs
*Controlled entry is a welcome security feature
of this pleasant family-run site. The touring
area and good quality toilets are centrally
located, and the grounds are particularly well
maintained. A 10-acre site with 80 touring
pitches, 75 static.*
Snooker, volleyball, football pitch, basket ball

Leisure: ⚊ ⚊ ⚊
Facilities: ⚊ ⊙ ⚊ ⚊ ⚊ ⚊ ⚊ ⚊ ⚊
Disabled facilities: toilets
Services: ⚊ ⚊ ⚊ ⚊ ⚊ ⚊ → ⚊ ⚊ ⚊ ⚊ ◎

MABLETHORPE   TF58

Golden Sands Holiday Park 🖾 66%

Quebec Road LN12 1QJ
☎ 01507 477871 🖷 01507 472066
Dir: 1m W of town off A1031,
Cleethorpes road

⚊ ⚊ ⚊
Open Apr-Oct Booking Advisable May/spring
bank hol & Jul-Sep Last arrival 20.00hrs Last
departure 10.00hrs
*A large, well-equipped seaside holiday park
with separate touring facilities on two sites,
including fully modernised toilets. The first
floor entertainment rooms are only accessible
via stairs (no lifts). A 127-acre site with 350
touring pitches, 1,300 static.*
Mini bowling alley, snooker/pool, indoor fun
palace

Leisure: ⚊ ⚊ ⚊ ⚊
Facilities: ⚊ ⚊ ⚊ ⚊ ⚊ ⚊
Disabled facilities: special caravans
Services: ⚊ ⚊ ⚊ ⚊ ⚊ ⚊ ⚊ ⚊ → ⚊ ⚊ ⚊
Notes: No single sex groups, some dog
breeds not accepted

MARKET RASEN TF18

Racecourse Caravan Park
►►► 66%

Legsby Road LN8 3EA
☎ 01673 842307 🖹 01673 844532
📧 marketrasen@rht.net
🌐 www.marketrasenraces.co.uk

Dir: E of Market Rasen on A631, turn R 300yds after lights into Legsby Rd, site racecourse entrance is 0.75m on L

★ � £8.35-£12.60 🚐 £8.35-£12.60
⚠ £7.60-£9.60

Open 29 Mar-7 Oct (rs race days shared toilet & shower on race days) Booking Advisable bank hols & race days Last arrival 20.00hrs Last departure 14.00hrs
Set in a grass paddock adjacent to, but separate from, the racecourse, and screened by a hedge. The site has a golf course with a discount for campers, and there is a large children's playground. A 3-acre site with 55 touring pitches.
Reduced rate for racing & golf

Leisure: ♠ 🅰
Facilities: 🎝 ⊙ ✳ 🕻 🔋 🛏
Disabled facilities: toilet & washbasin on racecourse complex
Services: 🔟 🕎 ☶ 🖬 🖉 🖽 → ∪ ℙ9 🖸
Notes: Family park

▨ ▨ ▨ 🆂

WOODHALL SPA TF16

Bainland Country Park
►►►►► 75%

Horncastle Road LN10 6UX
☎ 01526 352903 🖹 01526 353730
📧 bookings@bainland.com
🌐 www.bainland.com

Dir: 1.5m from town, on B1191

★ 🛏 £11-£31.50 🚐 £11-£31.50
⚠ £9-£24.50

Open all year Booking Advisable all year Last arrival 21.30hrs Last departure 11.30hrs
More a country club than a purely touring park, this is one of the best equipped parks in the country with an impressive array of leisure facilities, combined with high standards of maintenance. The touring pitches are all screened by shrubs and trees, and many are fully serviced. Children are well catered for, and there is an indoor swimming pool. A 12-acre site with 170 touring pitches, 51 hardstandings and 10 static.
Jacuzzi, solarium, sauna, par 3 putting, boules

Leisure: ₴ ◖ ♠ 🅰 🖵
Facilities: ➡ 🎝 ⊙ 🖰 ✳ 🕻 🔋 🛒 🛏
Disabled facilities: toilet & shower, moveable ramps
Services: 🔟 ✗ 📠 ☶ 🕎 ☶ 🖙 🖉 🖽 → ∪
ℙ18 ♨ 🗩 ◎ ⚲
Notes: Under 18s must be accompanied by an adult, single sex groups at manager's discretion

▨ ▨ ▨ 🆂

E4 CHINGFORD TQ39

Lee Valley Campsite ▶▶▶ 72%

Sewardstone Road E4 7RA
☎ 020 8529 5689 📠 020 8559 4070
[E] scs@leevalleypark.org.uk
[W] www.leevalleypark.com

Dir: From M25 J26 to A112 and signed

★ 🚐 fr £11.90 🚌 fr £11.90 ⛺ fr £11.90

Open Apr-Oct Booking Advisable bank hols & Jul-Aug Last arrival 22.00hrs Last departure noon

Overlooking King George's Reservoir and close to Epping Forest, this parks has excellent modern facilities and a very peaceful atmosphere. A bus calls at the site hourly to take passengers to the nearest tube station, and Enfield is easily accessible. This impressive park is maintained to a high standard. A 12-acre site with 200 touring pitches, 20 hardstandings.

Leisure: 🛝

Facilities: 🚿 ⊙ 🧺 ✳ 📞 🛒 🐕

Disabled facilities: toilets & showers

Services: [T] 🚐 ⛛ 🧼 ⛽ 🍃 ⇳ → ∪ ⛳18 🎥 🎣 ◎

Notes: No single sex groups, no unaccompanied under 18s

AMERICAN EXPRESS · AMERICAN EXPRESS · VISA · Barclays CONNECT · DELTA · [S]

N9 EDMONTON TQ39

Lee Valley Camping & Caravan Park ▶▶▶ 74%

Meridian Way N9 0AS
☎ 020 8803 6900 📠 020 8884 4975
[E] leisurecentre@leevalleypark.org.uk
[W] www.leevalleypark.com

Dir: From M25 J25, A10 S, 1st L on A1055, approx 5m to Leisure Centre. From A406 (North Circular), N on A1010, L after 0.25m, R (Pickets Lock Ln)

★ 🚐 fr £12 🚌 fr £12 ⛺ fr £12

Open Booking Advisable Jul-Aug Last arrival 22.00hrs Last departure noon

A pleasant, open site within easy reach of London yet peacefully located close to two large reservoirs. The very good toilet facilities are beautifully kept by dedicated wardens, and the site has the advantage of being adjacent to a restaurant and bar, and a multi-screen cinema. A 4.5-acre site with 160 touring pitches, 60 hardstandings.

Kitchen, cinema, 18-hole golf course

Leisure: 🔍 🛝

Facilities: 🚿 ⊙ 🧺 ✳ 📞 🛒 🧺 🐕

Disabled facilities: toilet & shower

Services: [T] 🍴 🥡 🚐 🚐 ⛛ 🧼 🍷 ⛽ 🍃 → ⛳18 ✈ 🎥 🎣 ⛵

Notes: No commercial vehicles, max length of units 26 feet

AMERICAN EXPRESS · VISA · Barclays CONNECT · DELTA · [S]

LONDON

SOUTHPORT SD31

Willowbank Holiday Home & Touring Park ▶▶▶ 73%

Coastal Road Ainsdale PR8 3ST
☎ 01704 571566 📠 01704 571566
[E] mail@willowbankcp.co.uk
[W] www.willowbankcp.co.uk

Dir: From A565 between Formby and Ainsdale turn at the Woodvale lights onto coastal road, site 150mtrs on L

🚐 🚚 ⛺

Open Mar-10 Jan Booking Advisable bank hols & special events Last arrival 22.00hrs Last departure 16.00hrs

Set in a wooded clearing on a nature reserve next to the beautiful sand dunes, this attractive park is just off the coastal road to Southport. The immaculate toilet facilities are well equipped. A 6-acre site with 64 touring pitches, 30 hardstandings and 230 static.

Baby changing facility

Leisure: /Π\

Facilities: 🚿 ⊙ 🧺 📞 🪑 🐕

Disabled facilities: toilet & shower room

Services: 🚐 🚰 🗑 🧯 🍃 → U ⛳18 ✈ 🎬 🎣 ◎ ⛵ 🏪

Notes: No single sex groups

💳 AMERICAN EXPRESS, VISA, Barclays CONNECT, DELTA, SWITCH

BARNEY TF93

The Old Brick Kilns ▶▶▶▶ 77%

Little Barney Lane NR21 0NL
☎ 01328 878305 📠 01328 878948
[E] enquire@old-brick-kilns.co.uk
[W] www.old-brick-kilns.co.uk

Dir: Follow brown tourist signs from A148 (Fakenham-Cromer) to Barney, then L into Little Barney Lane - site at end of lane

★ 🚐 £13-£15.25 🚚 £13-£15.25
⛺ £10.75-£13

Open Mar-6 Jan (rs low season bar food/takeaway selected nights only) Booking Advisable bank hols & Jul-Aug Last arrival 22.00hrs Last departure noon

A secluded and peaceful park approached via a quiet leafy country lane. The park is on two levels with its own boating and fishing pool and many mature trees. Excellent, well-planned toilet facilities can be found in two blocks, and there is a short dog walk. A 12.73-acre site with 65 touring pitches, 65 hardstandings.

Boules, outdoor draughts, chess, family games area

Leisure: 🔍 /Π\ 📺

Facilities: 🚿 ⊙ 🧺 ✳ 📞 🏪 🏠 🪑 🐕

Disabled facilities: toilets, washbasin & shower in separate room

Services: [T] ✖ 🚐 🗑 🍷 🧯 🍃 ⊞ → 🎣 ◎ ⛵

💳 AMERICAN EXPRESS, VISA, MASTERCARD, Barclays CONNECT, DELTA, SWITCH

BELTON

Rose Farm Touring & Camping Park ►►► 72%

Stepshort NR31 9JS
☎ 01493 780896 📄 01493 780896
🌐 www.members.aol.com/rosefarm04

Dir: Follow signs to Belton off A143, R at lane called Stepshort, site 1st on R

★ 🚐 £8-£10 🚙 £8-£10 ▲ £8-£10

Open all year Booking Advisable Jul-Aug
A former railway line is the setting for this very peaceful site which enjoys rural views. The ever-improving facilities are spotlessly clean, and the park is brightened with many flower and herb beds. A 6-acre site with 80 touring pitches.

Leisure: 🌊 🛝 ⛳
Facilities: 🕭 ⊙ ⚒ ♜
Disabled facilities: toilets
Services: 🚱 🖾 🛢 🖉 🗓 → ∪ ℾ18 ↳ ✦ 🍴

CLIPPESBY

Clippesby Hall ►►► 72%

Clippesby Hall NR29 3BL
☎ 01493 367800 📄 01493 367809
🅴 holidays@clippesby.com
🌐 www.clippesby.com

Dir: From A47 rdbt take A1064, after 2m L onto B1152, 0.5m turn L opposite village sign, 400yds on R

★ 🚐 £13-£19.50 🚙 £13-£19.50

▲ £13-£19.50

Open Spring BH-18 Sep (rs Etr-23 May No swimming/tennis. Pub/café BH wkd only) Booking Advisable school hols Last arrival 17.30hrs Last departure 11.00hrs
A lovely country house estate with secluded pitches hidden among the trees or in sheltered sunny glades. There are good toilet facilities, and amenities include a café, clubhouse and family crazy-golf. A 30-acre site with 100 touring pitches.
Bicycle hire & mini golf

Leisure: 🎾 🎯 🌊 🛝
Facilities: 🕭 ⊙ 🎏 ⚒ ♻ 🛁 ♜
Disabled facilities: toilet & shower, pub & shop accessible
Services: 🆃 ✕ 🚱 🖾 🖵 🛢 🖉 🗓 → ∪ ↳ ✦ ◎
Notes: Dogs must be kept on leads, no large groups of young people

CROMER
TG24

Forest Park Caravan Site
▶▶▶ 65%

Northrepps Road NR27 0JR
☎ 01263 513290 📠 01263 511992
📧 forestpark@netcom.co.uk

🌐 www.forest-park.co.uk

Dir: A140 from Norwich, L at T-jct signed Cromer, R signed Northrepps, R then immediate L, L at T-jct , park on R

★ 🚐 £9-£16 🚙 £9-£16 ▲ £9-£16

Open Mar-Jan Booking Advisable Etr, Spring bank hol & Jul-Aug Last arrival 22.00hrs Last departure 14.00hrs

Surrounded by forest, this gently sloping park offers a wide choice of pitches. Visitors have the use of a heated indoor swimming pool, and a large clubhouse with entertainment. A 85-acre site with 344 touring pitches, 372 static.

BMX track, hair salon

Leisure: 🌊 ⚓ 🎠

Facilities: � ⊙ 🖓 ❄ ⚓ 🏪 🎋

Disabled facilities: toilet and shower

Services: 🔟 ✕ 🚐 🔋 ♨ ♀ ⓘ ∅ 🅷 → ∪ ⌒18 ⛽ 🐕
♪ ◎

CROMER
TG24

Seacroft Camping Park
▶▶▶▶ 70%

Runton Road NR27 9NH
☎ 01263 511722 📠 01263 511512
🌐 www.ukparks.co.uk/seacroft

Dir: 1m W of Cromer on A149 coast road

🚐 £11-£18 🚙 £11-£18 ▲ £11-£18

Open Mar-Oct Booking Advisable school hols, 22-31 May & 4 Sep Last arrival 23.00hrs Last departure 11hrs

A very good touring site, well laid out and landscaped. Touring pitches are well screened for privacy, and there is a separate large playing field with children's play equipment. Toilets and showers in the sanitary buildings are tiled and spotless. There is a heated swimming pool and bar/restaurant. A 5-acre site with 120 touring pitches.

Baby change

Leisure: 🌊 ⚓ 🎠 🏓

Facilities: 🌣 ⊙ 🖓 ❄ ⚓ 🏪 🎣 🎋 🐕

Disabled facilities: toilet, shower & washbasin

Services: 🔟 ✕ 🛁 🚐 🔋 ♀ ⓘ ∅ 🅷 → ∪ ⌒18 🐕
♪ ◎ ♨

GREAT YARMOUTH   TG50

Vauxhall Holiday Park 🏕 68%

4 Acle New Road NR30 1TB
☎ 01493 857231 📠 01493 331122
📧 vauxhall.holidays@virgin.net
🌐 www.vauxhall-holiday-park.co.uk

Dir: On A47 approaching Great Yarmouth

★ 🚐 £13-£28 🚐 £13-£28 ▲ £13-£28

Open Etr, mid May-Sep & Oct half term
Booking Advisable mid Jul-Aug Last arrival
21.00hrs Last departure 10.00hrs

*A very large holiday complex with plenty of
entertainment and access to beach, river,
estuary, lake and A47. The touring pitches are
laid out in four separate areas, each with its
own amenity block, and all arranged around
the main entertainment. A 40-acre site with
220 touring pitches, 421 static.*

Children's pool, sauna, solarium, fitness centre

Leisure: 🏊 🎾 🔍 🎯 🎱 🎮

Facilities: 🛁 ⊙ ❄ 🔌 ⚃

Disabled facilities: toilets & ramps

Services: 🔲 ✗ 🏧 🚽 🍴 🍺 🛢 🚿 → ∪ ⌂18
🔥 ♨ ♪ ◎ ♨

Notes: ✈

🏧 💳 💳 🔦 ⑤

HUNSTANTON   TF64

Searles of Hunstanton 🏕 71%

South Beach PE36 5BB
☎ 01485 534211 📠 01485 533815
🌐 www.searles.co.uk

Dir: A149 to Hunstanton. At rdbt follow South
Beach signs. Searles on L

★ 🚐 £11-£27 🚐 £16-£30 ▲ £11-£23

Open Feb half term-New Year (rs Feb-May &
Oct-Dec outdoor pool closed) Booking
Advisable bank hols & Jul-Aug Last arrival
20.45hrs Last departure 11.00hrs

*A large seaside holiday complex with well-
managed facilities, adjacent to sea and beach.
The tourers have their own areas, including
two excellent toilet blocks and pitches are
individually lined with small maturing shrubs
for privacy. The bars and entertainment,
restaurant, heated pools, golf, fishing and
bowling green make this park popular. A 50-
acre site with 332 touring pitches, 100
hardstandings and 460 static.*

Leisure: 🏊 🎾 🔍 🎱 🎮

Facilities: 🚻 🛁 ⊙ ⚄ ❄ 🔌 🚿 🏪 🎣 🐕

Disabled facilities: toilet facilities,
adapted caravans

Services: 🔲 ✗ 🏧 🚽 🍴 🍺 🛢 🚿 → ∪ ⌂18 🔥
♨ ♪ ◎ ♨

Notes: No single sex groups, minimum
booking age 25yrs

🏧 💳 💳 🔦 ⑤

ST JOHN'S FEN END — TF51

Virginia Lake Caravan Park
▶▶▶ 67%

Sneeth Road Marshland PE14 8JF
☎ 01945 430332 📄 01945 430676
Ⓦ www.virginialake.co.uk

Dir: From A47 E of Wisbech follow tourist board signs to Terrington St John. Park on L

★ 🏕 fr £12 🚐 fr £12 ⛺ fr £12

Open all year Last arrival 23.30hrs Last departure noon

A well-established park beside a 2-acre fishing lake with good facilities for both anglers and tourers. A clubhouse serves a selection of meals and offers weekend entertainment. A good base for touring West Norfolk. A 5-acre site with 100 touring pitches, 20 hardstandings.

Fishing

Leisure: 🏊

Facilities: 🏕⊙🔍☼❄✆🏪⌕📶🐾

Services: ✖🛒🏕♨🚽🅿🔋🍴⌀🖃→∪🏪18 ☻ ♪⊚

SANDRINGHAM — TF62

Camping & Caravanning Club Site
▶▶▶▶ 75%

The Sandringham Estate Double Lodges PE35 6EA
☎ 01485 542555
Ⓦ www.campingandcaravanningclub.co.uk

Dir: From A148 turn L onto B1440 signed West Newton. Follow signs to site. Or take A149 turning L & following signs to site

★ 🏕 £15.35-£18.35 🚐 £15.35-£18.35
⛺ £15.35-£18.35

Open Feb-Nov Booking Advisable bank hols & peak periods Last arrival 21.00hrs Last departure noon

A prestige park, very well landscaped and laid out in mature woodland, with toilets and other buildings blending in with the scenery. There are plenty of walks from the site, and this is a good touring base for the rest of Norfolk. A 28-acre site with 275 touring pitches, 2 hardstandings.

Leisure: 🏊

Facilities: 🏕⊙🔍☼✆🏪⌕

Disabled facilities: toilet, shower, washbasin & razor point

Services: 🅃🏕🔋🍴⌀🖃→∪🍴

SCRATBY

Scratby Hall Caravan Park
▶▶▶ 67%

NR29 3PH

☎ 01493 730283

Dir: Signed off B1159

🚐 🚐 Å

Open Spring bank hol-mid Sep (rs Etr-Spring bank hol & mid Sep-Oct reduced hours & shop closed) Booking Advisable Spring bank hol wk & Jul-Aug Last arrival 22.00hrs Last departure noon

A neatly-maintained site with a popular children's play area, well-equipped shop and outdoor swimming pool with sun terrace. The toilets are kept spotlessly clean, and the beach and the Norfolk Broads are close by. A 5-acre site with 108 touring pitches.
Food preparation room

Leisure: 🔍 /八\

Facilities: ⚕ ⊙ ⌐ ☀ ✆ �

Disabled facilities: toilet, shower & washing facilities

Services: 🔟 🚐 🖴 🛢 ⌀ 🗄 → ∪ ⌐18 ⤸ ✈

STANHOE

The Rickels Caravan & Camping Park ▶▶▶ 70%

Bircham Road PE31 8PU

☎ 01485 518671 📄 01485 518969

Dir: From King's Lynn take A148 to Hillington, and B1153 to Great Bircham. Then B1155 to x-rds, straight over, site 100yds on L

★ 🚐 £8.50-£10 🚐 £8.50-£10 Å £8.50-£10

Open Mar-Oct Booking Advisable bank hols Last arrival 21.00hrs Last departure 11.00hrs

Set in three acres of grassland, with sweeping country views and a pleasant, relaxing atmosphere. The meticulously maintained grounds and facilities are part of the attraction, and the slightly sloping land has some level areas and sheltering for tents. Children using the play equipment can be safely watched from all pitches. A 3-acre site with 30 touring pitches.

Leisure: /八\ ⌐

Facilities: ⚕ ⊙ ☀ 🚮

Services: 🚐 🛢 ⌀ 🗄 → ✈ 🚮

Notes: Dogs must be on leads, no ground sheets

SWAFFHAM TF80

Breckland Meadows Touring Park ▶▶▶ 71%

Lynn Road PE37 7PT
☎ 01760 721246
🅔 info@brecklandmeadows.co.uk
🆆 www.brecklandmeadows.co.uk

Dir: 1m W of Swaffham centre on the old A47

★ 🚐 £10-£12 🚐 £10-£12 ▲ £6-£12

Open all year (rs Nov-Feb strictly bookings only) Booking Advisable Nov-Feb & BH's Last arrival 21.00hrs Last departure noon
An immaculate, well-landscaped little park on the edge of Swaffham. The impressive toilet block is well equipped, and there are hardstandings and full electricity. Plenty of planting is resulting in attractive screening. A 2.5-acre site with 45 touring pitches, 13 hardstandings.
Tourist info centre

Leisure: 🄰
Facilities: 🌤 ⊙ ✻ 🚭 🛱 🛏
Disabled facilities: toilet & washbasin with grab rails
Services: 🖃 🖹 ⌀ 🖃 → ∪ 🖿18 🌙 🖾 🖺

▩ ▩ ▩ ▨ �

BAMBURGH NU13

Waren Caravan Park ▶▶▶▶ 67%

Waren Mill NE70 7EE
☎ 01668 214366 🖹 01668 214224
🅔 waren@meadowhead.co.uk
🆆 www.meadowhead.co.uk

Dir: 2m E of town on B1342. From A1 turn onto B1342 signed Bamburgh and take unclass road past Waren Mill, signed Budle

🚐 🚐 ▲

Open Apr-Oct (rs Nov-Feb Bar, shop and restaurant closed) Booking Advisable Spring bank hol & Jul-Aug Last arrival 20.00hrs Last departure noon
Attractive seaside site with footpath access to the beach, surrounded by a slightly sloping grassy embankment giving shelter to caravans. The park offers excellent facilities including several family bathrooms. A 4-acre site with 180 touring pitches, 11 hardstandings and 300 static.
100 acres of private heathland

Leisure: ⚛ ◗ 🄰
Facilities: ➜ 🌤 ⊙ 🖎 ✻ 🌭 🛢 🚭 🛱 🛏
Disabled facilities: toilet, shower & caravan holiday home
Services: 🖹 ✗ 🖮 🖃 ⌀ 🖾 🖂 🖹 ⌀ 🖃 → ∪ 🖿18 🌙 ◎
Notes: No single sex groups

▩ ▩ ▩ ▨ �

Ord House Country Park
▶▶▶▶▶ 76%

East Ord TD15 2NS
☎ 01289 305288 📠 01289 330832
📧 enquiries@ordhouse.co.uk
🌐 www.ordhouse.co.uk

Dir: On A1, Berwick bypass, turn off at 2nd rdbt at East Ord, follow 'Caravan' signs

★ ⊞ £11-£17.40 ⊞ £11-£17.40

⬩ £6-£17.40

Open all year Booking Advisable bank hols & Jul-Aug Last arrival 23.00hrs Last dep noon
A very well run park set in the pleasant grounds of a country house. Touring pitches are marked and well spaced; some fully-serviced. The very modern toilet facilities include family suites, and first class disabled rooms. There is a six-hole golf course and an outdoor leisure shop with a good range of camping and caravanning spares, as well as clothing and equipment. A 42-acre site with 79 touring pitches, 46 hardstandings and 217 static.
Crazy golf, table tennis

Leisure: ⚑

Facilities: ➡ 🐾 ⊙ 🐾 ☀ 📞 🛒 🏠 🐕 ★

Disabled facilities: toilets, showers, ramp/lift access into barn

Services: 🆃 ✖ ➡ 🕯 🗑 🗐 🛒 🎯 → 🛉18 ❄ 🍽 ♪ ◎

Notes: No single sex groups

Haggerston Castle 🏰 72%

Beal TD15 2PA
☎ 01289 381333 📠 01289 381443
📧 lisamcewan@bourne-leisure.co.uk
🌐 www.british-holidays.co.uk/haggerstonecastle

Dir: On A1, 5.5m S of Berwick-upon-Tweed and signed

★ ⊞ ⊞

Open Mar-Nov Last arrival mdnt Last departure 10.00hrs
A large holiday centre with a very well equipped touring park, offering comprehensive holiday activities. The entertainment complex contains amusements for the whole family, and there are several bars, an adventure playground, boating on the lake, a children's club, a 9-hole golf course, tennis courts, and various eating outlets. A 7-acre site with 156 touring pitches, 1,200 static.

Leisure: 🎣 🎿 🏊 🎯 ⚑ 📺

Facilities: 🐾 ⊙ 🐾 ☀ 📞 🛒 🏠 🐕 ★

Services: ✖ 🛗 🗐 🗐 🛒 🎯 → 🛉 9 ❄ ◎ ⌂

CRASTER NU21

Camping & Caravanning Club Site ▶▶▶ 68%

Dunstan Hill Dunstan NE66 3TQ
☎ 01665 576310
ⓦ www.campingandcaravanningclub.co.uk

Dir: From A1 travelling N take B1340 signed Seahouses. Continue to T-jct at Criston Bank, turn R. Next R signed Embleton. R at x-rds then 1st L signed Craster

★ ⊟ £12.95-£16.35 ⊟ £12.95-£16.35
▲ £12.95-£16.35

Open Mar-Nov Booking Advisable BH's & peak periods Last arrival 21.00hrs Last departure noon

An immaculately maintained site with pleasant landscaping, close to the beach and Craster harbour. The historic town of Alnwick is nearby, as is the ruined Dunstanburgh Castle. A 14-acre site with 150 touring pitches, 5 hardstandings.

Leisure: ⚙
Facilities: ⚑⊙⚑✳⚔⚗⚘
Disabled facilities: toilet, shower, washbasin & hand dryer
Services: ⚏⚙⚗⚗⚗⚗→↑18⚗⚗⚗

ROTHBURY NU00

Coquetdale Caravan Park ▶▶▶ 65%

Whitton NE65 7RU
☎ 01669 620549 📄 01669 620559
ⓔ enquiries@coquetdalecaravanpark.co.uk
ⓦ www.coquetdalecaravanpark.co.uk

Dir: 0.5m SW of Rothbury on road to Newtown

★ ⚑ £10-£14 ⚑ £10-£14 ▲ £8-£14

Open mid Mar/Etr-Oct Booking Advisable bank hol wknds & school hols Last arrival 20.00hrs Last departure evening

A very pleasant mainly static site in a lovely location beside the River Coquet, with good open views of moorland and the Simonside Hills. Tourers are on the site's upper area with their own purpose-built toilet facilities. An ideal place for relaxing and touring. A 13-acre site with 50 touring pitches, 160 static. Adventure playground for older children/adults

Leisure: ⚙
Facilities: ⚑⊙✳⚔⚗⚗⚘
Services: ⚏⚗⚗→↑9⚗⚗
Notes: Families & couples only, no single sex groups

RADCLIFFE ON TRENT SK63

Thornton's Holt Camping Park
▶▶▶ 66%

Stragglethorpe Road Stragglethorpe NG12 2JZ
☎ 0115 933 2125 ▤ 0115 933 3318
ⓔ camping@thorntons-holt.co.uk
ⓦ www.thorntons-holt.co.uk

> **Dir:** Take A52, 3m E of Nottingham. Turn S at lights towards Cropwell Bishop. Park 0.5m on L. Or A46 SE of Nottingham. N at lights. Park 2.5m on R

🚐 £8.50-£10 🚐 £8.50-£10 ▲ £8.50-£10
Open all year Apr-1 Nov (rs 2 Nov-Mar No pool, shop or washing up) Booking Advisable bank hols & wknds mid May-Oct Last arrival 21.00hrs Last departure 13.00hrs
A well-run family site in former meadowland, with pitches located among young trees and bushes for a rural atmosphere and outlook. The toilets are housed in converted farm buildings, and an indoor swimming pool is a popular attraction. A 13-acre site with 155 touring pitches, 35 hardstandings.
Pub & Restaurant within 150mtrs.

Leisure: ⚡ 🎱 ⚓ ▱
Facilities: ⬕ ⊙ ◵ ✳ 🝙 🝙 ⛫ ♜
Disabled facilities: toilet, shower & washroom
Services: ▣ ✕ 🛢 ⑃ 🛢 🝙 ⊘ ▣ → ∪ ୮18 ⅄
♨ ♪ △
Notes: 10.30pm noise curfew

TUXFORD SK77

Orchard Park Touring Caravan & Camping Park ▶▶▶ 70%

Marnham Road NG22 0PY
☎ 01777 870228 ▤ 01777 870320
ⓔ info@orchardcaravanpark.co.uk
ⓦ www.caravanparksnottinghamshire.com

> **Dir:** Turn off A1 at Tuxford via slip road onto A6075, towards Lincoln. After 0.5m turn R into Marnham Road & site is 0.75m on R

🚐 £10-£12 🚐 £10-£12 ▲ £10-£12
Open mid Mar-Oct (rs Winter use restricted to hard standings) Booking Advisable bank hols & Jul-Aug Last arrival mdnt Last departure 18.00hrs
A rural site set in an old fruit orchard with spacious pitches arranged in small groups separated by shrubs. Many of them are served with water and electricity. This peaceful park's position in the middle of Sherwood Forest makes it an ideal touring base, and it is easily accessed from the A1. A 7-acre site with 60 touring pitches, 30 hardstandings.
Family shower room

Leisure: ⚓
Facilities: ⬕ ⊙ ◵ ✳ ⛫ 🝙 ᑎ ♜
Disabled facilities: shower, washbasin & toilet
Services: ▣ 🛢 🛢 ⊘ ▣ → ∪ ♪

BLETCHINGDON SP51

Diamond Farm Caravan & Camping Park ►►► 73%

Islip Road OX5 3DR
☎ 01869 350909 🖹 01869 350059
🖲 warden@diamondpark.co.uk
🕅 www.diamondpark.co.uk

Dir: From M40 J9 onto A34 S for 3m, then B4027 to Bletchingdon. Site 1m on L

🚐 � Å

Open Mar-Nov Booking Advisable bank hols & Jul-Sep Last arrival 22.00hrs Last departure noon
A well-run, quiet rural site in good level surroundings, and ideal for touring the Cotswolds. Situated 7m north of Oxford in the heart of the Thames Valley. This popular park is well planted, and offers a heated outdoor swimming pool and a games room for children. A 3-acre site with 37 touring pitches, 13 hardstandings.

Leisure: ⚊ ♣ ⚙

Facilities: ➡ 🏳 ⊙ ⏱ ☼ 🜂 🛠

Services: 🔟 🚐 🖳 🖪 🍴 🛢 🖉 🔃 ➔ ⊦18 🗡

CHARLBURY SP31

Cotswold View Touring Park ►►►► 71%

Enstone Road OX7 3JH
☎ 01608 810314 🖹 01608 811891
🖲 bookings@gfwiddows.f9.co.uk
🕅 www.cotswoldview.co.uk

Dir: Signed from A44 on to B4022

🚐 � Å

Open Etr or Apr-Oct Booking Advisable bank hols Last arrival 21.00hrs Last departure noon
A good Cotswold site, well screened and with attractive views across the countryside. The toilet facilities include fully-equipped family rooms and bathrooms, and there are spacious, sheltered pitches, some with hardstandings. Breakfast and take-away food available from the shop. A 10-acre site with 125 touring pitches.

Off-licence, cycle hire, skittle alley

Leisure: ⚊ ♣ ⚙

Facilities: ➡ 🏳 ⊙ ⏱ ☼ 🜂 🛠 🐾 🛠

Disabled facilities: 2 separate disabled rooms with walk/drive-in showers

Services: 🔟 ➡ 🚐 🖪 🛢 🖉 🔃 ➔ 🗡

STANDLAKE

Lincoln Farm Park ▶▶▶▶▶ 79%

High Street OX29 7RH
☎ 01865 300239 📄 01865 300127

Dir: In village off A415 between Abingdon & Witney, 5m SE of Witney

★ ⊞ £10.70–£17.45 ⊞ £10.70–£17.45

▲ £10.70–£17.45

Open Feb-Nov Booking Advisable bank hols, Jul-Aug & most wknds Last arrival 21.00hrs Last departure noon

An attractively landscaped park in a quiet village setting, with superb facilities and a high standard of maintenance. Family rooms, fully-serviced pitches, two indoor swimming pools and a fully-equipped gym are part of the comprehensive amenities. A 9-acre site with 90 touring pitches, 42 hardstandings and 19 static.

Indoor leisure centre, putting green, outdoor chess

Leisure: ⚐ ⚘

Facilities: ➡ ⋔ ⊙ ⚑ ✻ ⌧ ⚐ ⊟ ⋔

Disabled facilities: shower & toilet

Services: 🔟 ⚑ ⚐ ⊽ 🗑 🔋 ⌀ ⊡ → ∪ ⋔18 ⚲ ⤴

BRIDGNORTH

Stanmore Hall Touring Park
▶▶▶▶ 77%

Stourbridge Road WV15 6DT
☎ 01746 761761 📄 01746 768069
🄴 stanmore@morris-leisure.co

Dir: 2m E of Bridgnorth on A458

★ ⊞ £13.85–£21.60 ⊞ £13.85–£21.60

▲ £13.85–£21.60

Open all year Booking Advisable school & bank hols & Jul-Aug Last arrival 20.00hrs Last departure noon

An excellent park in peaceful surroundings offering outstanding facilities. The pitches, many of them fully serviced, are arranged around the lake in Stanmore Hall, home of the Midland Motor Museum. Handy for touring Ironbridge and the Severn Valley Railway, while Bridgnorth itself is an attractive old market town. A 12.5-acre site with 131 touring pitches, 44 hardstandings.

Leisure: ⚘

Facilities: ⋔ ⊙ ⚑ ✻ ⌧ ⚐ ⊟ ⋔

Disabled facilities: toilet & shower

Services: 🔟 ➡ ⚐ ⊽ 🗑 🔋 ⌀ ⊡ → ∪ ⋔18 ⚲ ⚏ ⤴

Notes: Max of 2 dogs

LYNEAL (NEAR ELLESMERE)   SJ43

Fernwood Caravan Park ▶▶▶▶ 68%

SY12 0QF
☎ 01948 710221 📠 01948 710324
📧 fernwood@caravanpark37.fsnet.co.uk
🌐 www.ranch.co.uk

Dir: From A495 in Welshampton take B5063, over canal bridge, turn R as signed

★ 🛖 £13.50-£18.00 🚐 £13.50-£18

Open Mar-Nov Booking Advisable bank hols
Last arrival 21.00hrs Last departure 17.00hrs
A peaceful park set in wooded countryside, with a screened, tree-lined touring area and fishing lake. The approach is past flower beds, and the static area which is tastefully arranged around an attractive children's playing area. There is a small child-free touring area for those wanting complete relaxation, and the park has 20 acres of woodland walks. A 26-acre site with 60 touring pitches, 165 static.
Lake for coarse fishing on site

Leisure: 🅰
Facilities: 📷⊙🔌☀🔥🛒📶
Disabled facilities: toilet
Services: 🖵 🔌 ⅏ 🗑 🍴 → 🔭 🥄

▨ ▨ ▨ ▨ 🛜 🅂

SHREWSBURY   SJ41

Oxon Hall Touring Park ▶▶▶▶ 78%

Welshpool Road SY3 5FB
☎ 01743 340868 📠 01743 340869
📧 oxon@morris-leisure.co.uk
🌐 www.morris-leisure.co.uk

Dir: Leave A5 ring road at jct with A458. Park shares entrance with 'Oxon Park & Ride'

🚐 🛖 👶
Open all year Booking Advisable high season
Last arrival 21.00hrs
A delightful park with quality facilities, and a choice of grass and fully-serviced pitches. An adults-only section is very popular with those wanting a peaceful holiday, and there is an inviting patio area next to reception and the shop, overlooking a small lake. This site is ideally located for visiting Shrewsbury and the surrounding countryside, and there is always a warm welcome here. A 15-acre site with 124 touring pitches, 60 hardstandings and 42 static.

Leisure: 🅰
Facilities: 📷⊙🔌🛒📶🛁📶
Disabled facilities: toilet & shower
Services: 🖵 🍴 🔌 ⅏ 🗑 🍴 ⌀ → ⌐18 🎪 🥄

▨ ▨ ▨ ▨ 🛜 🅂

BATH ST76

Newton Mill Caravan and Camping Park ►►►► 75%

Newton Road BA2 9JF
☎ 01225 333909 ⧉ 01225 461556
🅔 newtonmill@hotmail.com
🅦 www.campinginbath.co.uk

Dir: From Bath travel W on A4 to A39 rdbt, take immediate L and site 1m on L

🏕 🚐 🛖

Open all year Booking Advisable public hols & Jul-Aug Last arrival 21.00hrs Last departure noon
An attractive park set in a sheltered valley and surrounded by woodlands, with a stream running through. The very good facilities include a restaurant and bar, and smart toilet facilities with private cubicles. The city is easily accessible by bus, and the site is beside the level traffic-free Bath/Bristol cycle path. A 42-acre site with 195 touring pitches, 85 hardstandings.
Fishing & satellite TV hook ups

Leisure: 🎣 🗚
Facilities: 🖚 🗢 ⊙ 🗟 ❄ 🗟 🖢 🏋
Disabled facilities: toilets, showers & ramps
Services: 🍽 ✕ 🖦 🗲 🗟 🗟 🗨 🗟 🗟 → ⋃ ⏸9 ⚒ 🗢 🖊 ▬ ▬ ▬ ▬ 🗟

BLUE ANCHOR ST04

Hoburne Blue Anchor ►►► 68%

TA24 6JT
☎ 01643 821360 ⧉ 01643 821572
🅔 enquiries@hoburne.com
🅦 www.hoburne.com

Dir: 0.25m E of West Somerset Railway Station on B3191

★ 🚐 £9.50-£16 🚐 £9.50-£16
Open Mar-Oct (rs Mar & Oct shop & swimming pool limited) Booking Advisable bank hols & Jul-Aug Last arrival 22.00hrs Last departure 10.00hrs
Large coastal site, partly wooded on level ground overlooking bay with individual areas screened. There is a very good play area away from the touring park for children, and the staff are friendly and helpful. A 29-acre site with 103 touring pitches, 331 static.
Crazy golf

Leisure: 🎣 🗚
Facilities: 🖚 ⊙ 🗟 ❄ 🗲 🖢
Disabled facilities: toilet
Services: ✕ 🖦 🗲 ⅏ 🗟 🗟 ⊘ 🗟 → ⋃ ⏸18 ⚒
◎ Notes: 🚫 ▬ ▬ ▬ ▬ 🗟

BREAN ST25

Northam Farm Caravan & Touring Park ►►► 75%

TA8 2SE
☎ 01278 751244 📠 01278 751150
📧 enquiries@northamfarm.co.uk
🌐 www.northamfarm.co.uk

Dir: From M5 J22 to Burnham-on-Sea. In Brean, Northam Farm on R 0.5m past Brean leisure park

★ 🚐 £5-£16.50 🚏 £5-£16.50 ▲ £5-£16.50

Open Apr-Oct (rs Mar & Oct shop & takeaway closed, no dog area) Booking Advisable bank & school hols Last arrival 21.00hrs Last departure 10.30hrs
An attractive site a short walk from the sea with game, coarse and sea fishing close by. The quality park also has lots of children's play areas, and is near a long sandy beach. It also runs the Seagull Inn about 600yds away, which includes a restaurant and entertainment. A 30-acre site with 350 touring pitches, 137 hardstandings and 112 static.

Leisure: ⚙

Facilities: ➡ ⋒ ⊙ ⦦ ✳ ⛽ ⚑ 🞈

Disabled facilities: full disabled washroom & WC. Radar key needed

Services: 🖵 ✕ 🛒 🔌 🖼 🛢 🧴 🗄 → ∪ ⋒18 🎵

◎ Notes: Families & couples only, no motorcycles

BREAN ST25

Warren Farm Holiday Centre ⌂ 68%

Brean Sands TA8 2RP
☎ 01278 751227
📧 enquiries@warren-farm.co.uk
🌐 www.warren-farm.co.uk

Dir: M5 J22 and follow B3140 past Burnham on Sea to Berrow and Brean. Park 1.5m past Brean Leisure Park

★ 🚐 £6-£12 🚏 £6-£12 ▲ £6-£12

Open Apr-mid Oct Booking Advisable BH's & school hols Last arrival 20.00hrs Last departure noon
A large family-run holiday park close to the beach, divided into several fields each with its own designated facilities. Pitches are spacious and level, and enjoy panoramic views of the Mendip Hills and Brean Down. A bar and restaurant are part of the complex, which provide entertainment for all the family, and there is also separate entertainment for children. A 100-acre site with 575 touring pitches, 800 static.
Fishing lake & ponds, indoor play area

Leisure: ⚓ ⚙ ▭

Facilities: ➡ ⋒ ⊙ ⦦ ✳ ⛽ ⚑ 🞈 🞱

Disabled facilities: toilet & shower facilities

Services: 🖵 ✕ 🛒 🔌 🚰 🖼 🛢 🧴 🗄 → ∪ ⋒18
🎵 Notes: No single sex groups, no commerical vehicles

BRIDGWATER ST23

Mill Farm Caravan & Camping Park
▶▶▶▶ 70%

Fiddington TA5 1JQ
☎ 01278 732286

Dir: From Bridgwater take A39 W, turn L at Cannington rdbt for 2m, then R just beyond Apple Inn towards Fiddington and follow camping signs

🏕 🚐 ⛺

Open all year Booking Advisable peak periods Last arrival 23.00hrs Last departure 10.00hrs
An established, mature site with plenty to interest all the family, and helpful owners. A waterfall, stream and safe boating pool are popular features, and there are heated indoor and outdoor swimming pools, with a 50-metre waterslide, a games room, and pony and horse riding school. The park is divided into three caravan areas and a large space for tents, each with its own facilities and play equipment. A 6-acre site with 125 touring pitches.
Canoeing, pool table, trampolines, entertainment

Leisure: 🏊 🎣 🎱 🎮 🎪
Facilities: 🚻 🕭 ⊙ ♨ ✲ 🚿 🛒 🎣 🐎
Disabled facilities: toilets
Services: 📺 🕭 🚐 🔧 ♨ 🛒 ∅ ⬚ → ↾🛢 🔧 ◉

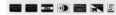

BURNHAM-ON-SEA ST34

Burnham-on-Sea Holiday Village
🏖 70%

Marine Drive TA8 1LA
☎ 01278 783391
🌐 www.british-holidays.co.uk

Dir: On A38 to Highbridge, cross railway bridge and turn R to Burnham-on-Sea. In 1m turn L into Marine Parade, and follow signs to site on L

🏕 🚐 ⛺

Open Mar-Oct Last arrival 22.00hrs Last departure noon
A large family-orientated holiday village complex with a separate touring park containing 43 super pitches. There is a wide range of activities including excellent indoor and outdoor pools, plus bars, restaurants and entertainment for all the family. The coarse fishing lake is very popular, and the seafront at Burnham is only 0.5m away. A 76-acre site with 75 touring pitches.

Leisure: 🏊 🎣 🎱 🎮 🎪
Facilities: 🛒
Services: ✕ 🕭 🚐 🛒 🍽 🛢
Notes: 🐕

CHARD ST30

Alpine Grove Touring Park
▶▶▶ 70%

Forton TA20 4HD
☎ 01460 63479 🖹 01460 63479
🄴 stay@alpinegrovetouringpark.com
🄦 www.alpinegrovetouringpark.com

Dir: Turn off A30 between Chard & Crewkerne towards Cricket St Thomas, follow signs. Park 2m on R

★ 🚐 £10.50-£12.50 🚍 £10.50-£12.50
🅰 £8-£10

Open Apr-1 Oct Booking Advisable bank hols & Jul-Aug Last arrival 21.00hrs Last departure 11.00hrs

An attractive, quiet wooded park with both hardstandings and grass pitches, close to Cricket St Thomas wildlife park, in a rural location. The park's nature trails are proving popular. A 8-acre site with 40 touring pitches, 15 hardstandings.

Leisure: ᔓ ⋀
Facilities: ฿ ⊙ ⦶ ⁕ ᚼ ⅃ 🖻 ㆆ ㅑ
Services: 🆃 🖵 🖴 🝙 ⌀ 🖃 → ∪ ↑18 ✒
Notes: Dogs must be kept on leads, no single sex groups

CHEDDAR ST45

Broadway House Holiday Caravan & Camping Park ▶▶▶▶ 65%

Axbridge Road BS27 3DB
☎ 01934 742610 🖹 01934 744950
🄴 enquiries@broadwayhouse.uk.com

Dir: From M5 J22 follow signs to Cheddar Gorge & Caves (8m). Park is midway between Cheddar & Axbridge on A371

★ 🚐 £10-£18.50 🚍 £9-£15 🅰 £8.50-£17

Open Mar-mid Nov (rs Mar-end May & Oct-Nov No bar or pool open, limited shop hours) Booking Advisable bank hols & end Jul-Aug Last arrival 23.00hrs Last departure noon

A well-equipped family park on the slopes of the Mendips with an exceptional range of activities for all ages. This is a busy and lively park in the main holiday periods, but can be quiet and peaceful off-peak. Broadway has its own activity centre based on the site, providing archery, shooting, climbing, caving, ballooning and much more. A 30-acre site with 200 touring pitches, 35 hardstandings and 37 static.

Sunbed, table tennis, crazy golf

Leisure: ᔓ ⦿ ⋀ ▢
Facilities: ➾ ฿ ⊙ ⦶ ⁕ ᚼ ⅃ 🖻 ㆆ ㅑ
Disabled facilities: toilet & shower facilities
Services: 🆃 ✕ 🖐 🖵 ∿ 🖴 🝙 ⌀ 🖃 → ∪ ↑18
✒ ◎
Notes: Children to be supervised at all times

CROWCOMBE ST13

Quantock Orchard Caravan Park
▶▶▶▶ 75%

TA4 4AW
☎ 01984 618618 🖷 01984 618618
🅴 qocp@flaxpool.freeserve.co.uk
🆆 www.flaxpool.freeserve.co.uk

Dir: Site set back from A358

♨ ♨ 🅰

Open all year Booking Advisable bank hols &
Jul-Aug Last arrival 22.00hrs Last departure
noon

*An attractive, quiet site with wonderful views,
sitting at the western foot of the Quantocks
midway between Taunton and Minehead. The
park is laid out in an old orchard with plenty
of colourful flower beds, and the quality
facilities are very well maintained. A fitness
complex next to the swimming pool offers
jacuzzi, sauna and exercise machines. Ideal
for visiting Exmoor National Park, and the
nearby West Somerset Steam Railway. A 3.5-
acre site with 75 touring pitches.*
Gym & leisure suite, off-licence on site

Leisure: ⚲ ⚓ ⌂ ▢
Facilities: ↔ 🅝 ☉ ☖ ✻ 📞 🌡
Disabled facilities: bathroom & toilet
Services: 🆃 ☎ ⬢ 🛢 ⌀ ☒ ⬚ → ∪ ⌂18 ⤴

🟦 🟦 🟦 🟦 🟦

DULVERTON SS92

Wimbleball Lake ▶▶▶ 65%

TA22 9NU
☎ 01398 371257
🆆 www.swlakestrust.org.uk

Dir: From A396 Tiverton-Minehead road
take B3222 signed Dulverton Services,
follow signs to Wimbleball Lake. Ignore 1st
entry (fishing) and take 2nd entry for
watersports & camping

★ ⚓ fr £10 🅰 fr £10

Open Apr-1 Nov Booking Advisable high
seasonhrs Last departure 14.00hrs
*A grassy site overlooking Wimbleball Lake, set
high up on Exmoor National Park. The
camping area is in its own paddock with
modern toilet facilities, and surrounded by
farmland in a quiet setting. The lake is
nationally renowned for its trout fishing, and
boats can be hired with advance notice. A
1.25-acre site with 30 touring pitches, 4
hardstandings.*
Watersports centre

Leisure: ⌂
Facilities: 🅝 ☉ 🌡
Disabled facilities: toilets
Services: ✗ ⚓ → ∪ ♨ ⤴ 🌡 △
Notes: Dogs must be kept on leads

🟦 🟦 🟦 🟦 🟦

FROME ST74

Seven Acres Caravan & Camping Site ▶▶▶ 66%

Seven Acres West Woodlands BA11 5EQ
☎ 01373 464222

Dir: On B3092 approx 0.75m from rdbt with A361, Frome bypass

★ 🚐 fr £8 🚌 fr£8 ⛺ fr £7

Open Mar-Oct

A level meadowland site beside the shallow River Frome, with a bridge across to an adjacent field, and plenty of scope for families (though no laundry, but launderette 0.5m away). Set on the edge of the Longleat Estate with its stately home, wildlife safari park, and many other attractions. A 3-acre site with 22 touring pitches, 22 hardstandings.

Leisure: 🛝

Facilities: 🚿 ⊙ □ ✳ 🪑 🐕

Disabled facilities: toilet & washbasin

Services: □ → ∪ □ □ □ □

Notes: Dogs must be kept on leads

PRIDDY ST55

Mendip Heights Camping & Caravan Park ▶▶▶▶ 72%

Townsend BA5 3BP
☎ 01749 870241 📠 01749 870368
[E] enquiries@mendipheights.co.uk
[W] www.mendipheights.co.uk

Dir: Take A39 N from Wells. After 3m turn L at lights onto B3135 to Cheddar. After 4.5m turn L. Site 200yds on R

★ 🚐 £8-£12 🚌 £8-£12 ⛺ £8-£12

Open Mar-15 Nov Booking Advisable bank & school hols Last arrival 20.30hrs Last departure 11.00hrs

A naturally sheltered country touring park nestling in a valley of the Mendip Hills, surrounded by trees. This rapidly improving site has a completely refurbished toilet block with plenty of en suite facilities. A shop selling local produce is popular, and evening meals and morning croissants and bread are also appreciated by visitors. A 4.5-acre site with 90 touring pitches, 13 hardstandings and 2 static.

Archery, canoeing, abseiling, caving, table tennis

Leisure: 🛝

Facilities: 🚿 ⊙ □ ✳ 📞 □ □ 🐕

Disabled facilities: family room suitable for disables visitors

Services: [T] □ □ □ □ □ □ □ → ∪ ◎

American Express Visa Barclays Connect Delta S

REDHILL ST46

Brook Lodge Farm Camping & Caravan Park ▶▶▶ 66%

Cowslip Green BS40 5RD
☎ 01934 862311 📠 01934 862311
📧 brooklodgefarm@aol.com
🌐 www.brooklodgefarm.com

Dir: M5 J18 follow signs for Bristol Airport. Park 3m on L of A38 at bottom of hill after passing Darlington Arms

★ 🚐 £12.50-£18.50 🚑 £10-£16.50

▲ £10.50-£17

Open Mar-Oct Booking Advisable 22 May-4 Sep Last arrival 22.30hrs Last departure noon
A naturally sheltered country touring park nestling in a valley of the Mendip Hills, surrounded by trees and a historic walled garden. Country walks can be enjoyed from the park, and there is trout fishing nearby. A 3.5-acre site with 29 touring pitches, 3 hardstandings.
Bicycle hire & walking maps provided

Leisure: ⚡ 🛆
Facilities: 🏪 ☉ ⚒ ✳ 🔧 ⚓ 🏇
Services: 🚱 🛢 🗑 → ∪ ↑18 🎵
Notes: Small dogs only & must be on lead

▭▭ ▭▭ ▭▭ ▭▭ 🅢

RODNEY STOKE ST44

Bucklegrove Caravan & Camping Park ▶▶▶▶ 66%

Wells Road BS27 3UZ
☎ 01749 870261 📠 01749 870101
📧 info@bucklegrove.co.uk
🌐 www.bucklegrove.co.uk

Dir: On A371 midway between Cheddar & Wells

★ 🚐 £5-£17 🚑 £5-£17 ▲ £5-£17

Open 5 Mar-2 Jan (rs Nov-Dec & Mar-Etr Pool closed) Booking Advisable bank hols & peak periods Last arrival 21.00hrs Last departure noon
A well-sheltered site on the southern slopes of the Mendip Hills providing superb views of Somerset. This popular park offers good facilities and amenities including an indoor swimming pool and a bar/restaurant. An ideal touring base, and a pleasant suntrap. A 7.5-acre site with 120 touring pitches, 24 hardstandings and 35 static.
Separate tourist information room

Leisure: ⚡ 🏊 🛆
Facilities: ⚓ 🏪 ☉ ⚒ ✳ 🔧 ⚓ 🎡
Disabled facilities: toilet & shower
Services: 🎫 ✗ 🚽 🚱 🛢 🗑 → ∪ ↑18 🎪 🎵 ◎
Notes: 🏇 No single sex groups

▭▭ ▭▭ ▭▭ ▭▭ 🅢

SPARKFORD   ST62

Long Hazel International Caravan/Camping Park ▶▶▶ 70%

High Street BA22 7JH
☎ 01963 440002 📄 01963 440002
✉ longhazelpark@hotmail.com
🌐 www.sparkford.f9.co.uk/lhi.htm

Dir: Turn off A303 at Hazlegrove rdbt follow signs for Sparkford. Park 400yds on L.

★ 🚐 £12-£14 🚃 £12-£14 ▲ £12-£14

Open 16 Feb-16 Jan Last arrival 22.00hrs Last departure 11.30hrs
A very neat, smart site next to the Sparkford Inn in the village high street. This attractive park is run by a friendly owner to a good standard. Nearby are the Haynes Motor Museum (1m) and Cadbury Castle (3m). A 3.5-acre site with 75 touring pitches, 40 hardstandings and 3 static.
Badminton, bowls, 9-hole putting green

Leisure: 🗛
Facilities: 🔦 ⊙ ⚒ ✳ ✆ 🔳 🎬 🗛 🛪
Disabled facilities: shower, toilet, washbasin. Accessibility scheme cat.2.
Services: 🗍 🕽 ∿ 🗆 🗟 🥤 🖃 → ∪ ᴘ18 🥩 ◎
Notes: No single sex groups, dogs must be kept on leads at all times & exercised off site

TAUNTON   ST22

Ashe Farm Camping & Caravan Site ▶▶▶ 66%

Thornfalcon TA3 5NW
☎ 01823 442567 📄 01823 443372
✉ camping@ashe-farm.fsnet.co.uk

Dir: From M5 J25 take A358 E for 2.5m. Turn R at Nags Head pub. Site 0.25m on R

★ 🚐 £9-£10.50 🚃 £9-£10.50 ▲ £9

Open Apr-Oct Booking Advisable Jul-Aug
A well-screened site surrounded by mature trees and shrubs, with two large touring fields. A facilities block includes smart toilets and a separate laundry room, while the old portaloos remain very clean and well-maintained. Not far from the bustling market town of Taunton, and handy for both coasts. A 7-acre site with 30 touring pitches, 8 hardstandings and 3 static.

Leisure: ९ 🗛
Facilities: 🔦 ⊙ ⚒ ✳ 🛪
Disabled facilities: toilet, shower & washbasin with ramp & aids
Services: 🛒 🕽 🗆 🥤 🖃 → ∪ ᴘ18 🥩 🥩 🗆 🥤

WATCHET   ST04

Home Farm Holiday Centre
▶▶▶ 71%

St Audries Bay TA4 4DP
☎ 01984 632487 📠 01984 634687
📧 dib@homefarmholidaycentre.co.uk
🌐 www.homefarmholidaycentre.co.uk

Dir: Follow A39 towards Minehead, fork R onto
B3191 at West Quantoxhead after St Audries
garage, then R after 0.25m

🏕 🚐 ⛺

Open all year Booking Advisable all year Last
arrival dusk Last departure noon
*In a hidden valley beneath the Quantock Hills,
this park overlooks its own private beach. The
atmosphere is friendly and quiet, and there
are lovely sea views from the level pitches.
Flower beds, woodland walks, and a koi carp
pond all enhance this very attractive site,
along with a lovely indoor swimming pool and
a beer garden. A 35-acre site with 40 touring
pitches, 35 hardstandings and 230 static.*

Leisure: 🏊 🎢
Facilities: 🌮 ⊙ 🔧 ❄ 🔌 🛒 🏪 🎋 🐾
Services: 🔲 💷 🔵 🅿 🌡 🔄 → 🐕

🔲 📶 📺 🅂

WESTON-SUPER-MARE   ST36

Country View Caravan Park
▶▶▶ 70%

Sand Road Sand Bay BS22 9UJ
☎ 01934 627595

Dir: From M5 J21 take A370 towards Weston-
Super-Mare. Immediately take L lane & follow
signs for Kewstoke/Sand Bay. Straight over 3
rdbts onto Norton Ln. At Sand Bay R into Sand
Rd, site on R

★ 🚐 £10-£21 🚐 £10-£21 ⛺ £10-£20

Open Mar-Jan Booking Advisable bank hols &
peak periods Last arrival 21.00hrs Last
departure noon
*A pleasant open site in a rural area few
hundred yards from Sandy Bay and beach. The
park is also well placed for energetic walks
along the coast at either end of the beach.
Facilities have been completely refurbished to
a good standard. A 8-acre site with 120
touring pitches, 90 hardstandings and 65
static.*

Leisure: 🎢 🔍 🎢
Facilities: 🌮 ⊙ 🔧 ❄ 🔌 🛒 🏪
Disabled facilities: toilet & washbasin
Services: 🔲 💷 🔵 🅿 🌡 🔄 → ∪ 🍴18 ⚡ 🍽 🔄 ◎
⛺

Notes: No single sex groups

WESTON-SUPER-MARE ST36

West End Farm Caravan & Camping Park ▶▶▶ 70%

Locking BS24 8RH
☎ 01934 822529 📄 01934 822529

Dir: From M5 J21 onto A370. Follow signs for International Helicopter Museum. Turn R at rdbt, follow signs to site

★ 🚐 £8–£11.50 🚑 £8–£11.50

▲ £8–£11.50

Open all year Booking Advisable peak periods Last arrival 22.00hrs Last departure noon
A delightful park bordered by hedges, with good landscaping and well-kept facilities. It is handily located next to a helicopter museum, and offers good access to Weston-Super-Mare and The Mendips. A 10-acre site with 75 touring pitches, 20 static.

Leisure: ◆ ⋀

Facilities: ♠ ⊙ ♦ ※ 👤 ㅑ

Disabled facilities: toilet & shower

Services: 🚐 📧 📋 🖉 → ∪ ⌂18 ﹀ 😊 🥎 ◎ ⬠

Notes: No single sex groups

LEEK SJ95

Camping & Caravanning Club Site ▶▶▶ 73%

Blackshaw Grange Blackshaw Moor ST13 8TL
☎ 01538 300285

🕸 www.campingandcaravanningclub.co.uk

Dir: 2m from Leek on A53 Leek to Buxton road. Site 200yds past sign for 'Blackshaw Moor' on L

★ 🚐 £12.95-£16.35 🚑 £12.95-£16.35

▲ £12.95-£16.35

Open all year Booking Advisable BH's & peak periods Last arrival 21.00hrs Last departure noon
A beautifully located Club site with well-screened pitches. The very good facilities are kept in pristine condition, and children will enjoy the new area. A 6-acre site with 70 touring pitches, 40 hardstandings.

Leisure: ⋀

Facilities: ♠ ⊙ ♦ ※ 📞 👤 🏛 ㅑ

Disabled facilities: toilet, shower, washbasin & razor point

Services: 🖵 🚐 ⩔ 📧 🍴 🖉 🖃 → ∪ ⌂18 🥄

OAKAMOOR   SK04

Star Caravan & Camping Park
▶▶▶ 68%

The Star Road Cotton ST10 3DW
☎ 01538 702219 📠 01538 703704
🅦 www.starcaravanpark.co.uk

Dir: 1.25m N of Oakamoor off B5417, 1.5m S
of A52. 1.25m from Alton Towers main
entrance

🏕 £10 🚐 £10-£12 ▲ £10-£12

Open Mar-Nov Booking Advisable especially
for EHU Last arrival 22.30hrs Last departure
noon

*This is a well-maintained and efficiently
managed grassland park with an open
outlook over the countryside. It is ideally
placed fo a variety of outdoor leisure activities
including fishing, country walking and cycling.
Ye Olde Starr Inn, a traditional country pub
serving good bar meals, is a two minute walk
away. A 25-acre site with 120 touring pitches,
20 hardstandings and 63 static.*

Leisure: ⚘

Facilities: ⚘ ⊙ ⌤ 🛒 🛏

Disabled facilities: shower/toilet, adapted
static. caravan

Services: 🖬 🚐 🗗 🛢 🖉 → 🛉18 🍴 🛒

Notes: No single sex groups, quiet after
11pm, no ground fires/disposable barbecues

BURY ST EDMUNDS   TL86

The Dell Touring & Caravan Park
▶▶▶▶ 72%

Beyton Road Thurston IP31 3RB
☎ 01359 270121 📠 01359 270121
🅔 thedellcaravanpark@btinternet.com

Dir: Signed off A14 at Beyton/Thurston, 4m
E of Bury St Edmunds. Also signed off A143
at Barton/Thurston

★ 🚐 £9.50-£11.50 🚐 £9.50-£11.50

▲ £9.50-£11.50

Open all year Booking Advisable bank hols
Last arrival anytime Last departure anytime
*A small site with enthusiastic owners which
has been developed to a high specification.
Set in a quiet spot with lots of mature trees,
the quality purpose-built toilet facilities
include family rooms, dishwashing and
laundry. An ideal base for exploring this
picturesque area, with many more
improvements planned. A 6-acre site with 100
touring pitches, 6 hardstandings.*

Facilities: 🛒 ⚘ ⊙ 🛒 ❋ 🛒 🛏

Disabled facilities: purpose built toilets
& showers

Services: 🖬 🚐 🗗 🛢 🖉 🖾 → 🛒

FELIXSTOWE TM33

Peewit Caravan Park ►►► 65%

Walton Avenue IP11 2HB
☎ 01394 284511 📠 01473 659824
E peewitpark@aol.com
W www.peewitcaravanpark.co.uk

Dir: Signed from A14 in Felixstowe, 100mtrs past dock gate, no. 1 on L

★ ⊕ £9-£16 ⊕ £9-£16 ▲ £8-£15

Open Apr or Etr-Oct Booking Advisable school & bank hols Last arrival 21.00hrs Last departure 11.00hrs

A grass touring area fringed by trees, with well-maintained grounds and a colourful floral display. This handy urban site is not overlooked by houses, and the toilet facilities are clean and well cared for. A function room contains a TV and library. The beach is a few minutes away by car. A 3-acre site with 55 touring pitches, 200 static.

Boules area, bowling green, adventure trail

Leisure: ⚑
Facilities: ⬤ ⬤ ✳ ⬤ ⬤
Disabled facilities: toilet & shower
Services: ⬤ ⬤ ⬤ ⬤ → ⬤ ⬤ ⬤ ⬤ ⬤ ◎ ⬤

IPSWICH TM14

Priory Park ►►►► 75%

IP10 0JT
☎ 01473 727393 📠 01473 278372
E jwl@priory-park.com
W www.priory-park.com

Dir: Leave A14 at Ipswich southern bypass towards town centre. After 300mtrs L towards Priory Park. Follow single carriageway into park

⊕ £16-£24 ⊕ £16-£24 ▲ £16-£24

Open Apr-Oct (rs Apr-Jun & Sep-Oct limited number of sites, club/pool closed) Booking Advisable At all times Last arrival 18.00hrs Last departure 14.00hrs

A well-screened and very peaceful south-facing park set close to the banks of the tidal River Orwell, and with panoramic views out over the water. The park is attractively landscaped, and offers superb toilet facilities with smartly-tiled, fully-serviced cubicles. A 100-acre site with 75 touring pitches, 59 hardstandings and 260 static.

9-hole golf, small boat launching, table tennis

Leisure: ⬤ ⬤ ⚑
Facilities: ⬤ ⬤ ⬤ ⬤ ✳ ⬤ ⬤ ⬤ ⬤
Services: ✕ ⬤ ⬤ ⬤ ⬤ ⬤ → ⬤ ⬤ ⬤ ⬤ ⬤
Notes: No commercial vehicles, pup tents or group bookings

Camping & Caravanning Club Site
▶▶▶▶ 70%

Suffolk Wildlife Park Whites Lane NR33 7SL
☎ 01502 742040
Ⓦ www.campingandcaravanningclub.co.uk

Dir: On A12 from Lowestoft at Kessingland rdbt, follow Wildlife Park signs, turn R through park entrance

★ ⊕ £12.95-£18.35 ⊕ £12.95-£18.35
▲ £12.95-£18.35

Open Mar-Nov Booking Advisable bank hols & peak periods Last arrival 21.00hrs Last departure noon
A well-screened open site next to Suffolk Wildlife Park, where concessions are available for visitors. An extensive renovation has created superb facilities, including three family rooms, a disabled unit, and smart reception. A well-equipped laundry and covered dishwashing sinks add to the quality amenities. A 5-acre site with 90 touring pitches.

Leisure: ⚙

Facilities: ⋒ ⊙ ⊛ ※ ₺ ⊞ ⊁

Disabled facilities: toilet, shower, washbasin & hand dryer

Services: ⊡ ⊕ ⊞ ⊡ ⊘ ⊞ → ∪ ⊾

▨ ▨ ▨ ▨ ⑤

Heathland Beach Caravan Park
▶▶▶▶ 74%

London Road NR33 7PJ
☎ 01502 740337 🖷 01502 742355
🅔 heathlandbeach@btinternet.com
Ⓦ www.heathlandbeach.co.uk

Dir: 1m N of Kessingland off A12 onto B1437

★ ⊕ £16-£21 ⊕ £16-£21 ▲ £7.50-£21

Open Apr-Oct Booking Advisable peak periods Last arrival 21.00hrs Last departure 11.00hrs
A well-run and maintained park offering superb toilet facilities. The park is set in meadowland, with level grass pitches, and mature trees and bushes. There is direct access to the sea and beach, and good provisions for families on site with a heated swimming pool and three play areas. A 5-acre site with 63 touring pitches, 200 static.
Freshwater/sea fishing

Leisure: ⋨ ⊛ ⚙

Facilities: ⋒ ⊙ ⊛ ※ ₺ ⊞ ⊞ ⊁

Disabled facilities: toilets & showers, ramp to bar

Services: ⊡ ⊕ ⊞ ⊠ ⊘ → ∪ ⏸18 ⊁ ⊞ ⊿ ⊿

Notes: 1 dog only per unit

▨ ▨ ▨ ▨ ⑤

S U F F O L K

WOODBRIDGE — TM24

Moon & Sixpence ►►►►► 78%

Newbourn Road Waldringfield IP12 4PP
☎ 01473 736650 📄 01473 736270
🅔 moonsix@dircon.co.uk
🅦 www.moonsix.dircon.co.uk

Dir: Follow caravan & Moon & Sixpence signs from A12 Ipswich (E bypass). Turn L at x-roads 1.5m from A12

★ 🚐 £16-£24 🚐 £16-£24 ▲ £16-£24

Open Apr-Oct (rs low season club, shop, reception open limited hours) Booking Advisable school & bank hols Last arrival 20.00hrs Last departure noon

A well-planned site, with tourers occupying a sheltered valley position around an attractive boating lake with a sandy beach. Toilet facilities are housed in a smart Norwegian cabin, and there is a laundry and dishwashing area. Leisure facilities include two tennis courts, a bowling green, fishing, boating and a games room. There is an adult-only area, and a strict no groups and no noise after 9pm policy. A 5-acre site with 65 touring pitches, 200 static.

Lake, cycle trail, 10 acre sports area, 9-hole golf

Leisure: ⚲ ⚭ ⚠

Facilities: ➔ 🏠 ⊙ ⚬ ⚒ ✻ ⚓ 🖾 🔔 🔭

Services: ✕ 🖾 ⚊ 🖾 ⚈ ▣ 🖉 ▣ → 📁18 💺 ⚚ ⚠

Notes: No group bookings or commercial vehicles. Quiet 9pm-8am

⬛ ⬛

EAST HORSLEY — TQ05

Camping & Caravanning Club Site ►►►► 68%

Ockham Road North KT24 6PE
☎ 01483 283273
🅦 www.campingandcaravanningclub.co.uk

Dir: M25 J10, proceed S & take 1st major turning off signed Ockham, Southend & Ripley, then turn L & site 2.5m on R. From S take A3 past Guildford & turn off towards Ripley on B2215

★ 🚐 £12.95-£16.35 🚐 £12.95-£16.35
▲ £12.95-£16.35

Open Mar-Nov Booking Advisable bank hols & peak periods Last arrival 21.00hrs Last departure noon

A beautiful lakeside site with plenty of trees and shrubs and separate camping fields, providing a tranquil base within easy reach of London. Toilet facilities are well maintained and clean. A 9.5-acre site with 130 touring pitches, 42 hardstandings.

Leisure: ⚭ ⚠

Facilities: 🏠 ⊙ ⚬ ✻ ⚓ 🖾 🔔

Disabled facilities: toilet, shower, hand basin & hand dryer

Services: ▣ 🖾 ⚈ 🖉 ▣ → ∪ 📁18 ⚚ 💺 ⚠

⬛ ⬛ ⬛ ⬛ ⬛ ⓢ

HORAM

Horam Manor Touring Park
▶▶▶ 69%

TN21 0YD
☎ 01435 813662
🄴 camp@horam-manor.co.uk
🅦 www.horam-manor.co.uk

Dir: On A267, 3m S of Heathfield and 10m N of Eastbourne

★ ♔ £13.50 ♔ £13.50 ▲ £13.50

Open Mar-Oct Booking Advisable peak periods Last arrival 22.00hrs Last departure 18.00hrs
A well landscaped park in a peaceful location on former estate land, set on gently-sloping grassland surrounded by woods, nature trails and fishing lakes. A 7-acre site with 90 touring pitches.
Parent and toddler room

Leisure: ९ ⁄A
Facilities: ᴎ ☉ ✳ ୯ 至 ⋒ ✝
Disabled facilities: toilet & shower
Services: ☎ ⌷ 🛉 🖉 🖃 → ∪ Ⱶ18 ⌡

PEVENSEY

Camping & Caravanning Club Site
▶▶▶ 69%

Norman's Bay BN24 6PR
☎ 01323 761190
🅦 www.campingandcaravanningclub.co.uk

Dir: From rdbt at jct of A27/A259 follow A259 signed Eastbourne. After entering Pevensey Bay village take 1st L signed Beachlands only. After 1.25m site on L

★ ♔ £12.95-£18.35 ♔ £12.95-£18.35
▲ £12.95-£18.35

Open Mar-Nov Booking Advisable bank hols & peak periods Last arrival 21.00hrs Last departure noon
A well-kept site with immaculate toilet block, right beside the sea. This popular family park enjoys good rural views towards Rye and Pevensey. A 3-acre site with 200 touring pitches.

Leisure: ९ ⁄A
Facilities: ᴎ ☉ ९ ✳ ୯ ⋒ ✝
Disabled facilities: toilet, shower, washbasin & razor point
Services: ⊤ ♔ ↯ ⌷ 🛉 🖉 🖃 → 至 △

SUSSEX, EAST

PEVENSEY BAY   TQ60

Bay View Caravan and Camping Park ▶▶▶ 72%

Old Martello Road BN24 6DX
☎ 01323 768688 📄 01323 769637
🖂 holidays@bay-view.co.uk
🌐 www.bay-view.co.uk

Dir: Signed from A259. On sea side of A259 along private road towards beach

★ 🚐 £11-£16 � £11-£16 ⚲ £10.30-£12

Open 24 Mar-2 Oct Booking Advisable bank & school hols Last arrival 22.00hrs Last departure noon

A pleasant well-run site just yards from the beach, in an area east of the town centre known as 'The Crumbles'. The level grassy site is very well maintained. A 6-acre site with 79 touring pitches, 9 hardstandings and 5 static.

Leisure: ⚲

Facilities: 🏕 ⊙ 🔧 ✳ 🌡 🦮

Services: 🔲 🚐 🖥 🛢 🔌 → 🍴18 ♨ 🜊 ◎ ⚱

Notes: Couples & families only, no commercial vehicles

DIAL POST   TQ11

Honeybridge Park ▶▶▶▶ 76%

Honeybridge Lane RH13 8NX
☎ 01403 710923 📄 01403 710923
🖂 enquiries@honeybridgepark.co.uk
🌐 www.honeybridgepark.co.uk

Dir: 10m S of Horsham on A24. Turn L 1m past Dial Post sign at Old Barn Nurseries, continue for 300yds park on R

🚐 £15-£20 � £15-£20 ⚲ £13-£18

Open all year Booking Advisable bank hols & high season Last arrival 22.00hrs Last departure 20.00hrs

An attractive and very popular park on gently-sloping ground surrounded by hedgerows and mature trees. A comprehensive amenities building houses upmarket toilet facilities including luxury family and disabled rooms, as well as a laundry, shop, takeaway and off-licence. There are plenty of hardstandings and electric hook-ups, and an excellent children's play area includes an aerial runway and other adventure equipment. A 15-acre site with 200 touring pitches, 55 hardstandings.

Leisure: ⚲ ⚲

Facilities: 🛁 🏕 ⊙ 🔧 ✳ 🌡 🦮 🥾

Disabled facilities: toilets & showers

Services: 🔲 🍺 🚐 🛁 🖥 🛢 🔌 🖥 → ∪ 🍴18 ♨ ⚱

Notes: No groups of under 18s

▨ ▨ ▨ 𝒮

LITTLEHAMPTON TQ00

White Rose Touring Park
▶▶▶ 70%

Mill Lane Wick BN17 7PH
☎ 01903 716176 📠 01903 732671
✉ snowdondavid@hotmail.com
🌐 www.whiterosetouringpark.co.uk

Dir: From A27 take A284 turn L into Mill Lane, after approx 1.5m just after Six Bells Pub.

★ 🚐 £14-£17 🚛 £14-£17 ▲ £12

Open 15 Mar-14 Dec Booking Advisable bank hols & Jul-Aug Last arrival 22.00hrs Last departure noon

Farmland surrounds this carefully maintained site located on well-drained ground close to Arundel and Littlehampton. The family-run site offers a choice of super pitches and mini pitches for tents, and there is good hedging and landscaping. A 7-acre site with 127 touring pitches, 13 static.

Leisure: ⚙

Facilities: 🛁 ⊙ 🕾 ※ 🐾 🖈

Disabled facilities: toilet & shower

Services: 🔲 🚐 🖾 🛢 🖉 🖫 → ∪ ↑18 ↳ ⚽ 🎣 ⑤ ⚠

SELSEY SZ89

Warner Farm Touring Park 🏕
72%

Warner Lane Selsey PO20 9EL
☎ 01243 604121 📠 01243 604499
🌐 warner.farm@btinternet.com

Dir: Turn R onto School Lane & follow signs

★ 🚐 £15-£27.25 🚛 £15-£27.25

▲ £13-£25.25

Open Mar-Oct Booking Advisable 4 wks prior to arrival Last arrival 20.00hrs Last departure 10.00hrs

A well-screened touring site adjoining the three static parks under the same ownership. A courtesy bus runs around the complex to entertainment and supermarkets. The park backs onto open grassland, and the leisure facilities with bar, amusements and bowling alley, and swimming pool/sauna complex are also accessible to tourers. A 10-acre site with 250 touring pitches, 45 hardstandings and 1,500 static.

Leisure: ⚡ 🎣 🐾 ⚙ 🏓

Facilities: 🛁 ⊙ 🕾 ※ 📞 🐾 🖻 🖈

Disabled facilities: toilets, showers & ramps

Services: 🔲 ✕ 🚰 🚐 ⛽ 🖾 🖉 🛢 🖉 → ∪ ↑18 ↳ 🎣 ◎ ⚠

WEST WITTERING SZ79

Wicks Farm Holiday Park

►►► 71%

Redlands Lane PO20 8QD

☎ 01243 513116 📠 01243 511296

[E] wicks.farm@virgin.net

[W] www.wicksfarm.co.uk

Dir: From Chichester take A286/B2179 to West Wittering. Follow road for 6m, then 2nd R after Lamb Inn.

★ 🚐 £12-£14 ⛺ £12-£14

Open 14 Mar-Oct Booking Advisable peak periods Last arrival 21.00hrs Last departure noon

A pleasant rural site, well screened by trees and with good clean toilet facilities. The park has a spacious recreation field, and good local walks, with the beach just 2m away. A 14-acre site with 40 touring pitches.

Leisure: 🎾 ⛺

Facilities: 🚿 ⊙ ⚗ ✱ 📞 🛒 🐕

Services: [T] 🚐 ⑂ 🗑 🔒 🍃 → ⛳9 🎣 ◎ ⛵

Notes: No touring caravans

💳 💳 💳 💳 💳

FRESHWATER SZ38

Heathfield Farm Camping

►►► 74%

Heathfield Road PO40 9SH

☎ 01983 756756 📠 01983 756756

[E] web@heathfieldcamping.co.uk

[W] www.ukparks.co.uk/heathfieldfarm

Dir: 2m W from Yarmouth ferry port on A3054, L to Heathfield Rd, entrance 200yds on R.

★ 🚐 £9-£12 🚐 £9-£12 ⛺ £7.50-£10.50

Open May-Sep Booking Advisable bank hols & Jul-Aug Last arrival 22.00hrs Last departure 22.00hrs

A good quality park with friendly owners and lovely views across the Solent to Hurst Castle. The toilet facilities which include a family room are immaculate, and this park is constantly improving to meet the needs of campers and caravanners. A 10-acre site with 60 touring pitches.

Separate playing field for ball games etc

Facilities: 🚿 ⊙ ⚗ ✱ 📞 🏠 ⛩ 🐕

Disabled facilities: toilet, shower & washbasin

Services: 🚐 ⑂ 🗑 🍃 → U ⛳19 ✈ 🎣 🛒 ◎ ⛵

Notes: Family camping only, no single sex groups

NEWBRIDGE SZ48

Orchards Holiday Caravan Park

►►►►► 76%

PO41 0TS

☎ 01983 531331 📠 01983 531666

[E] info@orchards-holiday-park.co.uk

[W] www.orchards-holiday-park.co.uk

Dir: 4m E of Yarmouth and 6m W of Newport on B3401.

★ 🚐 £11-£15.30 🚙 £11-£15.30

⛺ £11-£15.30

Open 14 Feb-3 Jan (rs Nov-Jan & Feb-mid Mar shop closed, pool closed Sep-May) Booking Advisable Etr, Spring BH, Jun-Aug, Oct half term Last arrival 23.00hrs Last dep 11.00hrs

A really excellent, well-managed park set in a peaceful location amid meadowland, with glorious downland views. Pitches are terraced, and offer good hardstandings, including super pitches. The toilet facilities are immaculate. There is excellent provision for families, and disabled access to all facilities.

A 8-acre site with 175 touring pitches, 62 hardstandings and 65 static.

Coarse fishing, petanque

Leisure: 🏊 🏊 ● 🛝 ▭

Facilities: 🚿 🚿 ⊙ 🧺 ✳ 📞 🛒 🐕

Disabled facilities: toilets, ramps & adapted caravan

Services: [T] ✕ 🍺 🚐 ▣ 🧯 ⊘ ▣ → ∪ 🎣

Notes: No single sex groups

💳 American Express, Visa, Barclays Connect, Delta, Switch

NEWCHURCH SZ58

Southland Camping Park

►►►►► 78%

PO36 0LZ

☎ 01983 865385 📠 01983 867663

[E] info@southland.co.uk

[W] www.southland.co.uk

Dir: Take A3056 to Sandown. Take 2nd road on L after Fighting Cocks pub towards Newchurch. Site 1m on L

🚐 £10-£14.60 🚙 £10-£14.60 ⛺ £10-£14.60

Open Etr-Sep Booking Advisable Jun, Jul-Aug Last arrival 21.30hrs Last departure 11.00hrs

Beautifully maintained site, peacefully located and impressively laid out on the outskirts of the village in the Arreton Valley. Spotless sanitary facilities including spacious family rooms enhance the park. Pitches are well screened by lovely trees and shrubs. A 9-acre site with 120 touring pitches.

12-volt transformers available

Leisure: 🛝

Facilities: 🚿 🚿 ⊙ 🧺 ✳ 📞 🛒 🏠 ⛩ 🐕

Disabled facilities: Grade 2 facilities, toilet, washbasin & shower

Services: [T] 🚐 🚐 ⩛ ▣ 🧯 ⊘ ▣ → ∪ ⛳18 ✈ 🎣 ◎ ⛵

💳 American Express, Visa, Barclays Connect, Delta, Switch

SANDOWN SZ58

Cheverton Copse Holiday Park
▶▶▶ 68%

Scotchells Brook Lane PO36 0JP
☎ 01983 403161 📠 01983 402861
✉ berriesdandm@aol.com
🌐 www.cheverton-copse.co.uk

Dir: 400yds from A3056 towards Newport,
1m from Lake

★ 🚐 £7-£10 🚃 £7-£10 ▲ £7-£10

Open Apr-Sep (rs Apr-Whit Clubhouse closed)
Booking Advisable 20 Jul-1 Sep Last arrival
21.00hrs Last departure noon
*A small park on the edge of open farmland
close to the resort attractions of Sandown and
Shanklin. The smart toilets offer excellent
sanitary facilities, and many of the pitches are
set on cut-away terraces in the slightly-sloping
land. A 1-acre site with 14 touring pitches,
57 static.*

Leisure: 🎱 🅰
Facilities: 🌁 ⊙ ⚲ ✳ 📞 📷
Services: 🔌 🚽 🍴 → ∪ ▐18 ↳ 🧺 ◎ ⟁ 🔋
Notes: ✗ No single sex groups

SANDOWN SZ58

Camping & Caravanning Club Site
▶▶▶▶▶ 73%

Lower Adgestone Road PO36 0HL
☎ 01983 403432
🌐 www.campingandcaravanningclub.co.uk

Dir: Turn off A3055 Sandown/Shanklin road
at Manor House pub, in Lake, continue past
school & golf course on L, turn R at T-jct,
park is 200yds on R

★ 🚐 £15.45-£18.95 🚃 £15.45-£18.95
▲ £15.45-£18.95

Open Mar-Oct Booking Advisable bank hols &
peak periods Last arrival 21.00hrs Last
departure noon
*A popular, well-managed park in a quiet, rural
location not far from Sandown. The level
pitches are imaginatively laid out, and
surrounded by beautiful flower beds and trees
set close to a small river. This planting offers
good screening as well as enhancing the
appearance of the park. Spotless sanitary
facilities include two family rooms, and there
is excellent provision for families in general. A
22-acre site with 270 touring pitches.*

Leisure: 🎣 🅰
Facilities: 🌁 ⊙ ⚲ ✳ 📞 🔋 📷 🚻
Disabled facilities: toilet, shower &
handbasin
Services: 🚰 🚽 🔌 🚽 🍴 📷 🔋 → ∪ ▐↳ 🧺 ⟁

Ninham Country Holidays
▶▶▶ 68%

Ninham PO37 7PL
☎ 01983 864243 📠 01983 868881
🅔 info@ninham.fsnet.co.uk
🅦 www.ninham-holiday.co.uk

Dir: Signposted off A3056 Newport to
Sandown road

🚐 �335 🏕

Open Etr-Sep Booking Advisable Jun-Sep
*Enjoying a lofty rural position with fine
country views, this delightful, spacious park
occupies two separate well-maintained areas
in a country park setting near the sea and
beach. A 8-acre site with 88 touring pitches.*
Coarse fishing

Leisure: 🕈 /🌑

Facilities: 🅚 ⊙ 🕈 ☀ ℄ 🖳 🎋 🛏 🐾

Services: 🔲 ✕ 🚐 🔌 🖥 🍴 🗓 → ∪ ⏵18 ⤬ 🍴
🍴 ⊚ 🔺

▨▨ 💳 🐾 🄢

Lower Hyde Holiday Park 🏖 67%

Landguard Road PO37 7LL
☎ 01983 866131 📠 01983 862532
🅔 holidaysales.lowerhyde@park-resorts.com
🅦 www.park-resorts.com

Dir: From Fishbourne ferry terminal follow
A3055 to Shanklin, Park is signed just
past lake

🚐 �335 🏕

Open 17 Apr-1 Nov Booking Advisable Aug
Last arrival 20.00hrs Last departure 10.00hrs
*A popular holiday park on the outskirts of
Shanklin, close to the sandy beaches. There is
an outdoor swimming pool and plenty of
organised activities for youngsters of all ages.
In the evening there is a choice of family
entertainment. Touring facilities are being
upgraded to a high standard in a new position
away from the main complex. A 65-acre site
with 115 touring pitches, 25 hardstandings
and 318 static.*

Leisure: 🕈 🕈 🔍 /🌑

Facilities: 🅚 ☀ ℄ 🖳

Disabled facilities: wc's/showers ramps

Services: ✕ 🖤 🚐 🖥 🍷 🍴 🗓 → ∪ ⏵18 ⤬ 🍴
🖥 ⊚

Notes: No single-sex groups, min age 21yrs

▨▨ 💳 🐾 🄢

WIGHT, ISLE OF

WHITECLIFF BAY   SZ68

Whitecliff Bay Holiday Park 71%

Hillway Road Bembridge PO35 5PL
☎ 01983 872671 📠 01983 872941
E holiday@whitecliff-bay.com
W www.whitecliff-bay.com

Dir: 1m S of Bembridge, signed off B3395 in village

★ 🚐 £8-£14 🚐 £8-£14 ▲ £8-£14

Open Mar-Oct Booking Advisable Jul-Aug Last arrival 21.00hrs Last departure 10.30hrs
A large seaside complex on two sites, with tourers and tents on one, and tourers and statics on the other. There is an indoor and outdoor swimming pool, a leisure centre, and plenty of traditional on-site entertainment, plus easy access to a lovely sandy beach. A 49-acre site with 400 touring pitches, 50 hardstandings and 227 static.
Leisure centre with fun pool, spa bath & sauna

Leisure: ⬡ ⬡ ◈ ⌂
Facilities: ➡ ⬡ ⊙ ⬡ ✳ ⬡ ⬡ ⬡
Disabled facilities: toilet & bath
Services: ▣ ✕ ⬡ ⬡ ⬡ ⬡ ⬡ ⬡ ⬡ ⬡ → ∪ ⌐9
⬡ ⬡ ◎
Notes: Adults (over 21) and families only, no single sex groups

▨ ▨ ▨ ⑤

WROXALL   SZ57

Appuldurcombe Gardens Caravan & Camping Park ►►► 66%

Appuldurcombe Road PO38 3EP
☎ 01983 852597 📠 01983 856225
E info@appuldurcombegardens.co.uk
W www.appuldurcombegardens.co.uk

Dir: From Newport take A3020, turning off towards Shanklin. Proceed through Rookley & Godshill. Turn R at Whiteley Bank rdbt towards Wroxall, then follow brown signs

🚐 🚐 ▲

Open Mar-Oct (rs Mar-Spring bank hol & Aug bank hol-Oct) Booking Advisable Jul-Aug Last arrival 22.00hrs Last departure noon
An attractive secluded site close to the ruins of Appuldurcombe House, with a stream running through it. The facilities include a good swimming pool, shop, bar/café and entertainment room, and plenty of tree planting will result in excellent screening. A 12-acre site with 100 touring pitches, 40 static.
Crazy golf & pitch & putt

Leisure: ⬡ ◈ ⌂
Facilities: ⬡ ⊙ ⬡ ✳ ⬡ ⬡ ⬡
Disabled facilities: toilet, bath & shower
Services: ▣ ✕ ⬡ ⬡ ⬡ ⬡ ⬡ ⬡ ⬡ → ∪ ⌐18
⬡ ⬡ ⬡ ◎ ⬡
Notes: Family groups during high season

▨ ▨ ▨ ▨ ⑤

DEVIZES

Camping & Caravanning Club Site
▶▶▶▶ 75%

Scout Lane Seend, Melksham SN12 6RN
☎ 01380 828839
🌐 www.campingandcaravanningclub.co.uk

Dir: From Devizes on A361 turn R onto A365, over canal, next L down lane beside 3 Magpies pub. Site on R

★ 🚐 £15.35-£16.35 🚍 £15.35-£16.35

▲ £15.35-£16.35

Open all year Booking Advisable BH's & peak periods Last arrival 21.00hrs Last departure noon

An excellent club site with well-designed, quality facilities and a high level of staff commitment. This popular park is set beside the Kennet and Avon Canal, with a gate to the towpath for walking and cycling, and with fishing available in the canal. Well situated for exploring Salisbury Plain and the Marlborough Downs. A 13.5-acre site with 90 touring pitches, 50 hardstandings.

Leisure: 🅰

Facilities: 🌡️ ⊙ ⚒ ✳ 🔧 🛍 🐾

Disabled facilities: toilet, shower, washbasin & hand dryer

Services: 🔟 🚗 ⚗ 🗑 🍴 🖊 🔌 → ∪ ◠18 🍴 🍴

⚠

🟦 🟥 🟦 🟩 🔲

SALISBURY

Coombe Touring Park
▶▶▶▶ 70%

Race Plain Netherhampton SP2 8PN
☎ 01722 328451 📠 01722 328451

Dir: Turn off A36 onto A3094, then 2m SW, adjacent to Salisbury racecourse

★ 🚐 £8-£11 🚍 £8-£11 ▲ £8-£11

Open all year Booking Advisable bank hols (by letter only) Last arrival 21.00hrs Last departure noon

A very neat and attractive site adjacent to the racecourse with views over the downs, and outstanding flower beds. The park is well landscaped with shrubs and maturing trees, and the very colourful beds are stocked from the owner's greenhouse. A comfortable park with a superb luxury toilet block. A 3-acre site with 50 touring pitches.

Children's bathroom

Facilities: 🌡️ ⊙ ⚒ ✳ 🔧 🕯️

Services: 🔟 🚗 🗑 🍴 🖊 🔌 🖊 → ∪ ◠18 🍴

WESTBURY ST85

Brokerswood Country Park
►►► 68%

Brokerswood BA13 4EH
☎ 01373 822238 📄 01373 858474
📧 woodland.park@virgin.net
🌐 www.brokerswood.co.uk

Dir: From M4 travel S on A350. R at
Yarnbrook to Rising Sun pub at North
Bradley, then L & follow lane for 1m to site
on R. Other approaches difficult for
caravans

★ 🚐 £8-£19 🚐 £8-£19 ▲ £8-£19

Open all year Booking Advisable peak season
& B/Hols Last arrival 21.30hrs Last departure
11.00hrs
*A pleasant site on the edge of an 80-acre
woodland park with nature trails and fishing
lakes. An adventure playground offers plenty
of fun for all ages, and there is a miniature
railway of one-third of a mile, an indoor play
centre, and a licensed café. A 6-acre site with
69 touring pitches, 21 hardstandings.
Country park with play grounds & fishing
lakes*

Leisure: 🅰
Facilities: 🌾 ⊙ ◖ ※ 📞 💺 🛋 🎋 🐾
Disabled facilities: shower & toilets
facilities with ramp, rails & help lights
Services: 🗊 ✗ 🚲 🔯 🔒 🗑 → 🖌
Notes: No single sex groups

▨▨ ▨▨ 🆔

BROADWAY SP03

Leedons Park ►►► 68%

Childswickham Road WR12 7HB
☎ 01386 852423 📄 01386 853655
Dir: From Evesham take A44 to Oxford.
Main island 3rd exit. Turn R down
Pennylands Bank. L then R into park.

🚐 🚐 ▲

Open all year Booking Advisable peak periods
& BH's Last arrival 20.00hrs Last departure
11.00hrs
*A large site on the edge of the Vale of
Evesham, 1m from the historical village of
Broadway; an ideal base from which to tour
the Cotswolds. The park enjoys 40 acres of
lawns and gardens, with duckponds proving
popular with children. Pet and pet-free areas
cater to all needs, and there is a large play
fort complex. A 16-acre site with 450 touring
pitches, 10 hardstandings and 86 static.*

Leisure: 🔧 🔍 ◓ 🅰
Facilities: 🌾 🌾 ⊙ ※ 📞 💺 🎋
Disabled facilities: toilets
Services: 🗊 ✗ 🚲 🔯 🗑 🔒 🗑 🗓 → ∪ 🖍18

▨▨ ▨▨ ▨▨ 🔧 🆔

HONEYBOURNE   SP14

Ranch Caravan Park ▶▶▶▶ 72%

Station Road WR11 7PR
☎ 01386 830744 📠 01386 833503
📧 enquiries@ranch.co.uk
🌐 www.ranch.co.uk

Dir: Through village x-rds towards Bidford, entrance 400mtrs on L

★ 🚐 £13.50-£18 🚐 £13.50-£18

Open Mar-Nov (rs Mar-May & Sep-Nov swimming pool closed, shorter club hours) Booking Advisable school hols Last arrival 20.00hrs Last departure noon
An attractive and well-run park set amidst farmland in the Vale of Evesham and landscaped with trees and bushes. Tourers have their own excellent facilities in two locations, and the use of an outdoor heated swimming pool in peak season. There is also a licensed club serving meals. Tents not accepted. A 12-acre site with 120 touring pitches, 30 hardstandings and 195 static.

Leisure: 🏊 🎱 🎣 🎮 ⊓
Facilities: 🌂 ⊙ 🔍 ✳ 📞 🐾 ⼌
Services: 🆃 ✕ 🛒 🌐 ⌁ ⍦ 🗄 🛢 🔌 🗄 → ∪ ✈
Notes: No unaccompanied minors, no single sex groups, no tents

■ ■ ⚑ 🄢

MALVERN   SO74

Riverside Caravan Park ▶▶▶ 66%

Little Clevelode WR13 6PE
☎ 01684 310475 📠 01684 310475
Dir: From A449 signed onto B4424

★ 🚐 fr £12 🚐 fr £12 ▲ fr £12

Open Mar-Dec (rs Barrier gate closes each evening) Booking Advisable bank hols & end May-end Aug Last arrival 20.00hrs Last departure noon
An open grassy field close to the Malvern Hills, with fishing in the River Severn which runs past the lower part of the park. The toilet facilities are good, and there is a bar/restaurant/shop. A 25-acre site with 70 touring pitches, 130 static.
Fishing on river

Leisure: 🎱 🎣 🎮 ⊓
Facilities: 🌂 ⊙ ✳ 🐾 ⼌
Services: 🆃 🌐 🗄 🛢 🔌 ⍦ → ∪ ⅏18 ✕ ✈
Notes: ✈ No bicycles & skateboards, barrier gate closed at night

ROMSLEY   SO98

Camping & Caravanning Club Site
▶▶▶ 70%

Fieldhouse Lane B62 0NH
☎ 01562 710015
Ⓦ www.campingandcaravanningclub.co.uk

Dir: Leave M5 at J3, take A456 then L on B4551 to Romsley. Turn R past Sun Hotel, take 5th L & next L for site in 330yds on L

★ 🚐 £12.95–£16.35 🚚 £12.95–£16.35
🛆 £12.95–£16.35

Open Mar-Nov Booking Advisable bank hols & peak periods Last arrival 21.00hrs Last departure noon

A very pretty, well tended park surrounded by wooded hills. The site offers excellent facilities, including hardstandings to provide flat pitches for motorhomes. Lovely views of the Clent Hills can be enjoyed from this park, and there are plenty of local scenic walks. A 7.5-acre site with 95 touring pitches, 18 hardstandings.

Leisure: ⚲
Facilities: 🏠⊙🤏☀️🜂🎣
Disabled facilities: toilet, handbasin, shower & razor point
Services: 🔟🚽🔋📷🖉🗄→🕈🅿18🎵🦺

WOLVERLEY   SO87

Camping & Caravanning Club Site
▶▶▶ 67%

Brown Westhead Park DY10 3PX
☎ 01562 850909
Ⓦ www.campingandcaravanningclub.co.uk

Dir: From Kidderminster A449 to Wolverhampton, turn L at lights onto B4189 signed Wolverley. Follow brown camping signs, turn R. Site on L

★ 🚐 £11.75–£15.35 🚚 £11.75–£15.35
🛆 £11.75–£15.35

Open Mar-Nov Booking Advisable bank hols & peak periods Last arrival 21.00hrs Last departure noon

A very pleasant grassy site on the edge of the village, with the canal lock and towpath close to the entrance, and a pub overlooking the water. The site has good access to and from nearby motorways. A 12-acre site with 120 touring pitches.

Leisure: ⚓⚲▭
Facilities: 🏠⊙🤏☀️🜂🎣🐾
Disabled facilities: toilet, shower, razor point & washbasin
Services: 🔟🚽🚰🔋📷🖉🗄→🕈🎵🦺🛆

BRANDESBURTON — TA14

Dacre Lakeside Park ▶▶▶ 66%

YO25 8RT
☎ 01964 543704 🖷 01964 544040
📧 dacresurf@aol.com
🌐 www.dacrepark.co.uk

Dir: Off A165 bypass, midway between Beverley and Hornsea

🐾 🐾 🛆

Open Mar-Oct Booking Advisable bank hols Last arrival 21.00hrs Last departure noon
A large lake popular with watersports enthusiasts is the focal point of this grassy site. The clubhouse offers plenty of indoor activities, and a fish and chip shop and Chinese takeaway can be found in the village. The lake is used for windsurfing, sailing and canoeing. A 8-acre site with 120 touring pitches.
Fishing & bowling

Leisure: ⚲ ⚬
Facilities: 🅿 ⊙ 🕾 ✳ 🌢 🐾 ⊁
Disabled facilities: shower & toilet
Services: 🖵 ➡ 🖈 🖻 🍺 🗗 🖉 🖃 → ∪ ⌂ 18 ➤ 🗸
🛆

BRIDLINGTON — TA16

Fir Tree Caravan Park ▶▶▶ 72%

Jewison Lane Sewerby YO16 6YG
☎ 01262 676442 🖷 01262 676442
📧 info@flowerofmay.com
🌐 www.flowerofmay.com

Dir: 1.5m from centre of Bridlington. Turn L off B1255 at Marton Corner & site is 600yds on L

🐾 🐾

Open Apr-Oct (rs Etr & late season) Booking Advisable Jul-Aug & bank hols Last arrival 21.00hrs Last departure noon
Fir Tree Park has a well laid out touring area with its own facilities within a large, mainly static park. It has an excellent swimming pool complex, and the adjacent bar with its new conservatory serves meals. There is also a family bar, games room and outdoor children's play area. A 22-acre site with 45 touring pitches, 45 hardstandings and 400 static.

Leisure: 🏊 ⚬ 🎠
Facilities: 🅿 ⊙ ✳ 🌢 🐾 ⊁
Disabled facilities: toilets
Services: ✗ 🖈 🖻 🍺 🗗 🖃 → ∪ ⌂ 18 ➤ 🐾 🗸
◎ 🛆
Notes: No single sex groups, dogs by arrangement only

RUDSTON TA06

Thorpe Hall Caravan & Camping Site ►►► 69%

Thorpe Hall YO25 4JE
☎ 01262 420393 📠 01262 420588
[E] caravansite@thorpehall.co.uk
[W] www.thorpehall.co.uk

Dir: 5m from Bridlington on B1253

★ 🚐 £9-£17 🚌 £9-£17 ⛺ £5.75-£12

Open Mar-Oct (rs reception & shop limited opening hours) Booking Advisable bank hols & peak periods Last arrival 22.00hrs Last departure noon

A delightful, peaceful small park within the walled gardens of Thorpe Hall yet within a few miles of the bustling seaside resort of Bridlington. There are numerous walks available locally, and a number of stately homes are within easy reach. A 4.5-acre site with 90 touring pitches.

Fishing, golf practice holes

Leisure: 🔍 ⛺ 📺

Facilities: ✈ 🚿 ⊙ 🧺 ✱ 📞 🛒 🪑 🐕

Disabled facilities: wash basin, toilet, bath & shower (free hot water)

Services: [T] 🚐 🔋 🧯 🌿 🧊 → ∪ 🎣

💳 AMERICAN EXPRESS · VISA · SWITCH

SKIPSEA TA15

Low Skirlington Leisure Park 🏖 75%

YO25 8SY
☎ 01262 468213 📠 01262 468105
[E] info@skirlington.com
[W] www.skirlington.com

Dir: From M62 towards Beverley then Hornsea. Between Skipsea & Hornsea on B1242

🚐 🚌 ⛺

Open Mar-Oct Booking Advisable Mar-Oct

A large well-run seaside park set close to the beach in partly-sloping meadowland with young trees and shrubs. The site has five toilet blocks, a supermarket and an amusement arcade, with occasional entertainment in the clubhouse. The wide range of family amenities include an indoor heated swimming pool complex with sauna, jacuzzi and sunbeds. A 10-pin bowling alley and indoor play area for children are planned for 2005. A 24-acre site with 285 touring pitches, 9 hardstandings and 450 static.

Putting green, pony trekking

Leisure: 🏊 🔍 ⛺ 📺

Facilities: ✈ 🚿 ⊙ 🧺 ✱ 📞 🛒 🪑 🐕

Disabled facilities: toilet & showers

Services: 🍴 🍺 🚐 🔋 🍷 🧯 🌿 🧊 → ∪ ⛳18 ✈ 🎣 ◎ ⛵

Notes: No single sex groups

💳 AMERICAN EXPRESS · VISA · Barclays CONNECT · SWITCH

SPROATLEY — TA13

Burton Constable Holiday Park
▶▶▶ 75%

Old Lodges HU11 4LN
☎ 01964 562508 ≣ 01964 563420
ⓔ info@burtonconstable.co.uk
ⓦ www.burtonconstable.co.uk

Dir: Off A165 onto B1238 to Sproatley. Follow signs to park

★ 🚐 £11-£14 🚏 £11-£14 ▲ £9.50-£14.50

Open Mar-Oct (rs Nov-Dec static caravans and cabins only) Booking Advisable bank hols Last arrival 22.00hrs Last departure 16.00hrs
A very attractive parkland site overlooking the fishing lakes, in the grounds of Burton Constable Hall. The toilet facilities are kept spotlessly clean, and the Lakeside Club provides a focus for relaxing in the evening. Children will enjoy the extensive adventure playground. A 30-acre site with 200 touring pitches, 14 hardstandings and 208 static. Two 10-acre fishing lakes

Leisure: Ⓐ
Facilities: 🌊⊙🕘❄🍴🔥🎣🐾
Disabled facilities: showers & toilet
Services: 🔲🚮⚡🔯🛒🔷🍴🗑🔲 → Ⓤ🏍18 🎣
Notes: Dogs must be kept on leads

ALLERSTON — SE88

Vale of Pickering Caravan Park
▶▶▶▶ 73%

Carr House Farm YO18 7PQ
☎ 01723 859280 ≣ 01723 850060
ⓔ tony@valeofpickering.co.uk
ⓦ www.valeofpickering.co.uk

Dir: On B1415, 1.75m off A170, Pickering to Scarborough road

★ 🚐 £10-£15 🚏 £10-£15 ▲ £10-£15

Open Mar-10 Jan (rs Mar) Booking Advisable BH's Last arrival 21.00hrs Last departure noon
An attractively maintained park with high quality facilities, and surrounded by mature hedges with lots of colourful landscaping. Set in open countryside within the North Yorkshire Moors National Park. A 13-acre site with 120 touring pitches, 80 hardstandings. Microwave

Leisure: Ⓐ
Facilities: 🚿🌊⊙🕘❄🍴🔥🐾
Disabled facilities: toilet, bath & washbasin
Services: 🔲🚮⚡🔯🛒🔷🔲 → Ⓤ🏍18 🎣
Notes: No single sex groups
🔲🔲🔲 Ⓢ

AYSGARTH

SE08

Westholme Caravan & Camping Park ▶▶▶ 76%

DL8 3SP
☎ 01969 663268
Dir: 1m E of Aysgarth off A684

★ 🚐 £10-£13 🚐 £10-£13 ▲ £8.50-£11

Open Mar-Oct Booking Advisable Bank hols & Jul-Aug Last arrival 22.00hrs Last departure noon

A beckside site with level grassy pitches in various paddocks set into the hillside. There is a well-equipped children's playground, a well-stocked shop, and a licensed bar and family room. The famous Aysgarth Falls are nearby. A 22-acre site with 70 touring pitches, 44 static.

Fishing free on site

Leisure: 🛝 🖵
Facilities: 📞 ⊙ 🖍 ※ 🕻 🐾 🛪
Services: 🗍 🚊 🖾 🍳 🗑 🚰 🖽 → 🗲

BOROUGHBRIDGE

SE36

Camping & Caravanning Club Site ▶▶▶▶ 72%

Bar Lane Roecliffe YO51 9LS
☎ 01423 322683
🕸 www.campingandcaravanningclub.co.uk
Dir: From A1(M) J48 follow signs for Bar Lane Ind Est & Roecliffe. Site 0.25m from rdbt

★ 🚐 £15.35-£16.35 🚐 £15.35-£16.35
▲ £15.35-£16.35

Open all year Booking Advisable bank hols & peak periods Last arrival 21.00hrs Last departure noon

A quiet riverside site with direct access onto the River Ure, with fishing and boating available. Close enough to the A1(M) but far enough away to hear little traffic noise, this site is a perfect stopover for longer journeys. The popular tourist centres of Ripon, Knaresborough, Harrogate and York are within easy reach, while the friendly little town of Boroughbridge offers plenty of facilities just a short walk away. A 5-acre site with 85 touring pitches, 14 hardstandings.

Leisure: 🛶 🛝
Facilities: 📞 ⊙ 🖍 ※ 🕻 🏛 🛪
Disabled facilities: toilet, washbasin, shower & razor point
Services: 🗍 🚊 �½ 🗑 🚰 🍳 🖽 → 🗲 🐾 🔺
▱▱ ▱▱ ▱▱ 🔖 🔄 💲

CAWOOD SE53

Cawood Park ▶▶▶▶ 66%

Ryther Road YO8 3TT
☎ 01757 268450
[E] cawoodpark@aol.com
[W] www.cawoodpark.com

Dir: A1 take B1222, turn at Cawood lights signed Tadcaster onto B1223 for 1m, park is on L

★ 🚐 £13-£20 🚌 £13-£20 ⛺ £10-£16

Open all year Booking Advisable bank hols & Jul-Aug Last arrival 21.00hrs Last departure 11.00hrs

An attractive park in a rural area with its own fishing lake, which the camping area overlooks. The site is bordered by hedges and mature trees, and is well away from the road, while amenities are modern. The club house with a comfortable bar is sited on one side of the lake, and there is occasional entertainment here. Coarse fishing is available. A 8-acre site with 60 touring pitches, 3 hardstandings and 10 static.

Leisure: 🏊 🔍 📺
Facilities: 🚿 ⊙ 🧺 ✻ 📞 🏪 🍖 🪑 🐕
Disabled facilities: toilets & bungalows to rent
Services: [T] 🚐 🗑 🍷 🔥 → ∪ ⛳18 🎣 ◎ ⛵

FILEY TA18

Crows Nest Caravan Park ▶▶▶ 67%

Gristhorpe YO14 9PS
☎ 01723 582206 📠 01723 582206
[W] www.crowsnestcaravanpark.com

Dir: On seaward side of A165, signed off rdbt

★ 🚐 £12-£20 🚌 £12-£20 ⛺ £12-£15

Open Mar-Oct Last departure noon

A beautifully situated park on the coast between Scarborough and Filey, with excellent panoramic views. This large and mainly static park offers lively entertainment, and two bars. The touring caravan area is near the entertainment complex, whilst the tenting pitches are at the top of the site. A 2-acre site with 49 touring pitches, 49 hardstandings and 217 static.

Leisure: 🏊 🔍 🛝
Facilities: 🚿 ⊙ ✻ 📞 🏪 🐕
Services: [T] 🍴 🚐 🗑 🍷 🔥 🌿 → ∪ ⛳18 🎣 ◎ ⛵

FILEY TA18

Primrose Valley Holiday Park 🏕
63%

YO14 9RF
☎ 01723 513771

Dir: Signposted off A165 Scarborough Bridlington road, 3m S of Filey.

🚐 🚙 ⛺

Open Mar-early Jan Last arrival 22.00hrs Last departure noon

A large all-action holiday centre with a wide range of sports and leisure activities to suit everyone from morning until late in the evening. A completely new touring area with its own facilities apart from the main holiday complex is planned for 2005, including a number of super pitches. A 160-acre site with 80 touring pitches, 1,200 static.

Facilities: 🛁
Services: ▣

▦ ▦ ▦

FILEY TA18

Reighton Sands Holiday Park 🏕
64%

Reighton Gap YO14 9SJ
☎ 01723 890476
🌐 www.havenholidays.com

Dir: On A165 5m S of Filey at Reighton Gap, signed

★ 🚐

Open Mar-Oct Last arrival 22.00hrs Last departure noon

A large, lively holiday centre with a wide range of entertainment and all-weather leisure facilities, located just 10 minutes' walk from a long sandy beach. Each of the three touring areas has its own facilities block, and the site is particularly geared towards families with young children. A 84-acre site with 303 touring pitches, 800 static.

Leisure: 🐟 🎣 ⚲ 🏓
Facilities: 🛁
Services: ✗ 🍴 ▣ ⚲

FILEY TA18

Blue Dolphin Holiday Park
67%

Gristhorpe Bay YO14 9PU
☎ 01723 515155
🕸 www.havenholidays.co.uk

Dir: Gristhorpe Bay 2m NW off A165

★ 🚐

Open all year Booking Advisable at all times
Last arrival 22.00hrs Last departure noon
*There are great clifftop views to be enjoyed
from this fun-filled holiday centre with an
extensive and separate touring area. The
emphasis is on non-stop entertainment, with
organised sports and clubs, all-weather leisure
facilities, heated swimming pools and plenty
of well-planned amusements. Pitches are
mainly on level or gently-sloping grass plus
some fully-serviced hardstandings, and the
beach is just 2 miles away. There is also an
interesting nature trail. A 80-acre site with
352 touring pitches.*

Leisure: ⚡ ⚡ ⚡ ⚓ ⛝ ☐
Facilities: 🛁
Services: ✗ 🖶 🔳 ⛾ 🔋

FILEY TA18

Flower of May Holiday Park
74%

Lebberston Cliff YO11 3NU
☎ 01723 584311 📠 01723 581361
🅔 info@flowerofmay.com

🕸 www.flowerofmay.com

Dir: Signed off A165 on Scarborough side
of Filey

🚐 🚐 🛆

Open Etr-Oct (rs early & late season) Booking
Advisable Spring BH wk, Jul-Aug & BH's Last
arrival 21.00hrs Last departure noon
*A delightful family site with level grassy
pitches and excellent facilities. This large
landscaped park offers a full range of
recreational activities, with plenty to occupy
everyone. Grass or hard pitches are available,
all on level ground, and arranged in avenues
screened by shrubs. A 13-acre site with 270
touring pitches, 100 hardstandings and 193
static.*
Squash, bowling, 9-hole golf & basketball
court

Leisure: ⚡ ⚡ ⚓ ☐
Facilities: 🛏 ⊙ ⚲ ✳ ⚴ 🛁 🛱 🛎
Disabled facilities: toilets
Services: 🔳 ✗ 🖶 🔌 🔳 ⛾ 🔋 🔲 → ∪ ⌐18 ⚅
🐾 🎵 ◎ ♨
Notes: No single sex groups, dogs by
arrangement only

HARROGATE SE35

High Moor Farm Park
►►►► 68%

Skipton Road HG3 2LT
☎ 01423 563637 ▤ 01423 529449

Dir: On A59 Harrogate-Skipton road

🚐 £12-£14 🚐 £12-£14 ⚠ £12-£14
Open Etr/Apr-Oct Booking Advisable public
hols Last arrival 23.30hrs Last departure
15.00hrs
*An excellent site with first class facilities, set
beside a small wood and surrounded by thorn
hedges. The numerous touring pitches are
located in meadowland fields, each area with
its own toilet block. A large heated indoor
swimming pool and a games room are very
popular, and there is a golf course, a full-sized
crown bowling green, and a bar serving meals
and snacks. A 15-acre site with 320 touring
pitches, 51 hardstandings and 158 static.*
Coarse fishing, 9-hole golf course, bowling
green

Leisure: ⚓ ⚘ ⚙

Facilities: 🚿 📡 ⊙ 🕭 ✳ ⚘ 🛒 🎋 �🐕 🎋

Disabled facilities: shower room with toilet
& washbasin

Services: 🆃 ✗ 🛒 🚐 🎛 🎅 ⚘ 🗑 → ∪ 𝄞18 🎪
♫ **Notes:** No single sex groups

▦ ▦ ▦ ▦ 5

HARROGATE SE35

Ripley Caravan Park
►►►►► 69%

Knaresborough Road Ripley HG3 3AU
☎ 01423 770050 ▤ 01423 770050

Dir: 3m N of Harrogate on A61. Turn R at
rdbt onto B6165 signposted Knaresborough.
Park 300yds L

★ 🚐 £7.50-£12 🚐 £7.50-£12 ⚠ £7.50-£12
Open Etr-Oct Booking Advisable bank hols
Last arrival 21.00hrs Last departure noon
*A well-run rural site in attractive meadowland
which has been landscaped with mature tree
plantings. The resident owners lovingly
maintain the facilities, and there is a heated
swimming pool and sauna, a games room,
and a covered play room for small children. A
18-acre site with 100 touring pitches, 30
static.*
Nursery playroom, sauna, football, TV in
games room

Leisure: ⚓ ⚘ ⚙

Facilities: 📡 ⊙ 🕭 ✳ ⚘ 🛒 🎋

Disabled facilities: toilet, shower
& washbasin

Services: 🆃 🚐 🎛 ⚘ 🗑 → ∪ 𝄞18 🌭 🎪 ♫

◎ **Notes:** Family camping only, dogs on
leads, BBQs must be off the ground

▦ ▦ ▦ ▦ 5

HARROGATE SE35

Rudding Holiday Park
▶▶▶▶▶ 74%

Follifoot HG3 1JH
☎ 01423 870439 📠 01423 870859
📧 holiday-park@ruddingpark.com
🌐 www.ruddingpark.com

Dir: From A1 take A59 to A658, turn S signed Bradford. Continue for 4.5m then R and follow signs

★ 🏕 £11.50-£27 🚐 ⚠ £7.50-£17

Open Mar-Jan (rs Nov-Jan) Booking Advisable bank hols Last arrival 22.30hrs Last dep 14.00hrs
A spacious park set in the stunning 200 acres of mature parkland with terraced pitches and dry-stone walls. A separate area houses super pitches where all services are supplied including a picnic table and TV connection. The toilet blocks are first class. There is an 18-hole golf course, plus the Deer House bar and restaurant, and a children's play area. A 55-acre site with 141 touring pitches, 60 hardstandings and 95 static.
Driving range

Leisure: ⚡ 🎱 🎢
Facilities: 🚿 🏧 ⊙ 🛒 🌊 🔥 🎯 📷 🐕
Disabled facilities: toilet & shower room
Services: 🔟 ✕ 🛒 🔧 🔲 🛢 💧 🚿 🚽 → ∪ ↑18 ⚓
⚡ 🔩

Notes: No single sex groups, min age unaccompanied 18yrs

▬ ▬ ▬ ▭ ◥ ⑤

HELMSLEY SE68

Golden Square Touring Caravan Park ▶▶▶▶ 74%

Oswaldkirk YO62 5YQ
☎ 01439 788269 📠 01439 788236
📧 barbara@goldensquarecaravanpark. freeserve.co.uk
🌐 www.goldensquarecaravanpark.co.uk

Dir: 1m from Ampleporth towards Helmsley on caravan route

★ 🏕 £9-£11.50

Open Mar-Oct Booking Advisable bank hols
Last arrival 21.00hrs Last departure noon
An all-round excellent site with manicured grounds and first class toilets. This friendly park is set in a quiet rural situation with lovely views over the North Yorks Moors. The park is terraced on three levels surrounded by trees, and caters particularly for families. Country walks and mountain bike trails start here, and the market town of Helmsley is just 2.5 miles away. Caravans are prohibited on the A170 at Sutton Bank between Thirsk and Helmsley. A 12-acre site with 129 touring pitches.
Microwave

Leisure: 🎱 🎢
Facilities: 🚿 🏧 ⊙ 🛒 🌊 🔥 🎯 📷 🐕
Disabled facilities: toilets & showers
Services: 🔟 🚿 🔧 🚐 🔲 🛢 💧 🚿 → ∪ ↑18 🔩
◎

HIGH BENTHAM   SD66

Riverside Caravan Park
▶▶▶▶ 69%

LA2 7HS
☎ 01524 261272 📄 01524 262163
📧 info@riversidecaravanpark.co.uk
🌐 www.riversidecaravanpark.co.uk

Dir: Off B6480, signed from town centre

★ 🚐 £2.25 🚐 £12.25 ▲ £12.25

Open Mar-Oct Booking Advisable bank hols
Last arrival 20.00hrs Last departure 13.00hrs
*A well-managed riverside park with level
grass pitches set in avenues separated by
trees. This attractive park has a well-equipped
amenities block including excellent facilities
for family tenters. The games room and
adventure playground are popular with
families, and the market town of High
Bentham is close by. A 12-acre site with 50
touring pitches, 7 hardstandings and 205
static.*
Free fishing permits for private stretch

Leisure: ✎ ⋀

Facilities: ↑ ⊙ ◱ ❄ ❈ ℄ 🕱 🏕

Disabled facilities: shower room,
RADAR key

Services: 🔟 ⛽ 🛢 ▨ ⌾ ▦ → ▶18 🖪

▦ ▦ ▦ ▧ ⑤

HUNMANBY   TA07

Orchard Farm Holiday Village
▶▶▶ 71%

Stonegate YO14 0PU
☎ 01723 891582 📄 01723 891582
📧 s.dugdale@virgin.net

Dir: Signed from A1039

★ 🚐 £10-£14 🚐 £10-£14 ▲ £10-£14

Open Mar-Oct (rs Nov-Mar not all facilities)
Booking Advisable bank hols & peak season
Last arrival 23.00hrs Last departure 11.00hrs
*Pitches are arranged around a large coarse
fishing lake at this grassy park. The young
owners are keen and friendly, and offer a
wide range of amenities including an indoor
heated swimming pool and a licensed bar. A
14-acre site with 91 touring pitches, 34
hardstandings and 46 static.*
Veg prep area, fishing

Leisure: ✎ ✎ ⋀ ▢

Facilities: ↑ ⊙ ◱ ❄ ℄ ℻ ⚘ 🕱 🏕

Disabled facilities: toilets, shower & ramps

Services: 🔟 ⛽ 🔟 ◉ 🛢 ▨ ▦ → ▶18 🖪 ◎ ◊

Notes: No single sex groups

MARKINGTON SE26

Yorkshire Hussar Inn Caravan Park
▶▶▶ 66%

High Street HG3 3NR

☎ 01765 677327

✉ yorkshirehussar@yahoo.com

Dir: Between Harrogate & Ripon (A61) turn W at Wormald Green, 1m into Markington

★ ♔ £10-£15 ♔ £10-£15 ▲ £7-£15

Open Apr-Oct Booking Advisable bank hols Last arrival 22.00hrs Last departure Noon *A terraced site behind the village inn with well-kept grass. This pleasant site offers spacious pitches with some hardstandings and electricity. A 5-acre site with 20 touring pitches, 2 hardstandings and 73 static.* Paddling pool

Leisure: ⚼

Facilities: ⬤ ⊙ ⚘ ✿ ☕

Services: ⊞ ⬚ ⬚ ♔ ⚑ ⊞ → ⋃ ↑18

Notes: Dogs must be kept on leads

NORTH STANLEY SE27

Sleningford Water Mill Caravan Camping Park ▶▶▶ 70%

HG4 3HQ

☎ 01765 635201

🌐 www.ukparks.co.uk/sleningford

Dir: Adjacent to A6108. 4m N of Ripon & 1m N of North Stainley

★ ♔ ♔ ▲

Open Etr & Apr-Oct Booking Advisable bank & school hols Last arrival 22.00hrs Last departure 12.30hrs *The old watermill and the River Ure make an attractive setting for this touring park which is laid our in two areas. Pitches are placed in meadowland and close to mature woodland, and the park is carefully maintained. This park is popular with canoeists. A 14-acre site with 80 touring pitches.* Off-licence, canoe access, fly fishing

Leisure: ⚓ ⚼

Facilities: ⬤ ⊙ ✿ ☕ ☕ ⚑ ⚛

Disabled facilities: toilet & shower

Services: ⊞ ♔ ⬚ ⬚ ⊘ ⊞ → ↑18 ⚒ △

Notes: Youth groups by prior arrangement only

RICHMOND NZ10

Swale View Caravan Park ►►► 69%

Reeth Road DL10 4SF
☎ 01748 823106 ▤ 01748 823106
✉ swaleview@teesdaleonline.co.uk

Dir: 3m W of Richmond on A6108, Reeth to Leyburn road

🏕 🚐 ⛺

Open Mar-Jan Booking Advisable bank & summer hols Last arrival 21.00hrs Last departure noon
Shaded by trees and overlooking the River Swale is this attractive, mainly grassy site. The facilities have been extensively upgraded by enthusiastic owners, and this park is a short distance from Richmond, and well situated for exploring Swaledale and Wensleydale. A 13-acre site with 60 touring pitches, 139 static.

Leisure: ⚓ ⌂ ▢
Facilities: ⌁ ⊙ ⚲ ⚘ ⚏ ⚑ ▦ 穴 ★
Disabled facilities: toilet facilities, adapted holiday homes, access throughout
Services: ▯ ➡ ⚑ ♨ ⊟ 🔋 ⊘ ⊞ → ∪ ⌗18 ♩
Notes: No single sex groups

▦ ▦ 𝒮

RICHMOND NZ10

Brompton-on-Swale Caravan & Camping Park ►►►► 69%

Brompton-on-Swale DL10 7EZ
☎ 01748 824629 ▤ 01748 826383
✉ brompton.caravanpark@btinternet.com
🌐 www.bromptoncaravanpark.co.uk

Dir: Take B6271 off A1 signed Richmond, site 1m on L

🏕 🚐 ⛺

Open Etr or Mar-Oct Booking Advisable school & bank hols Last arrival 20.00hrs Last departure noon
A peaceful riverside park on former meadowland with mature trees and other natural features. Fishing is available on the River Swale which flows through the park, and there is a good children's playground. A 14.5-acre site with 77 touring pitches, 22 static.
Fishing on site

Leisure: ⌂
Facilities: ⌁ ⊙ ⚲ ⚘ ⚏ ⚑ ▦ ★
Disabled facilities: toilet & shower blocks
Services: ▯ ⚑ 🔋 ♨ ⊘ ⊞ → ∪ ⌗18 ♩ 🔋 ⚠

▦ ▦ ▦ ▧ 𝒮

RIPON   SE37

Riverside Meadows Country Caravan Park ▶▶▶ 72%

Ure Bank Top HG4 1JD
☎ 01765 602964 📠 01765 604045
📧 info@flowerofmay.com
🌐 www.flowerofmay.com

Dir: On A61 at N end of new bridge out of Ripon, then W along riverside, do not cross river. Site 400yds, clearly signed

🏕 🚐 ▲

Open Etr-Oct (rs Mar-Apr bar open wknds only) Booking Advisable bank hols & high season Last arrival 21.00hrs Last departure noon
This pleasant, well-maintained site stands on high ground overlooking the River Ure, 1m from the town centre. The site has an excellent club with family room and quiet lounge. There is no access to the river from the site. A 28-acre site with 131 touring pitches, 269 static.

Leisure: 🏊 🅿 🎱

Facilities: 🌂 ⊙ ✳ ⚟ 🛒 🎋 🐾

Disabled facilities: toilets

Services: 🆃 🚐 🚽 🖙 🛢 ⌀ 🅓 → ∪ ⌖ 18 🌫 ♨ 🎣

⚠ **Notes:** No single sex groups, dogs by arrangement only

ROBIN HOOD'S BAY   NZ90

Grouse Hill Caravan Park ▶▶▶ 69%

Flask Bungalow Farm Fylingdales YO22 4QH
☎ 01947 880543 📠 01947 880543
Dir: Off A171 (Whitby-Scarborough road), entered via a loop road, at the Flask Inn

🏕 🚐 ▲

Open Spring bank hol-Sep (rs Etr-May shop & reception restricted) Booking Advisable public hols Last arrival 22.00hrs Last departure noon
A spacious site on a south-facing slope, with many terraced pitches overlooking the North Yorkshire Moors National Park. The owners are constantly improving the park, and it is an ideal base for walking and touring. A 14-acre site with 175 touring pitches.

Leisure: 🏊 🅿

Facilities: 🌂 ⊙ ✳ ⚟ 🛒 🎋

Disabled facilities: toilets & ramps

Services: 🆃 🚐 🚽 🛢 ⌀ 🅓 → ∪ ⌖9

Notes: No singles groups, no motorcycles

SCARBOROUGH — TA08

Killerby Old Hall ▶▶▶ 68%

Killerby YO11 3TW
☎ 01723 583799 📄 01723 583799

Dir: Direct access via B1261 at Killerby, near Cayton

★ 🏕 £11-£14

Open Mar-Oct Booking Advisable BHs & school holidays Last departure noon
A small secluded park, well sheltered by mature trees and shrubs, located at the rear of the old hall. Use of the small indoor swimming pool is shared by visitors to the hall's holiday accommodation. A 2-acre site with 20 touring pitches, 20 hardstandings. Grassed play area

Leisure: 🏊 🎣
Facilities: 🅿 ⊙ 🖵 🖵 🕭
Services: 🔌 🖤 🖵 ⊞ → U M18 🗄 ◎ ▲
Notes: No single sex groups

🔲 🔲 🔳

SCARBOROUGH — TA08

Jacobs Mount Caravan Park ▶▶▶▶ 71%

Jacobs Mount Stepney Road YO12 5NL
☎ 01723 361178 📄 01723 361178
📧 jacobsmount@yahoo.co.uk
🌐 www.jacobsmount.co.uk

Dir: Direct access from A170

★ 🏕 £10.50-£15 🚐 £10.50-£15

▲ £10.50-£15

Open Mar-Oct (rs Mar-May & Oct limited hours at shop/bar) Booking Advisable bank hols & late Jun-early Sep Last arrival 21.00hrs Last departure noon
An elevated family-run park surrounded by woodland and open countryside, yet only 2m from the beach. Touring pitches are terraced gravel stands with individual services. A licensed bar and family room provide meals and snacks, and there is an adjoining games room. A 18-acre site with 156 touring pitches, 131 hardstandings and 60 static.
Food preparation area

Leisure: 🎣 ⚲ 🖵
Facilities: ➡ 🅿 ⊙ 🖵 🔆 🕭 ⚓ 🕭
Disabled facilities: toilet facilities incl wheelchair entry shower
Services: 📺 ✖ 🖳 🖤 ⅄ 🗄 🖤 🍽 🗄 ⊞ → U M18 ✈ 🍽 🗄 ◎ ▲

🔲 🔲 🔳 🔳 🔳

SCARBOROUGH TA08

Spring Willows Touring Caravan Park ►►►► 71%

Main Road Staxton Roundabout YO12 4SB
☎ 01723 891505 📠 01723 892123
[E] fun4all@springwillows.fsnet.co.uk
[W] www.springwillows.co.uk

Dir: A64 to Scarborough, then take A1039 to Filey. Entrance on R

🚐 🚙 ⛺

Open Mar-Jan (rs Mar & Oct bar, pool, take-away, restaurant restricted) Booking Advisable bank hols, Etr, Jul & Aug Last arrival 18.00hrs Last departure 11.00hrs

A family park offering a full evening entertainment programme, and a restaurant serving food throughout the day and evening. Other amenities include a Mexican themed bar, and a popular children's club. Pitches are divided by shrubs and bushes, and sheltered by high sand dunes, with a natural spring running through the park. A 26-acre site with 184 touring pitches.

Sauna, solarium, coffee lounge

Leisure: 🏊 🔍 ⛺ 📺
Facilities: 🚿 ⊙ 🧺 ✱ 📞 🛒 🍽 ⛩ 🐕
Disabled facilities: toilet, shower & sink
Services: [T] ✖ 🧁 🔌 🍴 🗑 🍷 🔒 🌿 ⊞ → ∪ ⚑18

AMEX VISA DELTA [S]

STAINFORTH SD86

Knight Stainforth Hall Caravan & Campsite ►►►► 60%

BD24 0DP
☎ 01729 822200 📠 01729 823387
[E] info@knightstainforth.co.uk
[W] www.knightstainforth.co.uk

Dir: From W on A65 take B6480 for Settle, turn L before swimming pool signed Little Stainforth. From E continue through Settle on B6480, over bridge to swimming pool, then turn R.

★ 🚐 £10-£12 🚙 £10-£12 ⛺ £10-£12

Open May-Oct Booking Advisable bank hols & Jul-Aug Last arrival 22.00hrs Last departure noon

Located near Settle and the River Ribble in the Yorkshire Dales National Park, this well-maintained family site is sheltered by mature woodland. It is an ideal base for walking or touring in the beautiful surrounding areas. The toilet block has been refurbished to a very high standard. A 6-acre site with 100 touring pitches, 60 static.

Fishing on site

Leisure: 🔍 ⛺ 📺
Facilities: 🚿 ⊙ 🧺 ✱ 📞 🛒 ⛩ 🐕
Disabled facilities: toilet & shower
Services: [T] 🔌 🍴 🗑 🔒 🌿 ⊞ → ∪ ⚑9 🎣
Notes: No groups of young people

AMEX VISA Barclays CONNECT DELTA [S]

STAXTON TA07

Spring Willows Touring Caravan Park ►►►► 71%

Main Road Staxton Roundabout YO12 4SB
☎ 01723 891505 📠 01723 892123
📧 fun4all@springwillows.fsnet.co.uk
🌐 www.springwillows.co.uk

Dir: A64 to Scarborough, then take A1039 to Filey. Entrance on R

🚐 🚐 🏕

Open Mar-Jan (rs Mar & Oct bar, pool, take-away, restaurant restricted) Booking Advisable bank hols, Etr, Jul & Aug Last arrival 18.00hrs Last departure 11.00hrs

A family park offering a full evening entertainment programme, and a restaurant serving food throughout the day and evening. Other amenities include a Mexican themed bar, and a popular children's club. Pitches are divided by shrubs and bushes, and sheltered by high sand dunes, with a natural spring running through the park. A 26-acre site with 184 touring pitches.

Sauna, solarium, coffee lounge

Leisure: 🎿 🎯 ⚙ 🖵
Facilities: 🌧 ⊙ 🔧 ✳ 🕯 🛒 🚾 🎋 🐾
Disabled facilities: toilet, shower & sink
Services: 🆃 ✖ 🕯 🛒 🚐 🗒 🖬 🛢 🔌 ⊘ 🖂 → ∪ ⁑18

🔲 🔳 🔳 🅂

SUTTON-ON-THE-FOREST SE56

Goosewood Caravan Park ►►►► 73%

YO61 1ET
☎ 01347 810829 📠 01347 811498
📧 edward@gooseparks.co.uk
🌐 www.ukparks.co.uk/goosewood

Dir: From A1237 take B1363. After 5m turn R. Take R turn after 0.5m & site on R

★ 🚐 £10-£16.50 🚐 £10-£16.50

Open Feb-14 Jan Booking Advisable BH's, Jul & Aug Last arrival 20.00hrs Last departure noon

An immaculately maintained park with its own lake and seasonal fishing, set in attractive woodland just six miles north of York. The generous patio pitches are randomly spaced throughout the site. This popular family park has a first class play area for younger children, whilst teenagers will enjoy meeting others in the recreation barn. The new health spa (for 2005) will ensure that adults can relax after a day's activity. A 20-acre site with 75 touring pitches, 75 hardstandings and 35 static.

Fishing lake

Leisure: 🎯 ⚙
Facilities: 🛏 🌧 ⊙ 🔧 ✳ 🕯 🛒 🎋 🐾
Services: 🆃 🛏 🚐 🛢 🔌 🖂 → ∪ ⁑18 🎱 🔧

🔲 🔳 🅂

WINKSLEY SE27

Woodhouse Farm & Country Park ►►► 71%

HG4 3PG
☎ 01765 658309
[E] woodhouse.farm@talk21.com
[W] www.woodhousewinksley.com

Dir: 6m W of Ripon off B6265 Pateley Bridge road, 2.5m from Fountains Abbey, signed Grantley

★ 🚐 £10-£16 🚙 £10-£16 ⛺ £9-£16

Open Mar-Oct Booking Advisable bank hols & mid Jul-Aug Last arrival 21.00hrs Last departure noon

An attractive rural site on a former working farm, with several camping areas screened by hedges. Visitors have access to surrounding meadowland, lake and mature woods. A former farm building has been converted into a country-style pub serving food mainly at weekends. A 16-acre site with 140 touring pitches, 62 static.

Coarse fishing lake

Leisure: 🔍 ⛫ ▭

Facilities: 🚿 ⊙ ⚒ ✱ 📞 🛒 🍖 ⛩ 🐕

Disabled facilities: toilet, shower & washbasin

Services: [T] ✕ 🚐 🗑 🍷 🔋 🍃 ⊡ → ∪ 🎣

Notes: No single sex groups, no commercial vehicles

💳 💳 💳

WYKEHAM SE98

St Helens Caravan Park ►►►► 75%

St Helens in the Park YO13 9QD
☎ 01723 862771 📠 01723 866613
[E] caravans@wykeham.co.uk
[W] www.wykeham.co.uk

Dir: On A170 in village, 150yds on L beyond Downe Arms Hotel towards Scarborough

🚐 🚙 ⛺

Open Feb-Jan (rs Nov-Jan shop/laundry closed) Booking Advisable bank hols & Jul-Aug Last arrival 22.00hrs Last departure 17.00hrs

Set on the edge of the North York Moors National Park this delightfully landscaped park is well maintained and thoughtfully laid out with top quality facilities. The site is divided into terraces with tree-screening creating smaller areas, including an adults' zone. A cycle route leads through the surrounding Wykeham Estate, and there is a short pathway to the adjoining Downe Arms country pub. A 25-acre site with 250 touring pitches, 2 hardstandings.

Caravan storage

Leisure: 🔍 ⛫

Facilities: 🛁 🚿 ⊙ ⚒ ✱ 📞 🛒 🍖 ⛩ 🐕

Disabled facilities: 2 disabled toilets + showers

Services: [T] ✕ 🍺 🍴 🚐 🗑 🔋 🍃 ⊡ → ∪ ⛳18 ✈ 🎣 ◎ △

💳 💳 💳 💳 💳

CATEL (CASTEL)

Fauxquets Valley Farm ▶▶▶ 71%

GY5 7QA
☎ 01481 255460 📄 01481 251797
✉ info@fauxquets.co.uk
🌐 www.fauxquets.co.uk

Dir: Off pier. 2nd exit off rdbt. Top of hill L onto Queens Rd. Continue for 2m. Turn R onto Candie Rd. Opposite sign for German Occupation Museum

Å

Open mid Jun-Aug (rs May-mid Jun & 1-15 Sep Haybarn restaurant and Bar closed) Booking Advisable last 2 wks Jul-1st 3 wks Aug

A beautiful, quiet farm site in a hidden valley close to the sea. Friendly helpful owners who understand campers' needs offer good quality facilities and amenities, including an outdoor swimming pool, bar/restaurant, nature trail and sports areas. A 3-acre site with 100 touring pitches.
Bird watching

Leisure: ⚛ ⚛ ⚙ ▢
Facilities: ⬕ ⊙ ⬚ ✻ ⬚ ⬚ ⬚ ⬚
Services: ✕ ⬚ ⬚ ⬚ ⬚ ⬚ ⬚ ⬚ → ∪ ⌐9 ⬚ ⬚
◎ ⬚

VALE

La Bailloterie Camping & Leisure ▶▶▶ 69%

Bailloterie Lane GY3 5HA
☎ 01481 243636 📄 01481 243225
✉ info@campinginguernsey.com
🌐 www.campinginguernsey.com

Dir: 3m N of St Peter Port, take Vale road to Crossways, turn R into Rue du Braye. Site 1st L at sign

★ Å £10-£12.50

Open 15 May-15 Sep Booking Advisable all times Last arrival 23.00hrs

A pretty rural site with one large touring field and a few small, well-screened paddocks. This delightful site has been in the same family ownership for over 30 years, and offers super facilities in converted outbuildings. A 12-acre site with 100 touring pitches.
Volleyball net & boules pitch

Leisure: ⚛ ⚙ ▢
Facilities: ⬕ ⊙ ⬚ ✻ ⬚ ⬚ ⬚ ⬚
Services: ✕ ⬚ ⬚ ⬚ ⬚ ⬚ ⬚ ⬚ ⬚ ⬚ → ∪ ⌐18 ⬚ ⬚
⬚ ◎ ⬚

Notes: No single sex groups without references, dogs allowed in restricted areas

ST MARTIN

Rozel Camping Park ▶▶▶▶ 70%

Summerville Farm JE3 6AX
☎ 01534 856797 📠 01534 856127
📧 rozelcamping@jerseyhols.com
🌐 www.jerseyhols.com/rozel

Dir: From St Helier follow A6 Bagatelle
Road or A7 Saviour's Road then B38

🚐 £13.60-£16.40 🚍 £13.60-£16.40
⛺ £13.60-£16.40

Open May-mid Sep Booking Advisable Jul-Aug
Last departure noon

*An attractive and well-maintained secluded
holiday site offering excellent amenities in a
lovely farm location. The site is divided into
paddocks, with hedges for screening and
shelter. It is only a short walk from the
beautiful sandy beach and harbour at Rozel
Bay. A 4-acre site with 100 touring pitches, 20
static.*

Leisure: ₹ ◆ 𝔸 ☐
Facilities: 🅝 ☉ ☜ ※ ☾ 🕱 🏛
Disabled facilities: toilet, shower & basin
with ramp access
Services: 🇹 🔥 🚐 🗑 🗞 🗑 ⊞ → ∪ ⌂ 18 ⤧ ⤨ △
Notes: ✖ No single sex groups mid Jul-mid
Aug

ST MARTIN

Beuvelande Camp Site ▶▶▶▶▶ 70%

Beuvelande JE3 6EZ
☎ 01534 853575 📠 01534 857788

Dir: Take A6 from St Helier to St Martin &
follow signs to campsite before St Martins
church.

⛺

Open May-15 Sep Last arrival anytime

*A well-established site with excellent toilet
facilities, accessed via narrow lanes in
peaceful countryside close to St Martin. An
attractive bar/restaurant is the focal point of
the park, especially in the evenings, and there
is a small swimming pool and playground.
Motorhomes and towed caravans will be met
at the ferry and escorted to the site if
requested when booking. A 6-acre site with
150 touring pitches.*

Leisure: ₹ ◆ 𝔸 ☐
Facilities: 🅝 ☉ ※ ☾ 🕱
Disabled facilities: 2 private rooms with
toilet, shower & wash basin
Services: ✖ 🔥 🚐 🗑 🗞 🗑 ⊞ → ∪ ⌂ 18 ⤧ ⤨

KINTORE NJ71

Hillhead Caravan Park ▶▶▶ 70%

AB51 0YX

☎ 01467 632809 & 08704 130870

🖨 01467 633173

📧 enquiries@hillheadcaravan.co.uk

🌐 www.hillheadcaravan.co.uk

Dir: 1m from village & A96 Aberdeen to Inverness road. From A96 follow caravan signs to park on B994 & taking unclass road to site

★ 🚐 £10.45-£12.35 🚐 £10.45-£12.35

🅐 £7.95-£9.85

Open all year Booking Advisable at all times Last arrival 22.00hrs Last departure 13.00hrs *A peaceful site in the River Don Valley, with pitches well screened by shrubs and trees, and laid out around a small central area containing a children's play space. Enthusiastic owners are constantly improving the facilities, and the park is very well maintained. A 1.5-acre site with 24 touring pitches, 3 hardstandings and 5 static.* Caravan storage

Leisure: 🅰

Facilities: 🅝 ⊙ 🦺 ⚓ 🌣 🌜 💆 🛒 🎋 🕇

Disabled facilities: toilets & showers, one static. caravan adapted

Services: 🔟 🚽 📧 🛢 🚿 🔌 🔁 → ⌐18 🎵

NORTH WATER BRIDGE NO66

Dovecot Caravan Park ▶▶▶ 66%

AB30 1QL

☎ 01674 840630 🖨 01674 840630

📧 dovecotcaravanpark@tinyworld.co.uk

🌐 www.dovecotcaravanpark.com

Dir: Take A90, 5m S of Laurencekirk. At RAF Edzell sign turn L. Site 500yds on L

★ 🚐 £9.50-£10.50 🚐 £9.50-£10.50 🅐 £7-£8

Open Apr-Oct Booking Advisable Jul & Aug for hook ups Last arrival 20.00hrs Last departure noon

A level grassy site in a country area close to the A90, with mature trees screening one side and the River North Esk on the other. The immaculate toilet facilities make this a handy overnight stop in a good touring area. A 6-acre site with 25 touring pitches, 8 hardstandings and 44 static.

Leisure: 🔌 🅰 🖵

Facilities: 🅝 ⊙ 🦺 🌣 🌜 💆 🕇

Disabled facilities: toilet & shower

Services: 🔟 🚽 🛢

ABERDEENSHIRE

East Bowstrips Caravan Park
▶▶▶▶ 72%

DD10 0DE

☎ 01674 850328 🖷 01674 850328

🅔 tully@bowstrips.freeserve.co.uk

🆆 www.caravancampingsites.co.uk
/aberdeenshire/eastbowstrips.htm

Dir: From S on A92 coast rd into St Cyrus.
Pass hotel on L. Take 1st L then 2nd R
signposted

★ 🚐 £10-£11 🚐 £10-£11 ▲ £7.50-£11

Open Etr or Apr-Oct Booking Advisable Jun-
Aug Last arrival 22.00hrs Last departure 22.00hrs
*A quiet, rural site close to a seaside village,
with thoughtfully modernised facilities and a
particular welcome for the disabled. The park
is surrounded by farmland on the edge of a
village, and there are extensive views to be
enjoyed. Touring pitches are sited on rising
ground amongst attractive landscaping with
ornamental trees and shrubs, and flowers. A
4-acre site with 33 touring pitches, 21
hardstandings and 18 static.*
Separate garden with boule pitch

Leisure: 🗛

Facilities: 🗈⊙🗣❄🗶🗜🎋🐾

Disabled facilities: toilet & shower in fully
equipped separate washroom

Services: 🆃🚐🗑🛢→∪🎵

Notes: If camping - no dogs allowed,
if touring - dogs must be kept on leads at all
times

Camping & Caravanning Club Site
▶▶▶ 68%

AB34 4UP

☎ 01339 881388

🅔 www.campingandcaravanningclub.co.uk

Dir: From Aberdeen on A93 turn R in
Aboyne at Struan Hotel onto B9094. After
6m take next R & then fork L before bridge,
continue for 600yds, site on L

★ 🚐 £11.75-£15.35 🚐 £11.75-£15.35

▲ £11.75-£15.35

Open Apr-Nov Booking Advisable bank hols &
peak periods Last arrival 21.00hrs Last
departure noon
*A pretty park on the edge of the village, laid
out on two levels. The upper area has
hardstandings and electric hook-ups, and
views over hills and moorland, while the
lower level is well screened with mature trees
and grassy. A 8-acre site with 90 touring
pitches, 22 hardstandings.*

Leisure: 🎣 🗛

Facilities: 🗈⊙🗣❄🗶🛉🎋

Services: 🆃🚐🗑🛢🗑🖩→∪🎵🛢♨

EDZELL
NO66

Glenesk Caravan Park ▶▶▶ 65%

DD9 7YP

☎ 01356 648565

Dir: Situated on unclass road to Glen Esk, 1m N of the B966

Open Apr-Oct Booking Advisable public hols & mid Jun-Aug Last arrival 22.00hrs Last departure 16.00hrs

A carefully-maintained woodland site with caravans spread amongst the trees around a fishing lake, and tents located in a separate area. The pleasant owner and warden create a friendly atmosphere. A 8-acre site with 45 touring pitches, 10 static.

Leisure: ♦ ⚏ ☐

Facilities: ⋒ ⊙ ⊕ ✶ ⚊ ⊞ ⚏ ⊓

Services: ⊤ ⊕ ⊕ ⊞ ⊘ ⊞ → ∪ ↑18 ↘ ♪ ⚊

MONIFIETH
NO43

Riverview Caravan Park ▶▶▶▶ 70%

Marine Road DD5 4NN

☎ 01382 535471 ▤ 01382 535375

⊕ riverviewcaravan@btinternet.com

ⓦ www.ukparks.co.uk/riverview

Dir: Signed in both directions from A930 in centre of Monifieth

★ ⚏ £13-£15 ⚏ £13-£15 ▲ £13-£15

Open Apr-Oct (rs Nov-Mar Holiday homes open) Booking Advisable Jul-Aug Last arrival 22.00hrs Last departure 12.30hrs

A well-landscaped seaside site with individual hedged pitches, and direct access to the beach. The modernised toilet block has first class facilities which are immaculately maintained. Amenities include a multi-gym, sauna and steam rooms. A 5.5-acre site with 60 touring pitches, 40 hardstandings and 25 static.

Leisure: ♦ ⚏

Facilities: ⋒ ⊙ ⊕ ✶ ⚊ ⚏ ⊓ ⊓

Disabled facilities: toilet & shower

Services: ⊕ ⊕ ⋁ ⊞ ⊞ → ∪ ↑18 ☺ ♪ ⚊
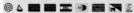
◎ ⚠ ▭ ▭ ▭ ⑩ ▭ ⚏ ⑤

BARCALDINE   NM94

Camping & Caravanning Club Site ►►► 68%

PA37 1SG

☎ 01631 720348

🌐 www.campingandcaravanningclub.co.uk

Dir: N on A828, 7m from Connel Bridge turn into site at Camping Club sign on R. Opposite the Marine Resource Centre

★ 🚐 £11.75-£15.35 🚐 £11.75-£15.35

▲ £11.75-£15.35

Open Apr-Nov Booking Advisable bank hols & peak periods Last arrival 21.00hrs Last departure noon

A sheltered site within a walled garden, bordered by Barcaldine Forest, close to Loch Creran. Tourers are arranged against the old garden walls, with some located outside in quiet grassed areas. There are pleasant woodland walks from the park, including the Sutherland memorial woods close by. A 4.5-acre site with 75 touring pitches, 27 hardstandings.

Leisure: �

Facilities: 🍴⊙🖉☀🕻🖳🖘🛏

Disabled facilities: toilet, washbasin, shower & razor point

Services: 🆃✗🖵↯🗉🖵🍴🛢⌀🅱→🗘

▨▨▨▨▨▨▨ 🔊

DUNOON   NS17

Stratheck Country Park ►►► 67%

PA23 8SG

☎ 01369 840472 🖨 01369 840504

🅔 enquiries@stratheck.com

🌐 www.stratheck.com

Dir: On A815, 7m N of Dunoon and 12m from Strachur, site on R at end of Loch Eck

★ 🚐 £12-£18 🚐 £12-£18 ▲ £8-£10

Open Mar-Oct (rs Mar-Jun & Nov-Dec restricted shop & bar opening hours) Booking Advisable Jul & Aug Last arrival 20.00hrs Last departure 16.00hrs

Spectacularly set in a beautiful valley within tree-lined hills and lying alongside the River Eachaig, this park is close to Loch Eck. It is an ideal centre for fishing and boating, and the countryside attracts walkers, climbers and cyclists. A 14-acre site with 40 touring pitches, 20 hardstandings and 85 static.

Leisure: 🔍 ⚲

Facilities: 🍴⊙🖉☀🕻🖳🛏

Services: 🆃🖵🗉🖵🍴🛢⌀→🗘🛢🍴🖳

GLENDARUEL NR98

Glendaruel Caravan Park ▶▶▶ 68%

PA22 3AB
☎ 01369 820267 📠 01369 820367
[E] mail@glendaruelcaravanpark.co.uk
[W] www.glendaruelcaravanpark.co.uk

Dir: From A83 take A815 to Strathur, then 13m to park on A886. By ferry from Gourock to Dunoon then B836, then A886 for approx 4m N. (This route is not recommended for towing vehicles as there is a 1:5 uphill gradient on B836)

🚐 🚌 ⛺
Open Apr-Oct Booking Advisable Spring bank hol & mid Jul-Aug Last arrival 22.00hrs Last departure noon
A very pleasant, well-established site in the beautiful Victorian gardens of Glendaruel House. The level grass and hardstanding pitches are set in 23 acres of wooded parkland in a valley surrounded by mountains, with many rare specimen trees. Facilities are immaculately maintained, and the owners are hospitable and friendly. A 3-acre site with 45 touring pitches, 34 hardstandings and 30 static.
Sea trout & salmon fishing

Leisure: 🎱 🛝
Facilities: 🚿 ⊙ 💨 ❄ ☎ 🛒 🏠 🧺 🐕
Services: [T] 🍽 🧼 🛢 🍃 🔋 → 🎣
Notes: Dogs must be kept on leads at all times
[AMERICAN EXPRESS] [VISA] [S]

INVERUGLAS NN30

Loch Lomond Holiday Park ▶▶▶▶ 70%

G83 7DW
☎ 01301 704224 📠 01301 704206
[E] enquiries@lochlomond-caravans.co.uk
[W] www.lochlomond-lodges.co.uk

Dir: On A82 3.5m N of Tarbet

★ 🚐 £13-£18 🚌 £13-£18
Open Mar-Oct (rs Dec-Jan main amenity building restricted hours) Booking Advisable May-Aug Last arrival 20.00hrs Last departure 11.45hrs
A lovely setting on the shores of Loch Lomond with views of forests and mountains, and boat hire available. The small touring area is beautifully situated overlooking the loch, and handily placed for the toilets and clubhouse. A 6-acre site with 18 touring pitches, 72 static.
Satellite TV, pool tables, boat hire

Leisure: 🎱 🛝 📺
Facilities: 🚿 ⊙ 💨 ❄ ☎ 🛒 🏠 🧺 🐕
Disabled facilities: toilet & shower
Services: [T] 🐦 🍽 🧼 🛢 🍃 → U ✈ 🎣 ⛵
[AMERICAN EXPRESS] [VISA] [DELTA] [S]

OBAN

Oban Caravan & Camping Park
▶▶▶ 67%

Gallanachmore Farm Gallanach Road PA34 4QH
☎ 01631 562425 📠 01631 566624
🅔 info@obancaravanpark.com

🔘 www.obancaravanpark.co.uk

Dir: From Oban centre follow signs for Mull Ferry, then take turning past terminal signed Gallanach, for 2m to site

★ 🚐 £10-£12.50 🚙 £10-£12.50

🅰 £10-£12.50

Open Etr/Apr-Oct Last arrival 23.00hrs Last departure noon

A well-equipped tourist park in an attractive location close to sea and ferries. This family park is an ideal boating centre, and offers two large rally areas in addition to the touring pitches, one with hardstandings and some electrics. A 15-acre site with 150 touring pitches, 35 hardstandings and 12 static. Indoor kitchen for tent campers

Leisure: ◕ ⚲ ⅏
Facilities: ℕ ⊙ ⓠ ☀ ⅃ ⌕ 🛉
Services: 🝘 🖳 ⱱ ⓥ 🖳 ⓘ ⊘ 🖽 → ∪ ⋒18 ⅄ ⛺
⌿ △ ▤ 🚍 🚍 📶 🅂

BALMINNOCH

Three Lochs Holiday Park
▶▶▶▶ 69%

DG8 0EP
☎ 01671 830304 📠 01671 830335
🅔 info@3lochs.co.uk

🔘 www.3lochs.co.uk

Dir: Follow A75 W towards Stranraer. Approx 10km from Newton Stewart rdbt turn R at small x-roads, follow signs to site, park 4m on R.

★ 🚐 £10.50-£12.50 🚙 £10.50-£12.50

🅰 £6-£10.50

Open Mar-Oct Booking Advisable bank hols & Jul-Aug Last arrival 22.00hrs Last departure 11.00hrs

A remote and very peaceful park set in beautiful moorland on the banks of Loch Heron, with further lochs and woodland nearby. This spacious grass park offers some fully-serviced pitches in a stunning location, and as well as being an ideal holiday spot for walkers and anglers, it provides a heated indoor swimming pool and well-equipped games room. A 22.5-acre site with 45 touring pitches, 20 hardstandings and 90 static. Snooker

Leisure: ♋ ◕ ⅏
Facilities: ℕ ⊙ ⓠ ☀ ⅃ ⌕ 🛉
Disabled facilities: toilets & showers
Services: 🝘 🖳 🖳 ⓘ ⊘ 🖽 → ⅄ ⌿

BRIGHOUSE BAY · NX64

Brighouse Bay Holiday Park
▶▶▶▶▶ 78%

DG6 4TS
☎ 01557 870267 📠 01557 870319
📧 aa@brighouse-bay.co.uk
🌐 www.gillespie-leisure.co.uk

Dir: Off B727 Kirkcudbright to Borgue or take A755 (Kirkcudbright) off A75 2m W of Twynholm. Clear signposting for 8m

★ ➡ £11.50-£15.50 ➡ £11.50-£15.50
▲ £11.50-£15.50

Open all year (rs Nov-Mar Leisure Club closed 2 days a wk) Booking Advisable Etr, Spring bank hol & Jul-Aug Last arrival 21.30hrs Last departure 11.30hrs

This grassy site enjoys a marvellous coastal setting adjacent to the beach and with superb sea views. Pitches have been imaginatively sculpted into the meadowland, with stone walls and hedges blending in with the site's mature trees. There are a large range of leisure facilities. A 30-acre site with 190 touring pitches, 120 static.

Mini golf, riding, fishing, quad bikes, 18-hole golf

Leisure: 🏊 🎣 🎢
Facilities: 🚿 📶 ⊙ 🍴 ✳ 📞 🛒 🏧 🐾
Disabled facilities: toilets & ramps
Services: 🔌 ✕ 🚽 🚐 🚿 🛒 🍴 🌀 🔋 → ∪ ♪9
♪ **Notes:** No single sex groups

CREETOWN · NX46

Creetown Caravan Park
▶▶▶ 71%

Silver Street DG8 7HU
☎ 01671 820377 📠 01671 820377
📧 beatrice.mcneill@btinternet.com
🌐 www.creetown-caravans.co.uk

Dir: Off A75 into Creetown, turn between clock tower & hotel, then L along Silver St

★ ➡ fr £9.50 ➡ fr £9.50 ▲ £9-£9.50

Open Mar-Oct Booking Advisable Jul & Aug Last arrival 22.30hrs Last departure 14.00hrs

A neat and well maintained park set in the village centre with views across the estuary on the coast of Wigtown Bay. Its attractive setting is beside the Moneypool Burn on the River Cree. Plenty of good amenities, including a heated outdoor swimming pool. A 3-acre site with 20 touring pitches, 50 static.

Games room

Leisure: 🏊 🎣 🎢
Facilities: 🚿 📶 ⊙ 🍴 ✳ 📞
Services: 🔌 🚐 🛒 🍴 🌀 🔋 → ♪ 🔋

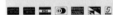

CREETOWN NX46

Castle Cary Holiday Park
▶▶▶▶▶ 74%

DG8 7DQ

☎ 01671 820264 📠 01671 820670

Dir: Signed with direct access off A75, 0.5m S of village

★ 🚐 £10.80-£13.50 🚚 £10.80-£13.50

🏕 £10.80-£13.50

Open all year (rs Oct-Mar reception/shop, no heated outdoor pool) Booking Advisable BH's & Jul-Aug Last arrival anytime Last departure noon

This attractive site in the grounds of Cassencarie House is sheltered by woodlands, and faces south towards Wigtown Bay. The park is in a secluded location with beautiful landscaping and excellent facilities. The bar/restaurant is housed in part of an old castle, and enjoys extensive views over the River Cree estuary. A 6-acre site with 50 touring pitches, 50 hardstandings and 26 static.

Mountain bike hire, crazy golf, coarse fishing

Leisure: 🎣 🏹 🔍 🎪 🛝

Facilities: 🚿 🏪 ⊙ 🌂 ❄ 🖎 🛒 🍴 🐕

Disabled facilities: toilet & wash hand basin

Services: 🅣 🍴 🛒 🚿 🗑 🔌 🛒 ♀ 🔥 ∅ 🖪 → 🛒 18 🎵 ◎

Notes: Dogs must be kept on leads at all times

▬▬ 🟦 📸 𝒮

CROCKETFORD NX87

Park of Brandedleys ▶▶▶▶ 75%

DG2 8RG

☎ 0845 4561759 📠 01556 690681

📧 brandedleys@holgates.com

🌐 www.holgates.com

Dir: In village on A75, from Dumfries towards Stranraer site on L up minor road, entrance 200yds on R

★ 🚐 £12.50-£21 🚚 £12.50-£21

🏕 £12.50-£21

Open all year (rs Nov-Mar bar/restaurant open Fri-Sun afternoon) Booking Advisable public hols & Jul-Aug Last arrival 22.00hrs Last departure noon

A well maintained site in an elevated position off the A75, with fine views of Auchenreoch Loch and beyond. This comfortable park offers a wide range of amenities, including a fine games room and a tastefully designed bar with adjoining bistro. Well placed for enjoying walking, fishing, sailing and golf. A 24-acre site with 80 touring pitches, 20 hardstandings and 63 static.

Badminton court & outdoor draughts

Leisure: 🎣 🏹 🔍 🎪

Facilities: 🚿 🏪 ⊙ 🌂 ❄ 🖎 🛒 🍴 🐕

Disabled facilities: toilet facilities & access to bar & restaurant

Services: 🅣 🍴 🛒 🚿 🗑 🔌 🛒 ♀ 🔥 ∅ 🖪 → 🎵

Notes: Guidelines issued on arrival

▬▬ 🟦 📸 𝒮

DALBEATTIE NX86

Glenearly Caravan Park

►►►► 71%

DG5 4NE

☎ 01556 611393 📠 01556 612058

Dir: From Dumfries take A711 towards Dalbeattie. Park entrance is past Edingham Farm on R, 200yds before boundary sign

★ 🚐 £8.50-£10.50 🚌 £8.50-£10.50 ⛺ £8.50-£10.50

Open all year Booking Advisable Jun-Aug Last arrival 19.00hrs Last departure noon

An excellent small park set in open countryside with panoramic views of Long Fell, Maidenpap and Dalbeattie Forest. The park is located in 84 beautiful acres of farmland which visitors are invited to enjoy.

A 10-acre site with 39 touring pitches, 17 hardstandings and 57 static.

Leisure: ● ⛛

Facilities: 🚿 ⊙ ✳ ☎ 🐕

Disabled facilities: Lockable bathroom with toilet, sink & shower

Services: 🚐 🗑 🔒 [⁝] → U ⛳18 ✈ 🎣 🛒

Notes: No single sex groups

ECCLEFECHAN NY17

Hoddom Castle Caravan Park

►►►►► 72%

Hoddom DG11 1AS

☎ 01576 300251 📠 01576 300757

[E] hoddomcastle@aol.com

[W] www.hoddomcastle.co.uk

Dir: From M74 J19, follow signs to site. From A75 W of Annan take B723 for 5m to signs

★ 🚐 £6-£11 🚌 £6-£11 ⛺ £6-£11

Open Etr or Apr-Oct (rs early season cafeteria closed) Booking Advisable bank hols & Jul-Aug Last arrival 21.00hrs Last departure 14.00hrs

The peaceful, well equipped park can be found on the banks of the River Annan, and offers a good mix of grassy and hard pitches, beautifully landscaped and blending into the surroundings. There are signed nature trails, maintained by the park's countryside ranger, a 9-hole golf course, trout and salmon fishing, and plenty of activity ideas for children.

A 28-acre site with 200 touring pitches, 150 hardstandings and 44 static.

Nature trails, visitor centre & 9-hole golf course

Leisure: ⚲ ● ⛛

Facilities: 🛏 🚿 ⊙ 🧺 ✳ ☎ 🛒 🏠 ⛩ 🐕

Disabled facilities: toilet, shower & access to bar, shop & cafeteria

Services: [T] ✕ 🍴 🚗 🚐 ⛛ 🗑 🍷 🔒 🌿 [⁝] → ⛳18 🎣 ◎ 💳 💳 💳 [S]

GATEHOUSE OF FLEET   NX55

Auchenlarie Holiday Park 🏕 70%

DG7 2EX

☎ 01557 840251 🖷 01557 840333

📧 enquiries@auchenlarie.co.uk

🌐 www.auchenlarie.co.uk

Dir: Direct access off A75, 5m W of Gatehouse of Fleet

★ 🚐 £20-£25 🚐 £20-£25 ▲ £15-£20

Open Mar-Oct Booking Advisable all year Last arrival 20.00hrs Last departure noon
A well-organised family park set on cliffs overlooking Wigtown Bay, with its own sandy beach. The tenting area, in sloping grass surrounded by mature trees, has its own sanitary facilities, while the marked caravan pitches are in paddocks with open views, and have high quality toilets. The leisure centre includes swimming pool, gym, solarium and sports hall. A 32-acre site with 49 touring pitches, 49 hardstandings and 350 static. Baby changing facilities

Leisure: 🏊 ⚽ 🎯 🅰

Facilities: 🛏 📵 ⊙ 🗑 ☀ 🍴 🛒 🏛 🛍 🖈

Disabled facilities: seperate toilet & shower rooms

Services: 🅣 ✕ 🖨 🔌 ⊕ 🍴 🚰 ◫ → ▸18 🌙 ◉

Notes: No single sex groups

▨ ▨ ◉ ▨ ▨ 🅢

GLENLUCE   NX15

Whitecairn Farm Caravan Park
▶▶▶ 69%

DG8 0NZ

☎ 01581 300267 🖷 01581 300434

📧 enquiries@whitecairncaravans.co.uk

🌐 www.whitecairncaravans.co.uk

Dir: Turn off A75 at Glenluce. Park signed from main street onto unclassified road to Glassnock Bridge. Park 1.5m N

★ 🚐 £10-£14 🚐 £10-£14 ▲ £10-£14

Open all year Last arrival 22.00hrs Last departure 11.00hrs
A well maintained farmland site, in open countryside with extensive views of Luce Bay. The park is next to the owner's working farm along a quiet country road. The refurbished toilets are centrally heated, and the laundry is well equipped. A 12-acre site with 10 touring pitches, 40 static.

Leisure: 🅰

Facilities: 📵 ⊙ 🗑 ☀ 🍴 🏛 🖈

Disabled facilities: ramp to caravan

Services: 🔌 🖨 ⊘ → 🚰 ▸18 🌙 🛒

GLENTROOL VILLAGE NX37

Glentrool Holiday Park ►►► 70%

Bargrennan DG8 6RN
☎ 01671 840280 📠 01671 840342
📧 enquiries@glentroolholidaypark.co.uk
🌐 www.glentroolholidaypark.co.uk

Dir: Leave Newton Stewart on A714 towards
Girvan, R at Bargrennan towards Glentrool.
Park on L before village.

★ 🚐 £8-£9 🚍 £8-£9 ▲ £5.50-£7

Open Mar-Oct Booking Advisable Jul-Aug &
BH's Last arrival 21.00hrs Last departure noon
*A small park close to the village of Glentrool,
and bordered by the Galloway National Park.
The keen owners are experienced
caravanners, and keep their site neat, clean
and freshly painted. The on-site shop is well
stocked. A 7.5-acre site with 14 touring
pitches, 12 hardstandings and 26 static.*

Leisure: ◕ ⋀
Facilities: ⋔ ⊙ ⊓ ※ � ⅃
Disabled facilities: toilet
Services: ▣ ⊕ ▮ ⌀ ⊞ → ⅃

GRETNA NY36

Bruce's Cave Caravan & Camping Park ►►► 72%

Cove Estate Kirkpatrick Fleming DG11 3AT
☎ 01461 800285 📠 01461 800269
📧 enquiries@bruce'scave.co.uk
🌐 www.brucescave.co.uk

Dir: Leave A/M74 J21 for Kirkpatrick Fleming
follow road N through village, pass Station Inn,
at London House Inn turn L and continue over
railway crossing to site entrance

★ 🚐 £8.50-£10 🚍 £8.50-£10 ▲ £7.50-£10

Open all year Apr-Nov (rs Nov-Mar Shop
closed) Last arrival 23.00hrs Last departure
19.00hrs
*The lovely wooded grounds of an old castle
and mansion are the setting for this pleasant
park. The mature woodland is a haven for
wildlife, and there is a riverside walk to
Robert the Bruce's Cave. The toilet block with
en suite facilities is of special appeal to
families. A 80-acre site with 75 touring
pitches, 60 hardstandings and 6 static.
BMX bike hire, course fishing, buggy travelcot*

Leisure: ⋀
Facilities: ↤ ⋔ ⊙ ⊓ ※ f ⅃ ⅏ 曲 芇 ㅏ
Disabled facilities: bathroom/shower/wc
& ramp
Services: ▣ ✕ ⊕ ⩒ ▮ ⌀ ⊞ → ∪ ⊩18 ⅃ 回
⚠ Notes: Dogs must be kept on lead

GRETNA NY36

Braids Caravan Park ▶▶▶▶ 68%

Annan Road DG16 5DQ
☎ 01461 337409 🖷 01461 337409
📧 enquiries@thebraidscaravanpark.co.uk
🌐 www.thebraidscaravanpark.co.uk

Dir: On B721, 0.5m from village on R,
towards Annan

★ 🚐 fr £11 🚐 fr £11 ▲ fr £8

Open all year Booking Advisable Jul-Sep Last
arrival 20.00hrs Last departure noon
*A well-maintained grassy site in the centre of
the village just inside Scotland. A new toilet
block has brought the facilities up to a high
standard, and a good number of hard pitches
further enhance this busy and popular park.
A 6-acre site with 74 touring pitches, 29
hardstandings and 5 static.*

Leisure: /A
Facilities: 🖭 ⊙ ⊠ ✳ ╲ 🚿
Disabled facilities: toilet & washbasin
Services: 🖽 🚐 ⅏ 🗑 🗎 ⌀ → ㅑ9 🌙 🖢

KIPPFORD NX85

Kippford Holiday Park ▶▶▶ 71%

DG5 4LF
☎ 01556 620636 🖷 01556 620607
📧 info@kippfordholidaypark.co.uk
🌐 www.kippfordholidaypark.co.uk

Dir: From Dalbeattie S on A710, site 3.5m on R,
300yds past jct for Kippford

🚐 £11-£17 🚐 £11-£17 ▲ £9-£11

Open all year Mar-Oct (rs Nov-Feb Booking
required, no shop) Booking Advisable at all
times Last departure noon
*An attractively landscaped park set in hilly
countryside close to the Urr Water estuary and
a sand/shingle beach, and with spectacular
views. The level touring pitches are on
grassed hardstands with private garden areas,
and many are fully serviced. The Doon Hill and
woodland walks separate the park from the
lovely Kippford village. A 18-acre site with 45
touring pitches, 22 hardstandings and 119
static.*
Golf, fly fishing, nature walk, playground,
cycle hire

Leisure: /A
Facilities: 🖭 ⊙ ⊠ ✳ ╲ 🖢 🚿 🗚 🧺
Disabled facilities: 2 combined
shower/toilet/washbasin rooms
Services: �# 🚐 ⅏ 🗑 🗎 ⌀ 🖽 → ∪ ㅑ9 🌙 ⊚ △
▥ ▤ 🛇

KIRKCUDBRIGHT NX65

Seaward Caravan Park
▶▶▶▶ 74%

Dhoon Bay DG6 4TJ
☎ 01557 870267 📠 01557 870319
🅔 aa@seaward-park.co.uk
🅦 www.gillespie-leisure.co.uk

Dir: 2m SW off B727 Borgue road

🚐 £9.50-£13.50 🚍 £9.50-£13.50
🏕 £9.50-£13.50

Open Mar-Oct (rs Mar-mid May & mid Sep-Oct swimming pool closed) Booking Advisable Spring bank hols & Jul-Aug Last arrival 21.30hrs Last departure 11.30hrs
A very attractive elevated park with outstanding views over Kirkcudbright Bay which forms part of the Dee Estuary. Access to a sandy cove with rock pools is just across the road. Facilities are well organised and neatly kept, and the park offers a very peaceful atmosphere. The leisure facilities of the other Gillespie parks are available to guests. A 8-acre site with 26 touring pitches, 30 static.
TV aerial hook-up, mini golf

Leisure: 🏊 🎣 ⚙ 🎮
Facilities: 🚿 🌳 ⊙ ⚑ ✳ ♿ 🛒 🌳 🔥
Disabled facilities: access to all facilities except launderette
Services: 🅟 🗑 🔌 ➔ ⛽ ₁₈ 🔧 ◎

MOFFAT NT00

Camping & Caravanning Club Site
▶▶▶ 73%

Hammerlands Farm DG10 9QL
☎ 01683 220436
🅦 www.campingandcaravanningclub.co.uk

Dir: Take Moffat sign from A74. After 1m turn R by the Bank of Scotland, R again in 200yds. Sign for site on R follow road round to site

★ 🚐 £12.95-£16.35 🚍 £12.95-£16.35
🏕 £12.95-£16.35

Open Mar-Nov Booking Advisable bank hols & peak periods Last arrival 21.00hrs Last departure noon
Well-maintained level grass touring site, with extensive views of the hilly countryside from many parts of the park. This busy stopover site is always well maintained, and looks bright and cheerful thanks to meticulous wardens. A 10-acre site with 180 touring pitches, 42 hardstandings.

Leisure: ⚙
Facilities: 🌳 ⊙ ⚑ ✳ ♿ 🛒 🌳 🔥
Disabled facilities: toilet, shower, washbasin & hand dryer
Services: 🅣 🅟 🔌 🗑 🔌 🗑 ➔ ⛽ ₁₈ 🔧 🅩
🏕 🍴 🍴 🍴 🏴 🅖

NEWTON STEWART   NX46

Creebridge Caravan Park
▶▶▶ 66%

Minnigaff DG8 6AJ
☎ 01671 402324 📠 01671 402324
📧 johnsharples@btopenworld.co.uk
🌐 www.creebridgecaravanpark.com

Dir: 0.25m E of Newton Stewart at Minnigaff on bypass, signed off A75

★ 🚐 £10 🚍 £10 ▲ £8-£10

Open Mar-Nov (rs Mar only one toilet block open) Booking Advisable Jul-Aug Last arrival 20.00hrs Last departure 10.00hrs
A small family-owned site a short walk from the town's amenities. The site is surrounded by mature trees, and offers good facilities including an indoor games room and outdoor draughts. A 5.5-acre site with 36 touring pitches, 12 hardstandings and 50 static.
Security street lighting

Leisure: ♠ ⚙
Facilities: 🏮⊙🔧🕾✳🐾🖾🎱🏌
Services: 🔌🖥💷🔋🚰🔌 → ♒ ▸18 🎯 ⌿

PALNACKIE   NX85

Barlochan Caravan Park
▶▶▶ 70%

DG7 1PF
☎ 01556 600256 📠 01557 870319
📧 aa@barlochan.co.uk
🌐 www.gillespie-leisure.co.uk

Dir: On A711 N of Palnackie, signposted.

★ 🚐 £9-£12 🚍 £9-£12 ▲ £9-£12

Open Apr-Oct (rs Apr-mid May & mid Sep-end Oct swimming pool) Booking Advisable Spring bank hol & Jul-Aug Last arrival 21.30hrs Last departure 11.30hrs
A small terraced park with quiet landscaped pitches in a level area backed by rhododendron bushes. There are spectacular views over the River Urr estuary, and the park has its own coarse fishing loch nearby. A 9-acre site with 20 touring pitches, 40 static.
Fishing, pitch & putt

Leisure: 🎣 ♠ ⚙ 🚪 □
Facilities: 🏮⊙🔧🕾✳🐾🖾🏌
Disabled facilities: toilet & ramps
Services: 🚽🔌🖥💷🔋🚰🔋 → ▸9 ⌿

PARTON NX67

Loch Ken Holiday Park ►►► 67%

DG7 3NE
☎ 01644 470282 📠 01644 470297
[E] office@lochkenholidaypark.freeserve.co.uk
[W] www.lochkenholidaypark.freeserve.co.uk

Dir: On A713, N of Parton

Open mid Mar-mid Nov (rs Mar/Apr (ex Etr) & late Sep-Nov restricted shop hours) Booking Advisable Etr, Spring bank hol & Jun-Aug Last arrival 20.00hrs Last departure noon

A busy and popular park with a natural water-borne emphasis, on the eastern shores of Loch Ken, with superb views. Family owned and run, it is in a peaceful and beautiful spot opposite the RSPB reserve, with direct access to the loch for boat launching. The park offers a variety of water sports, as well as farm visits and nature trails. A 7-acre site with 52 touring pitches, 33 static.

Bike, boat & canoe hire, fishing on loch

Leisure:
Facilities:
Disabled facilities: toilet & wash facilities, 2 specially designed caravans
Services: [T] →9

SANDHEAD NX04

Sands of Luce Holiday Park ►►►► 71%

Sands of Luce DG9 9JN
☎ 01776 830456 📠 01776 830477
[E] info@sandsofluceholidaypark.co.uk
[W] www.sandsofluceholidaypark.co.uk

Dir: From S & E - L off A75 onto B7084 signed Drummore. Site signed at jct with A716. From N - A77 through Stranraer towards Portpatrick, 2m & follow A716 signed Drummore, site signed in 5m

★ fr £12 fr £12 fr £12

Open Mar-Oct Booking Advisable Jul-Aug Last arrival 22.00hrs Last departure noon

A friendly site on grassy banks on the edge of a beautiful sandy beach, with lovely views across Luce Bay. Facilities are well-maintained and clean, and the area around the park is protected by the Nature Conservancy Council. A 30-acre site with 50 touring pitches, 160 static.

Boat launching

Leisure:
Facilities:
Disabled facilities: toilet, shower & wash basin, ramp to shop & games room
Services: →

VISA [S]

SANDYHILLS   NX85

Sandyhills Bay Leisure Park
▶▶▶ 71%

DG5 4NY

☎ 01557 870267 📠 01557 870319

📧 info@sandyhills-bay.co.uk

🌐 www.gillespie-leisure.co.uk

Dir: On A710 coast road, 7m from Dalbeattie, 6.5m from Kirkbean

★ 🚐 £9-£13 🚚 £9-£13 ▲ £9-£13

Open Apr-Oct Booking Advisable Spring bank hol & Jun-Aug Last arrival 21.30hrs Last departure 11.30hrs

A well maintained park in a superb location beside a 'blue-flag' beach, and close to many attractive villages. The flat, grassy site offers access to south-facing Sandyhills Bay and beach, and is sheltered by woods and hills. A 6-acre site with 26 touring pitches, 34 static.

Leisure: 🅰

Facilities: 🏕⊙🥤❄🔌🛒🎿🖥🐾

Services: 🚽🚿🛢🚰⚡🖥📶🖥→∪ি🛒

Notes: No single sex groups

▬▬ 🵵

Barnsoul Farm ▶▶▶ 67%

DG2 9SQ

☎ 01387 730249 📠 01387 730453

📧 barnsouldg@aol.com

🌐 www.barnsoulfarm.co.uk

Dir: Leave A75 between Dumfries & Crocketford at site sign onto unclass road signed Shawhead. At T-jct turn R & immediate L. Site 1m on L, follow Barnsoul signs.

★ 🚐 £8-£10 🚚 £8-£10 ▲ £8-£10

Open Apr-Oct (rs Feb-Mar chalets & bothies only) Booking Advisable Jul & Aug Last arrival 23hrs Last departure noon

A very spacious, peaceful and scenic farm site with views across open countryside in all directions. Set in 250 acres of woodland, parkland and farmland, and an ideal centre for touring this unspoilt area. It offers excellent kitchen facilities and a dining area for lightweight campers. A 10-acre site with 30 touring pitches, 8 hardstandings and 6 static.

Leisure: 🅰

Facilities: 🏕⊙🥤❄🔌🛒🏬🎿🐾

Disabled facilities: toilet and shower

Services: 🛢🚰🖥🖥→∪🛒🐾⚠

Notes: No unbooked groups, no loud noise after 11pm

SOUTHERNESS NX95

Southerness Holiday Village 71%

DG2 8AZ
☎ 01387 880256 ▤ 01387 880429
✉ enquiries@southerness.co.uk
ⓦ www.southerness.co.uk

Dir: From S take A75 from Gretna to Dumfries. From N take A74, exit at A701 to Dumfries. Take A710 coast road. Approx 16m, site easily seen

★ ⊟ £9-£15 ⊟ £9-£15 ▲ £9-£15

Open Mar-Oct Booking Advisable Jul-Aug & BH's Last arrival 22.00hrs Last departure 16.00hrs

A continually improving holiday centre with the emphasis on family entertainment. On-site facilities include all-weather pitches, a supermarket, large laundry and a leisure centre. A sandy beach on the Solway Firth is close by. A 8-acre site with 90 touring pitches, 59 hardstandings and 350 static.
Amusement centre, live entertainment & kids' club

Leisure: ⧎ ⬤ ⚠
Facilities: ⋒ ⊙ ⊙ ⚲ ※ ⚲ ⚑ ⚹ ⚸ ⟲
Disabled facilities: shower
Services: ⊡ ✕ ⚌ ⊟ ⊡ ⊠ ⚹ ⊘ ⊞ → ⌐18 ⚹ ◎
Notes: No single sex groups

STRANRAER NX06

Aird Donald Caravan Park
▶▶▶▶ 70%

London Road DG9 8RN
☎ 01776 702025 ▤
✉ enquiries@aird-donald.co.uk
ⓦ www.aird-donald.co.uk

Dir: Turn L off A75 on entering Stranraer, (signed). Opposite school, site 300yds

★ ⊟ £10 ⊟ £10 ▲ £4.80-£8.90

Open all year Last departure 16.00hrs
A spacious touring site, mainly grass but with tarmac hard-standing area, with pitches large enough to accommodate a car and caravan overnight without unhitching. On the fringe of town screened by mature shrubs and trees. Ideal stopover en route to Northern Irish ferry ports. A 12-acre site with 100 touring pitches.

Leisure: ⚠
Facilities: ⋒ ⊙ ⚲ ※ ⚹
Disabled facilities: toilet & washbasin
Services: ⊟ ⚹ ⊘ ⊞ → ∪ ⌐18 ⚹ ⚌ ⚹ ⊟ ⚙

DUNBAR NT67

Belhaven Bay Caravan & Camping Park ▶▶▶ 67%

Belhaven Bay EH42 1TU
☎ 01368 865956 📠 01368 865022
[E] belhaven@meadowhead.co.uk
[W] www.meadowhead.co.uk

Dir: Turn off A1 onto A1087 towards Dunbar. Situated within John Muir Park on L into Dunbar

★ 🚐 £8-£15 🚙 £8-£15 ⛺ £6-£15

Open Mar-Oct Last departure 12.00hrs
Small, well maintained park in a sheltered location and within walking distance of the beach. This is an excellent spot for seabird watching, and there is a good rail connection with Edinburgh from Dunbar. A 40-acre site with 52 touring pitches, 11 hardstandings and 64 static.
internet café

Leisure: ⛹
Facilities: 🚿 ⊙ 🔌 ✳ 📞 🛒 🍴 ⛩ 🐕
Disabled facilities: shower, wc & washbasin
Services: [T] 🚐 ⚡ ▣ → ∪ ⛳18 🎣 ◎ ⛵
Notes: Dogs on leads at all times

AMERICAN EXPRESS VISA Switch

DUNBAR NT67

Thurston Manor Holiday Home Park ▶▶▶▶▶ 76%

Innerwick EH42 1SA
☎ 01368 840643 📠 01368 840261
[E] mail@thurstonmanor.co.uk
[W] www.thurstonmanor.co.uk

Dir: 4m S of Dunbar, signposted off A1

★ 🚐 £10-£14 🚙 £10-£14 ⛺ £10-£14

Open Mar-8 Jan (rs 1-23 Dec wknds only) Booking Advisable Etr, bank hols & high season Last arrival 21.00hrs Last dep noon
A pleasant park set in 250 acres of unspoilt countryside. The touring and static areas of this large park are in separate areas. The main touring area occupies an open, level position, and the toilet facilities are modern and exceptionally well maintained. The park boasts a well-stocked fishing loch, a heated indoor swimming pool, steam room, sauna, jacuzzi, mini-gym and fitness room and seasonal entertainment. A 250-acre site with 100 touring pitches, 45 hardstandings and 420 static.
Private lake, pony trekking, fitness room

Leisure: 🏊 ♠ ⛹ 📺
Facilities: 🚿 ⊙ 🔌 ✳ 📞 🛒 ⛩ 🐕
Disabled facilities: ramps, shower & chair lift in pool
Services: [T] ✖ 🧺 🐕 🚐 ▣ 🍷 🔋 🌿 [⇕] → 🎣
Notes: No single sex groups under age 25

AMERICAN EXPRESS VISA Barclays CONNECT DELTA Switch

LONGNIDDRY NT47

Seton Sands Holiday Village
68%

EH32 0QF
☎ 01875 813333 📠 01875 813531

Dir: Take A1 to Tranent slip road, then B6371 to Cockenzie & R onto B1348. Park 1m on L

★ 🚐 🚙

Open Mar-Oct Last arrival 23.00hrs Last departure noon

A well equipped holiday centre with plenty of organised entertainment, clubs and bars, restaurants, and sports and leisure facilities. A multi-sports court, heated swimming pool, and various play areas ensure that there is plenty to do, and there is lots to see and do in and around nearby Edinburgh. The good touring facilities are separate from the large static areas. A 1.75-acre site with 60 touring pitches, 648 static.

Leisure: 🏊 🏌 🎯 /🎱

Facilities: 🌂 ⊙ 🎇 🐧 🛝 🚾 🎣 🛒 ⼽

Services: 🛈 ✕ 🍺 🔌 💷 🖾 🔧 🖉 🛢 → U ⼽18 ⛽

MUSSELBURGH NT37

Drum Mohr Caravan Park ►►►►
73%

Levenhall EH21 8JS
☎ 0131 665 6867 📠 0131 653 6859
✉ bookings@drummohr.org
ⓦ www.drummohr.org

Dir: Leave A1 at jct with A199 towards Musselburgh, at rdbt turn R onto B1361 signed Prestonpans, take 1st L & site 400yds

★ 🚐 £12-£14.50 🚙 £12-£14.50

▲ £12-£14.50

Open Mar-Oct Booking Advisable Jul-Aug Last arrival 20.00hrs Last departure noon

This attractive park is sheltered by mature trees on all sides, and carefully landscaped within. The park is divided into separate areas by mature hedging and planting of trees and ornamental shrubs. Pitches are generous in size, and there are a number of fully serviced pitches with water, waste, electricity and hardstanding. The first-class amenities are immaculately clean and maintained to a very high standard. A 9-acre site with 120 touring pitches, 50 hardstandings and 5 static.

Leisure: /🎱

Facilities: 🌂 ⊙ 🎇 ❄ 🐧 🛝 ⼽

Disabled facilities: toilet & shower

Services: 🛈 🍺 ⼳ 🖾 🖉 🛢 → ⼽18 ⛽

NORTH BERWICK NT58

Meadowhead's Tantallon Caravan & Camping ►►►► 71%

Dunbar Road EH39 5NJ
☎ 01620 893348 📠 01620 895623
[E] tantallon@meadowhead.co.uk
[W] www.meadowhead.co.uk

Dir: Off A198 Dunbar road

★ 🚐 £10-£17 🚙 £10-£17 ⛺ £10-£15

Open Mar-Oct Booking Advisable Jul-Aug Last arrival 20.00hrs Last departure noon

A large and well-serviced grassland site with outstanding views across the water to the coast of Fife. The site is convenient for the town and Edinburgh, with direct access to the beach and many local attractions. A 10-acre site with 147 touring pitches, 10 hardstandings and 60 static.

Putting green

Leisure: 🔍 ⛺ ▭

Facilities: 🚿 ⊙ 🧺 ✲ 📞 🏪 ⛱ 🐕

Disabled facilities: toilets, shower & caravan holiday home

Services: [T] 🔧 🚰 🗑 🧯 🧺 ▦ → ∪ ⛳18 ⚓

VISA Barclays CONNECT

EDINBURGH NT27

Meadowheads Mortonhall Caravan & Camping Park ►►►► 69%

38 Mortonhall Gate Frogston Road East EH16 6TJ
☎ 0131 664 1533 📠 0131 664 5387
[E] mortonhall@meadowhead.co.uk
[W] www.meadowhead.co.uk

Dir: Take city by-pass to jct with A702 & follow signs to Mortonhall

🚐 £10-£16 🚙 £10-£16 ⛺ £10-£16

Open mid Mar-5 Jan (rs Nov-Jan shop closed) Booking Advisable Jul-Aug Last arrival 22.00hrs Last departure noon

This park is set in the 200-acre Mortonhall country estate to the south of Edinburgh, and provides a spacious camping area with grass-based and hard pitches, some with full service, bordered by mature trees. The excellent facilities are kept spotlessly clean and well cared for. A 22-acre site with 250 touring pitches, 43 hardstandings and 19 static.

Leisure: 🔍 ⛺ ▭

Facilities: 🚿 ⊙ 🧺 ✲ 📞 🏪 🐕

Disabled facilities: toilets, showers & caravan holiday home

Services: [T] 🍴 🔧 🚰 🗑 🍷 🧯 🧺 ▦ → ∪ ⛳18 🎥

Notes: No single sex groups

VISA Barclays CONNECT

ST ANDREWS NO51

Craigtoun Meadows Holiday Park
►►►►► 78%

Mount Melville KY16 8PQ
☎ 01334 475959 ▤ 01334 476424
🄴 craigtoun@aol.com
🄦 www.craigtounmeadows.co.uk

> **Dir:** From M90 J8 onto A91 to St Andrews. After Guardbridge R for Strathkinness. At 2nd x-rds after Strathkinness L for Craigtoun

★ ⌑ ⊞ £14.50-£21 ▲ £14.50-£18.50

Open Mar-Oct (rs Mar-Etr & Sep-Oct shops and restaurant open shorter hrs) Booking Advisable BH's & Jun-Aug Last arrival 21.00hrs Last departure noon
An attractive site set unobtrusively in mature woodlands, with large pitches in hedged paddocks. All pitches are fully serviced. The modern toilet block provides cubicled en suite facilities as well as spacious showers, baths, disabled facilities and baby changing areas. Located near the sea and sandy beaches. A 32-acre site with 58 touring pitches, 58 hardstandings and 157 static.

Leisure: ९ ◕ ⋀
Facilities: ➡ ⋔ ⋒ ⊙ ⬲ ✳ ℄ 🖳 🅐 🗇
Disabled facilities: toilet, shower & washbasin
Services: 🆔 ✕ ⬥ ⬗ 🖲 🄸 🄰 ⬀ 🄴 → ∪ ⌂18 🛢 ♪
Notes: ✗ No groups under 18yrs
▦ ▦ ▨ 𝒮

BOAT OF GARTEN NH91

Campgrounds of Scotland
►►► 67%

PH24 3BN
☎ 01479 831652 ▤ 01479 831450
🄴 briangillies@totalise.co.uk
🄦 www.campgroundsofscotland.com

> **Dir:** From A9 take A95 to Grantown-on-Spey, then follow signs for Boat of Garten. Park is situated in centre of village.

★ ⬲ £10.50-£17.50 ⬗ £10.50-£17.50
▲ £5.50-£15

Open all year Booking Advisable 26 Dec-2 Jan & 25 Jul-7 Aug Last arrival 22.00hrs Last departure 11.00hrs
A very attractive site in a beautiful location with outstanding views. Young trees and bushes enhance the park, which is set in mountainous woodland near the River Spey and Loch Garten. A 3.5-acre site with 37 touring pitches, 20 hardstandings and 60 static.

Leisure: ⋀
Facilities: ⋒ ⊙ ⬲ ✳ ℄ 🖳
Disabled facilities: toilet facilities
Services: 🆔 ✕ ⬥ 🖲 🄸 ⬀ 🄴 → ⌂18 ♪

CANNICH — NH33

Cannich Caravan and Camping Park ►►► 64%

IV4 7LN

☎ 01456 415364 📠 01456 415364
📧 enquiries@highlandcamping.co.uk
🌐 www.highlandcamping.co.uk

Dir: On A831, 200yds SE of Cannich Bridge

★ 🚐 £6.50-£9.50 🚐 £6.50-£9.50 ▲ £6-£8

Open Mar-Oct (rs Dec-Feb Winter opening by arrangement) Booking Advisable Jul & Aug Last arrival 23.00hrs Last departure noon *Quietly situated in Strath Glass, close to the River Glass and Cannich village. This family-run park has attractive mountain views, and is set in ideal walking and naturalist country. A 6-acre site with 43 touring pitches, 15 hardstandings and 15 static.*
Mountain bike hire

Leisure: 🎣 🛝 ☐
Facilities: 🅿 ⊙ 🌰 ☀ ⚲ 🚿 🎨
Disabled facilities: shower & toilet
Services: 🖵 �

Notes: Dogs must be kept on leads

DORNOCH — NH78

Grannie's Heilan Hame Holiday Park 🏕 68%

Embo IV25 3QD

☎ 01862 810383 & 810753 📠 01862 810368
📧 enquiries@parkdean.com
🌐 www.parkdean.com

Dir: A949 to Dornoch, turn L in square & follow signs for Embo

★ 🚐 £10-£23 🚐 £8-£23 ▲ £8-£19.50

Open Mar-Oct Booking Advisable Jul-Aug & BH's Last arrival 23.30hrs Last departure 10.00hrs
A holiday centre with a wide range of leisure facilities, including indoor swimming pool with sauna and solarium, separate play areas for under and over fives, putting green, tennis courts and very much more. The sanitary facilities are clean and well maintained, and the park is set on the beach yet handy for the Highlands. A 60-acre site with 200 touring pitches, 158 static.
Spa bath, sauna, solarium & mini ten-pin bowling

Leisure: 🏊 🎱 🎣 🛝
Facilities: 🅿 ⊙ 🌰 ☀ ⚲ 🐾 🎯
Services: 🖵 ✗ 🍴 🚐 🎨 🚰 🖵 → �18 🚗 ◎
Notes: No single sex groups under 25yrs

GAIRLOCH   NG87

Sands Holiday Centre ▶▶▶ 65%

IV21 2DL
☎ 01445 712152 🖷 01445 712518
🄴 litsands@aol.co.uk
🆆 www.highlandcaravancamping.co.uk

Dir: 3m W of Gairloch on B8021

★ 🚐 £8.50-£12 🚙 £8.50-£12 ▲ £8.50-£12

Open 20 May-10 Sep (rs Apr-19 May & 11
Sep-mid Oct shop & some toilets closed)
Booking Advisable Jul-Aug Last arrival
22.00hrs Last departure noon
*Close to a sandy beach with a panoramic
outlook towards Skye, a well maintained park
with very good facilities. A large laundry and
refitted toilets make this an ideal family site.
A 51-acre site with 360 touring pitches, 20
static.*
Boat slipway

Leisure: ♦ ⋀
Facilities: ⋔ ⊙ ⌦ ※ ⌕ ⚲ ⌂ ⊼ ⼡
Disabled facilities: toilet & shower room
Services: ⛽ ⌸ ⊟ 🗑 ⌲ ⊞ → ∪ ⍾ 🌣 ⌡

▭ ▭ ▭ ▰ ⑤

GLENCOE   NN15

Invercoe Caravan & Camping Park
▶▶▶▶ 70%

PH49 4HP
☎ 01855 811210 🖷 01855 811210
🄴 invercoe@sol.co.uk
🆆 www.invercoe.co.uk

Dir: Turn R off A82 at Glencoe Hotel onto B863
for 0.25m

★ 🚐 £14-£18 🚙 £14-£18 ▲ £14-£18

Open all year Booking Advisable Jul-Aug for
electric hook ups Last departure noon
*Level grass site set on the shore of Loch
Leven, with excellent mountain views. The
area is ideal for both walking and climbing,
and also offers a choice of several freshwater
and saltwater lochs. Convenient for the good
shopping at Fort William. A 5-acre site with
60 touring pitches, 5 static.*

Leisure: ⋀
Facilities: ⋔ ⊙ ⌦ ※ ⌕ ⚲ ⼡
Disabled facilities: toilet facilities
Services: ⛽ ⌸ ⊟ 🗑 ⌲ ⊞ → ⍾ 🌣 ⌡
Notes: No large group bookings

▭ ▭ ⑤

GRANTOWN-ON-SPEY NJ02

Grantown-on-Spey Caravan Park
▶▶▶▶ 75%

Seafield Avenue PH26 3JQ
☎ 01479 872474 📠 01479 873696
📧 team@caravanscotland.com
🌐 www.caravanscotland.com

Dir: From town turn N at Bank of Scotland Park, straight ahead from 0.25m

🚐 £13-£16 🚐 £13-£16 ⚠ £10-£15
Open 29 Mar-Oct Booking Advisable Etr, May day, Spring BH & Jul-Aug Last arrival 22.00hrs
A scenic park in a mature setting near the river, surrounded by hills, mountains, moors and woodland. The park is very well landscaped, and is in a good location for golf, fishing, mountaineering, walking, sailing and canoeing. Fully-serviced pitches are sought after, and there is a luxury toilet block. A 29-acre site with 120 touring pitches, 60 hardstandings and 45 static.
Picnic tables, football pitch

Leisure: ♦ ⚠
Facilities: 🏧 ⊙ ⏱ ✳ 📞 🛒 🖶 🎋 🐾
Disabled facilities: toilet, shower & washbasin
Services: 🆃 🚽 🚙 🕳 🖻 🛢 🖉 🖂 → ∪ ⋒18 ⤵

INVERNESS NH64

Torvean Caravan Park
▶▶▶▶▶ 75%

Glenurquhart Road IV3 8JL
☎ 01463 220582

Dir: 1m W of Inverness on A82 at Tomnahuich Canal bridge

🚐 🚐
Open Apr-Oct Booking Advisable Jun-Aug Last arrival 21.00hrs Last departure noon
Located on the Caledonian Canal, this park is quiet and well secluded yet close to Inverness town centre. Every feature of the park has been planned, constructed and maintained to the highest standard, The landscaped grounds are immaculate, and there is a good quality children's play area. A 3-acre site with 50 touring pitches, 10 static.

Leisure: ⚠
Facilities: 🏧 ⊙ ⏱ ✳ 📞 🖂
Services: 🆃 🚙 🖻 🛢 🖉 🖂 → ∪ ⋒18 ✚ ♨ ⤵ 🛒
Notes: No single sex groups, no motorcycles, no traders

NAIRN NH85

Camping & Caravanning Club Site
▶▶▶ 68%

Delnies Wood IV12 5NX
☎ 01667 455281
🌐 www.campingandcaravanningclub.co.uk

Dir: Off A96 Inverness to Aberdeen Rd. 2m W of Nairn

★ 🚐 £10.75-£13.65 🚐 £10.75-£13.65
🅰 £10.75-£13.65

Open Apr-Nov Booking Advisable BH's & peak periods Last arrival 21.00hrs Last departure noon
An attractive site set amongst pine trees, with facilities maintained to a good standard. The park is close to Nairn with its beaches, shopping, golf and leisure activities. A 14-acre site with 75 touring pitches, 3 hardstandings.

Leisure: ♦ ⚗
Facilities: 🅁 ⊙ ⛱ ❄ 🔧 🗄 ⼎
Services: 🕕 🚰 📶 🛢 🗑 ⊞ → ∪ 🍴9 🗡 ⬛

▭ ▭ ▭ ▭ 🛒 🆔

TAIN NH78

Dornoch Firth Caravan Park
▶▶▶ 67%

Meikle Ferry South IV19 1JX
☎ 01862 892292 📠 01862 892292
🅴 will@dornochfirth.co.uk
🌐 www.dornochfirth.co.uk

Dir: Follow A9 N past Tain to Meikle ferry rdbt, straight across onto A836 then immediate 1st R.

★ 🚐 £11-£14 🚐 £11-£14 🅰 £6.50-£8.50

Open all year (rs Nov-Mar static caravans closed) Booking Advisable Jul-Aug Last arrival 22.00hrs Last departure noon
A pleasant family site with open views of Dornoch Firth and the lovely coastal and country scenery. The immaculately maintained facilities and lovely flower beds make this a delightful base for touring the immediate vicinity with its many places of interest. A 2-acre site with 30 touring pitches, 10 hardstandings and 20 static.
Bar/Restaurant adjacent to site

Leisure: ⚗
Facilities: 🅁 ⊙ ⛱ ❄ 🔧 ⼎
Services: 🚰 📶 🗑 ⊞ → ∪ 🍴18 🗡 🗡 ◎ ⬠

▭ ▭ 🆔

Broomfield Holiday Park ▶▶▶ 65%

West Shore Street IV26 2UR
☎ 01854 612020 🖨 01854 613151
🄴 sross@broomfieldhp.com
🆆 www.broomfieldhp.com

Dir: Take the 2nd R past Harbour

★ 🚐 fr £12 🚌 fr £11 ▲ £8-£12

Open Etr/Apr-Sep Booking Advisable for group bookings only Last departure noon
Set right on the water's edge of Loch Broom and the open sea, with lovely views of the Summer Isles. The toilets are very well equipped and clean, and the park is close to the harbour and town centre with their restaurants, bars and shops. A 12-acre site with 140 touring pitches.

Leisure: ⚆

Facilities: 🅁 ⊙ ✳ 🛒 🖃 🏧

Disabled facilities: toilet & washbasin

Services: 🔌 🗑 🗓 🖃 → ⁑9 ✕ ✈ ◎

▩ ▩ ▩ ⑤

Ardmair Point Camping & Caravan Park ▶▶▶ 70%

IV26 2TN
☎ 01854 612054 🖨 01854 612757
🄴 sales@ardmair.com
🆆 www.ardmair.com

Dir: 3m N of Ullapool on A835, enter at telephone box on beach at Ardmair

★ 🚐 fr £10 🚌 fr £10 ▲ fr £10

Open May-Sep Booking Advisable Jul-Aug Last arrival 21.00hrs Last departure noon
An excellent touring site on small peninsula, with superb mountain and sea loch views, and an interesting children's play area. Pitches adjoin and overlook the beaches, and there is a shop. A 7-acre site with 60 touring pitches, 14 hardstandings.
Boats, canoes for hire

Leisure: ⚆

Facilities: 🅁 ⊙ 🕴 ✳ ✆ 🐕 🏇

Disabled facilities: toilet & shower

Services: 🎀 🔌 🗓 🛢 🖉 🖃 → ⁑9 ✕ ✈

▩ ▩ ▨ ⑤

HIGHLAND

CRAIGELLACHIE — NJ24

Camping & Caravanning Club Site ▶▶▶ 68%

AB38 9SD

☎ 01340 810414

🌐 www.campingandcaravanningclub.co.uk

Dir: From S leave A9 at Carrbridge, follow A95 to Grantown-on-Spey, leaving Aberlour on A941. Take next L turn B9102 signed Archiestown. Site 3m on L

★ 🚐 £12.95-£16.35 🚙 £12.95-£16.35

▲ £12.95-£16.35

Open Apr-Nov Booking Advisable bank hols & peak periods Last arrival 21.00hrs Last departure noon

A very nice rural site with views across meadowland towards Speyside, and the usual high Club standards. Hardstandings are well screened on an upper level, and grass pitches with more open views are sited lower down. A 7-acre site with 75 touring pitches, 13 hardstandings.

Leisure: 🅰

Facilities: 🏪 ⊙ 🤚 ✳ ⚞ 🐴 ⭐

Disabled facilities: toilet, shower, washbasin & hand dryer

Services: 🛨 🍺 🔌 ⚗ 🔣 ⚑ 🔣 → 🔣 🔣

▧ ▧ ▧ ▧ 🅂

FOCHABERS — NJ35

Burnside Caravan Park ▶▶▶ 65%

IV32 7ET

☎ 01343 820511 📠 01343 821291

Dir: Located 0.5m E of town off A96

★ 🚐 £10-£14 🚙 £10-£14 ▲ £10

Open Apr-Oct Booking Advisable Jul-Aug Last departure noon

Attractive site in a tree-lined, sheltered valley with a footpath to the village. Owned by the garden centre on the opposite side of the A96. A 5-acre site with 51 touring pitches, 30 hardstandings and 101 static.

Jacuzzi & sauna

Leisure: 🤽 ⚡ 🅰 ⚞

Facilities: 🏪 ⊙ 🤚 ⚞ 🐴 ⭐

Disabled facilities: toilet & shower

Services: 🛨 🍺 🔌 ⚗ → ∪ ⌐18 🔣 ◎

▧ ▧ ▧ 🅂

LOSSIEMOUTH NJ27

Silver Sands Leisure Park ►►►► 67%

Covesea West Beach IV31 6SP
☎ 01343 813262 📠 01343 815205
✉ holidays@silversands.freeserve.co.uk
🌐 www.travel.to/silversands

Dir: From Lossiemouth follow B9040 2m W to site

🚐 🚗 ⛺

Open Apr-Oct (rs Apr, May & Oct shops & entertainment restricted) Booking Advisable Jul-Aug Last arrival 22.00hrs Last dep noon
A large holiday park with entertainment for all during the peak season, set on the links between the coast road and the shore of the Moray Firth. Touring campers and caravans are catered for in three areas: one offers de-luxe facilities including water, drainage, electricity and hard and grassed area, while the other areas are either unserviced or include electric hook-ups and water. A well-stocked shop sells holiday gear, and there is a clubroom and bar plus takeaway food outlet. A 7-acre site with 140 touring pitches, 200 static.
Children's entertainment

Leisure: 🔦 🔦 🛝 🎱
Facilities: 🚿 🌂 🏪 ⊙ 🍴 ※ 🛡 🖾 🛒 🌲 🍴
Services: 🗓 ✕ 🏪 💷 🛢 🗜 💡 🖾 → ∪ ⊓ 18 ⚡
⚡ ◎ ⚠ **Notes:** Over 14yrs only in bar

🟦 ▬ 🟥 🆑

CRAIGNURE NM73

Shieling Holidays ►►► 68%

PA65 6AY
☎ 01680 812496
🌐 www.shielingholidays.co.uk

Dir: From ferry, L onto A849 to Iona. After 400mtrs L at church, follow campsite signs towards sea

★ 🚗 £12.50-£14 🚐 £12.50-£14
⛺ £12.50-£14
Open Apr-Oct Booking Advisable Spring bank hol & Jul-Aug Last arrival 22.00hrs Last departure noon
A lovely site on the water's edge with spectacular views, and less than 1m from ferry landing. There is a campers' shelter in a disused byre which is especially popular in poor weather. Hardstandings and service points are provided for motorhomes, and there are astro-turf pitches for tents. The park now offers bunkhouse accommodation for families. A 7-acre site with 65 touring pitches, 20 hardstandings and 15 static.
Adventure playground, bikes

Leisure: 🔦 🛝 🎱
Facilities: 🌂 ⊙ 🍴 ※ 🛡 🖾 🛒 🌲 🍴
Disabled facilities: facilities from 2005
Services: 🗓 🏪 🚰 🛢 🗜 → 🍴 9 ⚡
🟦 ▬ 🟥 🆑

MOTHERWELL   NS75

Strathclyde Country Park Caravan Site ►►► 66%

366 Hamilton Road ML1 3ED
☎ 01698 266155 ▤ 01698 252925
ⓔ strathclydepark@northlan.gov.uk

Dir: From M74 J5, direct access to park

🚐 �঩ Å

Open Apr-Oct Booking Advisable Jun-Aug Last arrival 22.30hrs Last departure noon
A level grass site situated in a country park amidst woodland and meadowland with lots of attractions. A large grass area caters for 150 tents, while 100 well-screened pitches, with electrics and some hardstandings, are also available. A site with 250 touring pitches, 100 hardstandings.

Leisure: 🛝
Facilities: 🖍 ⊙ ❤ 🝒 🚿 🌂 🏞 🛖
Disabled facilities: toilets & showers
Services: ✕ 🚮 🖳 🏧 🗎 ⌀ → ∪ ⌂18 ⚲ 👪 🎵
△ Notes: Site rules available on request by post

BLAIR ATHOLL   NN86

Blair Castle Caravan Park ►►►►► 73%

PH18 5SR
☎ 01796 481263 ▤ 01796 481587
ⓔ mail@blaircastlecaravanpark.co.uk
ⓦ www.blaircastlecaravanpark.co.uk

Dir: From A9 jct with B8079 at Aldclune, then NE to Blair Atholl. Park on R after bridge

★ 🚐 £10-£13 🚛 £10-£13 Å £8-£13

Open Mar-Nov Booking Advisable bank hols & Jul-Aug Last arrival 21.30hrs Last dep noon
Attractive site set in impressive seclusion within the Atholl Estate, surrounded by mature woodland and the River Tilt. Although a large park, the various groups of pitches are located throughout the extensive parkland, and each has its own sanitary block with all-cubicled facilities of a very high standard. There is a choice of grass pitches, hard standings, or fully-serviced pitches. This park is particularly suitable for the larger type of motorhome. A 32-acre site with 280 touring pitches, 105 static.
Internet gallery

Leisure: 🎣 🛝
Facilities: 🏊 🖍 ⊙ 🝒 ✳ ❤ 🝒 🌂 🏞 🛖
Disabled facilities: toilets and bathroom
Services: 🆃 🚮 🖳 ⋁ 🗎 ⌀ ⌷ → ∪ ⌂9 🎵 ◎
Notes: No unaccompanied young or single sex groups

🏧 💳 🔲 🔲 🔲 🔲

KENMORE   NN74

Kenmore Caravan & Camping Park
▶▶▶▶ 67%

PH15 2HN
☎ 01887 830226 📠 01887 829059
📧 info@taymouth.co.uk
🌐 www.taymouth.co.uk

Dir: A9 to Ballinluig, W on A827 to Aberfeldy.
6m to Kenmore, over bridge park on R

★ 🚐 £11.50-£12.50 🚉 £11.50-£12.50
⛺ £11-£12

Open mid Mar-end Oct Booking Advisable mid
Jul-mid Aug & wknds Last arrival 22.00hrs
Last departure 14.00hrs
*A pleasant riverside site with an air of
spaciousness and a very good licensed
bar/restaurant. Set on the banks of the River
Tay, it has good views of the mountains, as
well as offering on-site river fishing (plus
fishing in a nearby loch). The modern facilities
include a laundry, family bathrooms, and two
children's playgrounds. A 14-acre site with
160 touring pitches, 60 hardstandings and 60
static.*
Cycle hire, boat hire

Leisure: ⚲ ♠ ⚠ ▢
Facilities: ⋔ ⊙ ⚒ ※ ⚰ 🖳 ⏦ ⛲
Disabled facilities: shower & toilet facilities
Services: ▥ ✕ 🛢 🛒 🖤 ⚱ 🖤 🍽 ♀ ⌀ ⍉ 🖾 → ∪
⚑18 (par 70) ⅄ ♣ △
Notes: Families and couples only

▬▬ ▬▬

PERTH   NO12

Camping & Caravanning Club Site
▶▶▶ 65%

Scone Palace Scone PH2 6BB
☎ 01738 552323
🌐 www.campingandcaravanningclub.co.uk

Dir: Follow signs for Scone Palace. Once
through continue for 2m. Turn L following site
signs. After 1m L into Racecourse Rd. Site
entrance from car park

★ 🚐 £11.75-£15.35 🚉 £11.75-£15.35
⛺ £11.75-£15.35

Open Mar-Nov Booking Advisable bank hols &
peak periods Last arrival 21.00hrs Last
departure noon
*A delightful woodland site, sheltered and well
screened from the adjacent Scone Racecourse.
Two very good amenity blocks are built of
timber and blend in well with the
surroundings of mature trees. New super
pitches and access roads add to the park's
appeal. A 16-acre site with 150 touring
pitches, 43 hardstandings.*

Leisure: ♠ ⚠
Facilities: ⋔ ⊙ ⚒ ※ ⚰ 🖳 🖾 ⛲
Disabled facilities: toilet, shower
& washbasin
Services: ▥ 🖤 🛢 🛒 ⌀ 🖾 → ∪ ♣ △
▬▬ ▬▬ ▬▬ ▬▬ 🄂

PITLOCHRY NN95

Faskally Caravan Park
▶▶▶▶ 70%

PH16 5LA
☎ 01796 472007 📠 01796 473896
✉ ehay@easynet.co.uk
🌐 www.faskally.co.uk

Dir: 1.5m N of Pitlochry on B8019

★ 🚐 £13-£14.40 🚗 £13-£14.40
🛖 £10.50-£12.10

Open 15 Mar-Oct Booking Advisable Jul-Aug
Last arrival 23.00hrs
A large park attractively divided into various sections by mature trees, occupying a rural position in gently-sloping meadowland beside the tree-lined River Garry. The excellent amenities include a leisure complex with heated indoor swimming pool, sauna and steam room, bar, restaurant and indoor amusements. There are extensive countryside views, and this park is well placed as a centre for touring, being close to but unaffected by the A9. A 27-acre site with 200 touring pitches, 130 static.
Steam room, spa & sauna

Leisure: 🎿 🌊 ⚱
Facilities: ⛫ ⊙ 🍴 ❄ 📞 🛒
Disabled facilities: toilets, showers, ramps
Services: 🖵 ✕ 🔌 💷 🚻 🛢 ⊘ → ∪ ⌐18 🍴 🔌
Notes: Tents-no single sex groups

🔲 🔲 💳 📶 🅢

TUMMEL BRIDGE NN75

Tummel Valley Holiday Park 🏚
67%

PH16 5SA
☎ 01882 634221 & 0870 420 2991
📠 01882 634302
✉ enquiries@parkdean.com
🌐 www.parkdean.com

Dir: From Perth take A9 N to bypass Pitlochry. 3m after Pitlochry turn onto B8019 signed to Tummel Bridge. Park in 11m on L

🚐 £10-£23 🚗 £8-£23
Open Apr-Oct Booking Advisable at all times
Last arrival 21.00hrs Last departure 10.00hrs
A well-developed site amongst mature forest in an attractive valley, beside the famous bridge. Play areas and the bar are sited alongside the river, and this is an ideal base in which to relax. A 55-acre site with 33 touring pitches, 152 static.
Bicycle hire, crazy golf, fishing rod hire

Leisure: 🎿 🌊 ⚱
Facilities: ⛫ ⛫ ⊙ 🍴 ❄ 📞 🛒 🛢 🎍 🍴
Disabled facilities: full toilet facilities
Services: ✕ 🛗 🔌 💷 🚻 🛢 → 🔌
Notes: No single sex groups under 25 yrs/
mixed groups under 21yrs

🔲 🔲 💳 📶 🅢

COLDINGHAM NT96

Scoutscroft Holiday Centre ►►►► 74%

St Abbs Road TD14 5NB
☎ 018907 71338 📠 018907 71746
[E] holidays@scoutscroft.co.uk
[W] www.scoutscroft.co.uk

Dir: From A1 take B6438 signed Coldingham & Scoutscroft is on the R, on the edge of Coldingham village

★ 🚐 £12-£17 🚙 £12-£14 ⛺ £8-£15

Open Mar-Oct (rs Mar-May, Sep, Oct Crofters Bar only, arcade wknds only) Booking Advisable BH's, Jul-Aug, wknds Last arrival mdnthrs Last departure noon

A large family-run site with good facilities and plenty of amenities including bars, restaurant, and children's games rooms. Set on the edge of the village and close to the sea, with separate areas and toilet blocks for tourers. A 16-acre site with 60 touring pitches, 32 hardstandings and 120 static.

Sub Aqua Centre, cash machine

Leisure: 🔍 ⛛ ▭
Facilities: 🛁 🚿 ⊙ ⚲ ✳ 📞 ⚒ 🏪 ⛩
Disabled facilities: toilets for walking disabled
Services: [T] ✕ 🍴 🚐 🗑 🍷 🔒 🌿 ⊞ → U ⛳18 ⚓
⛵ **Notes:** No single sex groups or groups under 21yrs

💳 💳 💳 💳 💳

JEDBURGH NT62

Jedwater Caravan Park ►►► 65%

TD8 6PJ
☎ 01835 869595 📠 01835 869595
[E] jedwater@clara.co.uk
[W] www.jedwater.co.uk

Dir: Located 3.5m S of Jedburgh on A68

🚐 🚙 ⛺

Open Etr-Oct Booking Advisable high season Last arrival mdnthrs Last departure noon

A quiet riverside site in a beautiful valley, run by resident owners as a peaceful retreat. The touring area is separate from statics, and this site is an ideal touring base. A 10-acre site with 60 touring pitches, 60 static.

Bike hire, trampoline, football field

Leisure: 🔍 ⛛ ▭
Facilities: 🚿 ⊙ ⚲ ✳ 📞 ⚒ 🏪 ⛩ 🐕
Services: [T] 🚐 🗑 🔒 🌿 ⊞ → U ⛳9 ⚓

KELSO NT73

Springwood Caravan Park ▶▶▶▶ 73%

TD5 8LS
☎ 01573 224596 📠 01573 224033
📧 admin@springwoodestate.co.uk
🌐 www.springwoodestate.co.uk

Dir: On A699, signed Newton St Boswells

★ 🚐 £16 🚐 £16

OAY 26 Mar-4 Oct Booking Advisable bank hols & Jul-Aug Last arrival 23.00hrs
Set in a secluded position on the banks of the tree-lined River Teviot, this well-maintained site enjoys a pleasant and spacious spot in which to relax. It is under the careful supervision of the owners, and offers a high standard of modern toilet facilities which are mainly contained in fully cubicled en suite units. Floors Castle and the historic town of Kelso are close by. A 4-acre site with 35 touring pitches, 220 static.

Leisure: ◀ ⋀

Facilities: 🏪 ⊙ ঀ ✳ ⚄ ⅄

Disabled facilities: toilets & showers

Services: 🚐 🖫 🛢 → ∪ ⅃18 ⛺ 🥄 🦺

Notes: No dogs if camping in tent

▬ ▬ ▦ ▨ 🆂

PEEBLES NT24

Rosetta Caravan & Camping Park ▶▶▶ 68%

Rosetta Rd EH45 8PG
☎ 01721 720770 📠 01721 720623

Dir: Signposted from all main roads from Peebles.

🚐 🚐 ⅄

Open Apr-Oct Booking Advisable BH's, Jul & Aug Last arrival 23.00hrs Last departure 15.00hrs
A pleasant site set in 40 acres of parkland around a late Georgian mansion and stable block. Some of the stable buildings house the toilet facilities and bar. A 25-acre site with 160 touring pitches, 48 static.
Bowling & putting greens

Leisure: ◀ ⋀ ▢

Facilities: 🏪 ⊙ ঀ ✳ ⚄ 🖴 ⅄

Services: 🖫 🚐 🖫 ঀ 🛢 ⌀ → ∪ ⅃18 🥄 🦺

PEEBLES NT24

Crossburn Caravan Park
▶▶▶▶ 68%

Edinburgh Road EH45 8ED
☎ 01721 720501 📠 01721 720501
📧 enquiries@crossburncaravans.co.uk
🌐 www.crossburncaravans.com

ⓘ Dir: 0.5m N of Peebles on A703

🚐 £12-£13 🚐 £12-£13 ▲ £12-£13
Open Apr-Oct Booking Advisable Jul-Aug Last
arrival 21.00hrs Last departure 14.00hrs
*A level site in a peaceful and relatively quiet
location, despite the proximity of the main
road which partly borders the site, as does the
Eddleston Water. There are lovely views
across the Eddleston Valley, and the park is
well stocked with trees, flowers and shrubs
which give it a particularly rural feel. Facilities
are maintained to a high standard, and the
site shop, which is comprehensively stocked,
also keeps a large supply of caravan spares.
Fully-serviced pitches are available, as well as
a choice of grass or hard pitches. A 6-acre site
with 45 touring pitches, 15 hardstandings and
85 static.*
9-hole putting course & mountain bikes for
hire

Leisure: ♦ /瓜
Facilities: ⊯ 🏠 ⊙ 🔌 🕯 🚰 🎋 🛒 🐾
Services: 🔟 🛒 🚐 🔓 🛢 🧴 🔜 → ∪ 🅿18 🎵
Notes: Dogs must be kept on leads,
no single sex groups

▨ ▨ ▧ 🄂

SELKIRK NT42

Victoria Park Caravan & Camping
Park ▶▶▶ 65%

Victoria Park Buccleuch Road TD7 5DN
☎ 01750 20897 📠 01750 20897
Dir: From A707/A708 N of town, cross river
bridge & take 1st L, then L again

🚐 🚐 ▲
Open Apr-Oct Booking Advisable Jul-Aug Last
arrival 20.00hrs Last departure 14.00hrs
*A consistently well-maintained site with good
basic facilities forming part of public park and
swimming pool complex close to River Ettrick.
A 3-acre site with 60 touring pitches.*
Fitness room & sauna

Leisure: 🏊 /瓜
Facilities: 🏠 ⊙ 🔌 ✴ 🕯 🚰 🛒 🎋 🐾
Disabled facilities: pool hoist & ramps
Services: ✕ 🚐 🛢 🛢 🔜 → ∪ 🅿9 🎵

 🄂

AYR · NS32

Craig Tara 70%

KA7 4LB
☎ 01292 265141
🌐 www.british-holidays.co.uk

★

Open Mar-Oct Last arrival 22.00hrs Last departure noon
A large, well-maintained holiday centre with on-site entertainment and sporting facilities to suit all ages. The touring area is set apart from the main complex at the entrance to the park, and campers can use all the facilities, including Water World, soft play areas, sports zone, show bars, and supermarket with in-house bakery. There is a bus service to Ayr. A 213-acre site with touring pitches.

Facilities: 🖧

Services: 🔘

COYLTON · NS41

Sundrum Castle Holiday Park 68%

KA6 5JH
☎ 01292 570057 📠 01292 570065
✉ enquiries@parkdean.com
🌐 www.parkdeanholidays.com

Dir: Just off A70, 4m E of Ayr near Coylton

★ 🚐 £12.50-£23.50 🚐 £12.50-£23.50
⛺ £9-£19.50

Open Mar-Oct Booking Advisable all times Last arrival 21.00hrs Last departure noon
A large family holiday centre, with plenty of on-site entertainment, just a 10 minute drive from the centre of Ayr. Leisure facilities include an indoor swimming pool, mini 10-pin bowling, clubs for teenies and teenagers, and the touring area is adequate and clean. A 30-acre site with 32 touring pitches, 190 static. Amusement arcade

Leisure: 🏊 ⚾ 🎢 ▢

Facilities: 🎣 ☉ ⚒ 📞 🖧

Services: ✕ 🛒 🚐 🐶 🗑 ♈ 🔌 ⊘ → ∪ ⌖18 ♨ ✈

Notes: No single sex groups, no under 25s, dogs kept on leads

---

MAYBOLE NS20

Camping & Caravanning Club Site ►►► 69%

Culzean Castle KA19 8JX
☎ 01655 760627
Ⓦ www.campingandcaravanningclub.co.uk

Dir: From N on A77 in Maybole turn R onto B7023 (signed Culzean & Maidens) and in 100yds turn L. Site 4m on R

★ ⊞ £12.95-£16.35 ⊞ £12.95-£16.35

▲ £12.95-£16.35

Open Mar-Nov Booking Advisable bank hols & peak periods Last arrival 21.00hrs Last departure noon

A mainly level grass park with some gently sloping pitches and hard stands along the bed of an old railway, situated at the entrance to the castle and country park. The park is surrounded by trees on three sides and with lovely views over Culzean Bay. A 10-acre site with 90 touring pitches, 25 hardstandings.

Leisure: ⚙

Facilities: ⚑ ⊙ ☜ ☀ ☰ ⛲

Disabled facilities: toilet, shower, washbasin & razor point

Services: ⬚ ⊕ ⊠ ⊟ ∅ ⊞ → ∪ ੧ ⌂

MAYBOLE NS20

The Ranch ►►►► 73%

Culzean Road KA19 8DU
☎ 01655 882446 ▤ 01655 882446
Ⓦ www.theranchscotland.co.uk

Dir: Situated on B7023, 1m S of Maybole towards Culzean

⊞ ⊞ ▲

Open Mar-Oct & wknds in winter Booking Advisable bank hols & Jul-Sep Last arrival 20.00hrs Last departure noon

A very attractive privately-run park with two distinct areas for statics and tourers, but all sharing the same excellent leisure facilities, including a heated indoor swimming pool. Touring pitches are fully serviced, and screened for privacy by shrubs and rose bushes. A 9-acre site with 40 touring pitches, 40 hardstandings and 68 static.

Mini gym, sauna & sunbed

Leisure: ≋ ♦ ⚙

Facilities: ⚑ ☜ ☀ ☰ ⛲ ☰ ⛲ ⌂

Disabled facilities: toilet

Services: ⬚ ⊕ ⊠ ⊟ → ∪ ੧ ⌦ ⌐

ABERFOYLE NN50

Trossachs Holiday Park
►►►► 73%

FK8 3SA
☎ 01877 382614 📠 01877 382732
📧 info@trossachsholidays.co.uk
🌐 www.trossachsholidays.co.uk

Dir: Access on E side of A81, 1m S of jct A821 & 3m S of Aberfoyle

★ 🚐 £12.50-£16 🚎 £12.50-£16

🅰 £12.50-£16

Open Mar-Oct Booking Advisable anytime Last arrival 21.00hrs Last departure noon
An imaginatively designed terraced site offering a high degree of quality all round, with fine views across Flanders Moss. All touring pitches are fully serviced with water, waste, electricity and TV aerial, and customer care is a main priority. Set in 20 acres of ground within the Queen Elizabeth Forest Park, with plenty of opportunities for cycling off-road on mountain bikes, which can be hired or bought on site. A 40-acre site with 65 touring pitches, 45 hardstandings and 70 static.
Cycle hire

Leisure: ✦ ⚠ 🖵
Facilities: 🅁 ⊙ 🔧 ✳ 🌡 🛒 🎍 🍴
Services: 🎦 🕹 🖾 🛢 🐟 🗑 → 🎵18 ⚓ ♫

⬛ ⬛ 🔀 🆂

AA CAMPSITE OF THE YEAR FOR SCOTLAND 2005

BALMAHA NS49

Camping & Caravanning Club Site
►►►► 74%

Milarrochy Bay G63 0AL
☎ 01360 870236
🌐 www.campingandcaravanningclub.co.uk

Dir: From A811 Balloch to Stirling Rd, take Drymen turning. In Drymen take B837 for Balmaha. After 5m road turns sharp R up steep hill. Site 1.5m further on

★ 🚐 £12.95-£16.35 🚎 £12.95-£16.35

🅰 £12.95-£16.35

Open Mar-Nov Booking Advisable BH's & peak periods Last arrival 21.00hrs Last departure noon
On the quieter side of Loch Lomond next to the 75,000-acre Queen Elizabeth Forest, this attractive site offers very good facilities. The toilets, including disabled and family rooms, are fitted to a high standard. A 12-acre site with 150 touring pitches, 25 hardstandings.

Leisure: ⚠
Facilities: 🅁 ⊙ 🔧 ✳ 🛒 🎍 🍴
Disabled facilities: toilet, washbasin, razor point & shower
Services: 🎦 🕹 🖾 🛢 🐟 🗑 → ♫ 🛒 🛆

⬛ ⬛ ⬛ 🔀 🆂

CALLANDER · NN60

Gart Caravan Park ▶▶▶▶ 69%

The Gart FK17 8LE
☎ 01877 330002 ▤ 01877 330002
✉ enquiries@gart-caravan-park.co.uk
ⓦ www.gart-caravan-park.co.uk

Dir: 1m E of Callander on A84

★ ⊞ fr £16 ⊞ fr £16

Open Etr or Apr-15 Oct Booking Advisable BHs
& Jul-Aug Last arrival 22.00hrs Last departure
11.30hrs
*A well-screened caravan park bordered by
trees and shrubs, near to the Queen Elizabeth
Park amidst ideal walking and climbing
country. A feature of the park is the careful
attention to detail in the maintenance of
facilities, and the owners are very helpful and
friendly. A 26-acre site with 122 touring
pitches, 66 static.*
Fishing on site

Leisure: ⋔
Facilities: ⋒⊙✳⚊⛵ ✠
Disabled facilities: toilet
Services: ☎ ⅋ ▢ ⅟ → ∪ ⋒18 ↺ ⊿
Notes: No single sex groups,
no unaccompanied young people,
no commercial vehicles

▬ ▬ ▧ ⑤

BALLOCH · NS38

Lomond Woods Holiday Park ▶▶▶▶ 70%

Old Luss Road G83 8QP
☎ 01389 755000 ▤ 01389 755563
✉ lomondwoods@holiday-parks.co.uk
ⓦ www.holiday-parks.co.uk

Dir: Turn R off A82, 17m N of Glasgow on to
A811 Stirling to Balloch road. Park 0.25m in
Balloch

★ ⊞ £13-£18 ⊞ £13-£18 ▲ £13-£18

Open all year Booking Advisable all dates Last
arrival 21.00hrs Last departure noon
*A mature park with well-laid out pitches
screened by trees and shrubs, surrounded by
woodland and hills. The park is within
walking distance of 'Loch Lomond Shores', a
complex of leisure and retailing experiences
which is the main gateway to Scotland's first
National Park. Amenities include an inspiring
audio-visual show, open-top bus tours, and
loch cruises. A 13-acre site with 110 touring
pitches, 80 hardstandings and 35 static.*
Leisure suite with sauna, spa bath & bike hire

Leisure: ⚓ ⋔ ▱
Facilities: ➔⋒⊙❄✳⚊⛵⊟✠
Disabled facilities: toilet & shower room
Services: ▣ ➔ ⅋ ⅟ ▢ ✎ ⊞ → ∪ ⋒18 ↺
⊿ ⊿ **Notes:** No single sex groups

▬ ▬ ▧ ⑤

EAST CALDER   NT06

Linwater Caravan Park ▶▶▶ 73%

West Clifton EH53 0HT
☎ 0131 333 3326 📄 0131 333 1952
📧 linwater@supanet.com
🌐 www.linwater.co.uk

Dir: Signposted along B7030 off M9 J1 or from
Wilkieston on A71

★ 🚐 £11-£13 🚐 £11-£13 ▲ £9-£11

Open late Mar-late Oct Booking Advisable
BH's & Aug Last arrival 21.00hrs Last
departure noon

*A farmland park in a peaceful rural area
within easy reach of Edinburgh. The very good
facilities are housed in a Scandinavian-style
building, and are well maintained by resident
owners. Nearby are plenty of pleasant
woodland walks. A 5-acre site with 60 touring
pitches, 8 hardstandings.*

Leisure: 🛝

Facilities: 🅁 ⊙ 🕾 ✳ 🌢 🛉

Disabled facilities: toilet & shower

Services: 🚱 🖃 🛢 🖉 🖯 → ∪ ↑27 ⅄ 🍴 🛒

🔲 🔲 🅂

BRYNSIENCYN   SH46

Fron Caravan & Camping Park
▶▶▶ 67%

LL61 6TX
☎ 01248 430310 📄 01248 430310
📧 froncaravanpark@brynsiencyn.fsnet.co.uk

Dir: Off A4080 Llanfair to Newborough road,
1m W of Brynsiencyn

🚐 🚐 ▲

Open Etr-Sep Booking Advisable Spring bank
hol & Jul-Aug Last arrival 22.00hrs Last
departure noon

*A quiet family site in a pleasant rural area,
ideally situated for touring Anglesey and
North Wales. The farm buildings which house
facilities are well maintained and mainly
attractive. A 5.5-acre site with 60 touring
pitches.*

Leisure: 🔩 🔍 🛝

Facilities: 🅁 ⊙ 🕾 ✳ 🌢 🛒 🛉

Disabled facilities: wheelchair access,
toilet, shower & washbasin

Services: 🅣 🚱 🛢 🖉 🖯 → ∪ ↑9 🍴

Notes: No single sex groups

DULAS

Tyddyn Isaf Caravan Park ►►►► 70%

Lligwy Bay LL70 9PQ
☎ 01248 410203 📠 01248 410667
📧 enquiries@tyddynisaf.demon.co.uk
🌐 www.tyddynisaf.demon.co.uk

Dir: Take A5025 through Benllech to Moelfre rdbt, L towards Amlwch to Brynrefail village. Turn R opposite craft shop. Park 0.5m down lane on R

★ 🚐 £14-£18 🚃 £14-£18 ⋏ £9.50-£15

Open Mar-Oct (rs Mar-Jul & Sep-Oct Bar & shop opening limited) Booking Advisable May bank hol & Jun-Aug Last arrival 22.00hrs Last departure 11.00hrs

A beautifully situated family park on quite steeply rising ground adjacent to sandy beach, and with magnificent views over Lligwy Bay. Access to the long sandy beach is by private footpath, or by car. Other paths lead to Dulas Bay and the small harbour village of Moelfre with its lifeboat station and seawatch centre. The park has very good toilet facilities, a well-stocked shop, and a clubhouse serving meals and takeaway food. A 16-acre site with 80 touring pitches, 20 hardstandings and 50 static. Baby changing unit

Leisure: 🅰 ☐
Facilities: ⋒ ⊙ 🕄 ※ ⅃ 🖳 ⼞ ⼙
Services: ⊤ ✕ ♨ ♥ 🔋 ⍾ ∅ ⊡ → ∪ ⼗18 ⼂
♩ Notes: No groups or single sex parties, dogs must be kept on leads

LLANBEDRGOCH
SH58

Ty Newydd Leisure Park ►►► 67%

LL76 8TZ
☎ 01248 450677 📠 01248 450711
📧 mike@tynewydd.com
🌐 www.tynewydd.com

Dir: A5025 from Brittania Bridge. After passing through Pentraeth village bear L at layby. Site 0.75m on R

★ 🚐 £10-£25 🚃 £10-£25 ⋏ £10-£25

Open Whit-mid Sep (rs Mar-Whit & mid Sep-Oct club/shop wknds only, outdoor pool closed) Booking Advisable Etr, Whit & Jul-Aug Last arrival 23.30hrs Last departure 10.00hrs

A low-density park with many facilities including a heated outdoor pool, a country club with restaurant, a good playground, and a fitness centre with pool and gym for which an extra charge is made. A 4-acre site with 48 touring pitches, 15 hardstandings and 60 static.

Sauna & Jacuzzi

Leisure: ⌇ ⼂ ◣ 🅰
Facilities: ⋒ ⊙ 🕄 ※ ⅃ 🖳 ⼞ ⼙
Disabled facilities: toilet, shower & handbasin
Services: ⊤ ✕ ♨ ⊡ 🔋 ♥ ⍾ ∅ ⊡ → ∪ ⼗9 ⼂ ♨

ISLE OF ANGLESEY

MARIAN-GLAS   SH58

Home Farm Caravan Park ►►►► 80%

LL73 8PH

☎ 01248 410614 ▤ 01248 410900

✉ enq@homefarm-anglesey.co.uk

🌐 www.homefarm-anglesey.co.uk

Dir: Located on A5025, 2m N of Benllech, with park entrance 300mtrs beyond church

★ ⊞ £10.25-£22 ⊞ £10.25-£20

▲ £10.25-£18

Open Apr-Oct Booking Advisable bank hols Last arrival 21.00hrs Last departure noon

A first class park in an elevated and secluded position sheltered by trees. The peaceful rural setting affords views of farmland, the sea, and the mountains of Snowdonia. The modern toilet block has helped to win numerous awards, and there are excellent play facilities for children both indoors and out. The area is blessed with sandy beaches, and local pubs and shops cater for everyday needs. A 6-acre site with 98 touring pitches, 21 hardstandings and 84 static.

Indoor adventure playground

Leisure: ⚲ ⚓ ⚤ ▭

Facilities: ➔ ⬡ ☉ ⚇ ✳ ⚲ ⚲ ⚲ ⚲

Disabled facilities: toilets & showers

Services: 🖵 ⚏ ⟟ ⬛ 🅰 ⬒ → ∪ ⌿18 ⚏ △

▨▨ ▨▨ ⬕ ▨ ⑤

PENTRAETH   SH57

Rhos Caravan Park ►►► 67%

Rhos Farm LL75 8DZ

☎ 01248 450214 ▤ 01248 450214

Dir: Site on L of A5025, 1m N of Pentraeth

★ ⊞ £8-£14 ⊞ £8-£14 ▲ £8-£12

Open Etr-Oct (rs Mar shop & showers restricted) Booking Advisable Spring bank hol & Jul-Aug Last arrival 22.00hrs Last departure 16.00hrs

A warm welcome awaits families at this spacious park on level, grassy ground with easy access to the main road to Amlwch. This 200-acre working farm has a games room, two play areas and farm animals to keep children amused, with good beaches, pubs, restaurants and shops nearby. The two toilet blocks are kept to a good standard by enthusiastic owners who are constantly improving the facilities. A 15-acre site with 98 touring pitches, 66 static.

Leisure: ⚤

Facilities: ⬡ ☉ ✳ ⚲ ⚲ ⚲ ⚲

Services: 🖵 ⚏ ⬛ 🅰 ⬒ → ∪ ⌿9 ⚏ ⚏ ⚏

Notes: No single sex groups

▨▨ ▨▨ ▨ ▨ ⑤

RHOSNEIGR
SH37

Ty Hen ►►► 63%

Station Road LL64 5QZ
☎ 01407 810331 📠 01407 811261
🅴 bernardtyhen@hotmail.com
🆆 www.tyhen.com

Dir: A55 across Anglesey. At exit 5 follow signs
to Rhosneigr, at clock turn R. Entrance adjacent
to Rhosneigr railway station.

★ ⊞ £14-£16 ⊞ £14-£16 ⚑ £8-£12

Open Mar-Oct Booking Advisable All year Last
arrival 21.00hrs Last departure noon
*Attractive seaside position near a large fishing
lake and riding stables, in lovely countryside.
A smart new toilet block is a welcome
addition to this popular family park with
friendly owners always on hand. A 7.5-acre
site with 38 touring pitches, 3 hardstandings
and 42 static.*
Fishing, family room

Leisure: ⚘ ⚘ ⚐
Facilities: 🏪 ⊙ ⚘ ✳ ⚘ ⚘
Disabled facilities: 2x (toilet, shower
& washbasin)
Services: ⚘ 🔳 ⊞ → ∪ ⌐18 ⚘ ⚘
Notes: 1 motor vehicle per pitch, dogs on
leads, children in tents/tourers/statics by 10pm
🔳 🔳 🆂

LLANGADOG
SN72

Abermarlais Caravan Park
►►► 67%

SA19 9NG
☎ 01550 777868
🅴 www.ukparks.co.uk/abermarlais

Dir: With direct access off A40 on Llandeilo
sideof A482, 6m W of Llandovery

★ ⊞ fr £8.50 ⊞ fr £8.50 ⚑ fr £8.50

Open 15 Mar-15 Nov (rs Nov, Dec & Mar 1
toilet block, water point no hot water)
Booking Advisable bank hols & 15 Jul-Aug
Last arrival 23.00hrs Last departure noon
*An attractive, well-run site with a welcoming
atmosphere. This part-level, part-sloping park
is in a wooded valley on the edge of the
Brecon Beacons National Park, beside the
River Marlais. A 17-acre site with 88 touring
pitches, 2 hardstandings.*
Volleyball, badminton court & softball
tennis net

Leisure: ⚐
Facilities: 🏪 ⊙ ✳ ⚘ ⚘ ⚘
Services: 🔳 ⚘ ▮ ⊘ ⊞ → ∪ ⚘
Notes: Dogs must be kept on leads, no open
fires, silence from 23.00hrs-8.00hrs

🔳 🔳 ⓞ 🔳 🆂

ISLE OF ANGLESEY / CARMARTHENSHIRE

NEWCASTLE EMLYN SN34

Afon Teifi Caravan & Camping Park

►►► 64%

Pentrecagal SA38 9HT
☎ 01559 370532
[E] afon.teifi@virgin.net
[W] www.afonteifi.co.uk

Dir: Signed off A484, 2m E of Newcastle Emlyn

★ £11-£12 £11-£12 ▲ £8-£12

Open Apr-Oct (rs Nov-Mar when facilities limited, no toilet block) Booking Advisable peak periods Last arrival 23.00hrs

Set on the banks of the River Teifi, a famous salmon and sea trout river, this park is secluded with good views. Family owned and run, and only 2 miles from the market town of Newcastle Emlyn. A 6-acre site with 110 touring pitches, 10 hardstandings and 10 static.

15 acres of woodland, fields & walks

Leisure:

Facilities:

Disabled facilities: toilets & shower

Services: → 9

NEWCASTLE EMLYN SN34

Cenarth Falls Holiday Park

►►►►► 73%

Cenarth SA38 9JS
☎ 01239 710345 01239 710344
[E] enquiries@cenarth-holipark.co.uk
[W] www.cenarth-holipark.co.uk

Dir: Off A484 on outskirts of Cenarth village, on Cardigan side.

£13-£22 £13-£22 ▲ £13-£22

Open Mar-9 Jan Booking Advisable bank hols & Jul-Aug Last arrival 20.00hrs Last departure 11.00hrs

A high quality park with excellent facilities, close to the village of Cenarth where the famous salmon and sea trout River Teifi cascades through the Cenarth Falls Gorge. A well landscaped park with a indoor heated swimming pool and fitness suite, and a restaurant and bar. A 2-acre site with 30 touring pitches, 30 hardstandings and 89 static.

Pool table, health & leisure complex

Leisure:

Facilities:

Disabled facilities: toilet & shower, ramps ot restaurant/bar

Services: →

Notes: No single sex groups, no dogs from 16 Jul-4 Sep

RHANDIRMWYN SN74

Camping & Caravanning Club Site
▶▶▶ 69%

SA20 0NT
☎ 01550 760257
Ⓦ www.campingandcaravanningclub.co.uk

Dir: From Llandovery take A483 L at sign
Rhandirmwyn, 7, L at post office, site on L
before river.

★ ♠ £12.95-£16.35 ♠ £12.95-£16.35

▲ £12.95-£16.35

Open Mar-Nov Booking Advisable bank hols &
peak periods Last arrival 21.00hrs Last
departure noon

*On the banks of the Afon Tywi near Towy
Forest and the Llyn Brianne reservoir, this
secluded park has superb views from all
pitches. The park is divided into paddocks by
mature hedging, and facilities and grounds
are very well tended. A 11-acre site with 90
touring pitches, 7 hardstandings.*

Leisure: ⚼

Facilities: ⚲ ⊙ ☜ ✻ ℂ 🏛 ⌦

Disabled facilities: toilet, shower, razor
point & washbasin

Services: 🔲 ⚡ ⅄ 🔋 🗎 ⧄ ⊞ → ◢ ⚍ △

ABERAERON SN46

Aeron Coast Caravan Park
▶▶▶ 69%

North Road SA46 0JF
☎ 01545 570349
Ⓔ aeroncoastcaravanpark@aberaeron.freeserve.co.uk
Ⓦ www.aberaeron.co.uk/aeron_coast/acoast2.htm

Dir: On A487 coastal road on northern edge of
Aberaeron, signposted. Filling station at
entrance

★ ♠ £10.50-£14 ♠ £10.50-£14

▲ £10.50-£14

Open Mar-Oct Booking Advisable bank &
school hols Last arrival 23.00hrs Last
departure 11.00hrs

*Set in a spacious 22 acres of coastal parkland,
with direct entry onto the beach and only
200yds from the attractive small town and
harbour. This park has a wide range of indoor
and outdoor activities, and caters well for the
whole family. A 22-acre site with 100 touring
pitches, 23 hardstandings and 200 static.
Indoor leisure rooms & entertainment hall*

Leisure: ⌇ ⚲ ⚌ ⚼ ⌨

Facilities: ⚲ ⊙ ✻ ℂ 🔋

Disabled facilities: toilet & shower
(plus toilet in pool area)

Services: 🔲 🍺 ⚡ ⅄ ⚡ 🛢 🗎 ⧄ ⊞ → ◢ ◎ △

Notes: Families only, no motorcycles, no
letting static caravans

BETTWS EVAN SN34

Pilbach Holiday Park ▶▶▶ 65%

SA44 5RT

☎ 01239 851434 📠 01239 851969

[E] info@pilbach.com

[W] www.pilbach.com

Dir: S on A487, turn L onto B4333

★ 🚐 £12-£20 🚙 £12-£20 ⛺ £8-£20

Open Mar-Oct (rs Mar-Spring BH & Oct swimming pool closed) Booking Advisable Spring BH & Jul-Aug Last arrival 22.00hrs Last departure noon

Set in secluded countryside, with two separate paddocks and pitches clearly marked in the grass. This park makes a good base for visiting this very scenic area and nearby seaside resorts. It has a heated outdoor swimming pool, and entertainment in the club two or three times a week in high season. A 15-acre site with 65 touring pitches, 10 hardstandings and 70 static.

Bike/skateboard parks

Leisure: 🏊 🎾 🛝

Facilities: 🚿 ⊙ 🧺 ✳ 📞 🏪 🛒 🐕

Services: [T] 🍴 🍟 🚐 🧼 🍷 🔥 🧊 [+] → ∪ ⛳18 🎬 🎣 💳

BORTH SN69

Brynowen Holiday Park 🏨 65%

SY24 5LS

☎ 01970 871366

[E] gmbrynowen@park-resorts.com

[W] www.park-resorts.com

★ 🚐 £5-£25 🚙 £5-£25

Open Mar-14 Jan Last arrival 20.00hrs Last departure 10.00hrs

Enjoying spectacular views across Cardigan Bay and the Cambrian Mountains, a small touring park in a large and well-equipped holiday centre. The well-run park offers a wide range of organised activities and entertainment for all the family from morning until late in the evening. A long sandy beach is a few minutes' drive away. A 52-acre site with 16 touring pitches, 480 static.

Leisure: 🏊 🛝

Facilities: 🚿 🧺 📞 🏪 🐕

Disabled facilities: purpose built toilet, caravans

Services: 🍴 🍟 🚐 🧼 🍷 → ⛳18

Notes: No single sex groups/groups under 18 years

💳

CROSS INN

Camping & Caravanning Club Site
▶▶▶ 67%

Llwynhelyg SA44 6LW
☎ 01545 560029
Ⓦ www.campingandcaravanningclub.co.uk

Dir: Left from A487 Cardigan-Aberystwyth at Synod Inn. Take A486 signed Newquay. In 2m in village of Cross Inn, L after Penrhiwgaled Arms Pub. Site 0.75m on R

★ ⊕ £11.75-£15.35 ⊕ £11.75-£15.35
▲ £11.75-£15.35

Open Mar-Oct Booking Advisable bank hols & peak periods Last arrival 21.00hrs Last departure noon

An excellent, attractive touring site in an elevated rural position with extensive country views. A footpath from the site joins the coastal walk, and the pretty village of New Quay is only a short drive away. A 14-acre site with 90 touring pitches, 6 hardstandings.

Leisure: ⚙

Facilities: ⛱ ⊙ ⚲ ⚡ ✳ ⚟ ⛽ ⛏ ⛊

Disabled facilities: toilet, shower & washbasin

Services: ☎ ⚙ ⚓ ⛽ ⚓ ∅ ⚡ → ∪ ⌂18 ⚓ ⚙

▨ ▨ ▨ ▨ ▨ ⑤

BETWS-YN-RHOS

Hunters Hamlet Caravan Park
▶▶▶ 70%

Sirior Goch Abergele LL22 8PL
☎ 01745 832237 ▤ 01745 833978
Ⓔ huntershamlet@aol.com
Ⓦ www.caravancampingsites.co.uk/conwy /huntershamlet.htm

Dir: From A55 westbound A547 into Abergele. Straight through lights, 1st L by George & Dragon onto A548. 2.75m R at x-rds onto B5381. Site 0.5m on L

★ ⊕ £12-£20 ⊕ £12-£15

Open 21 Mar-Oct Booking Advisable BHs and Jul-Aug Last arrival 22.00hrs Last departure noon

A quiet working farm next to the owners' Georgian farmhouse. Pitches are in two grassy paddocks with pleasant views, and the beach is 3 miles away. The very good toilets include unisex bathrooms and are kept spotlessly clean. A 2-acre site with 23 touring pitches, 23 hardstandings.
Baby bath and changing facilities

Leisure: ⚙

Facilities: ⛟ ⛱ ⊙ ⚲ ✳ ⚡ ⛉ ⛏

Disabled facilities: toilet, washbasin & shower, superpitch can be reserved

Services: ⚙ ⛽ ⚡ → ⌂9 ⚓ ⛊

Notes: No tents, dogs must not be left unattended. No ball games on central grass areas

▨ ▨ ▨ ▨ ⑤

C E R E D I G I O N / C O N W Y

CERRIGYDRUDION   SH94

Glan Ceirw Caravan Park
▶▶▶ 69%

Ty Nant LL21 0RF
☎ 01490 420346 🖹 01490 420346
🅔 glanceirwcaravanpark@tinyworld.co.uk
🅦 www.ukparks.co.uk/glanceirw

Dir: From A5 Betws-y-Coed onto unclass road 1m after Cerrig-y-Druiden, and park 0.25m on L. From Corwen for 8m, then 2nd L onto unclass road after Country Cooks

★ ♣ £10-£18 ♣ £10-£18 ▲ £6-£12

Open Mar-Oct Booking Advisable bank hols & Jul-Sephrs Last departure noon
A small riverside site in a rural location, with pleasant owners. Guests can enjoy the use of two games rooms, a bar lounge, a jacuzzi, and an amenity block. An ideal touring point for Snowdonia and North Wales. A 4.5-acre site with 15 touring pitches, 9 hardstandings and 29 static.

Leisure: ♦ ⅊ ▢
Facilities: ♠ ☉ ✳ ⅃ ♨ ⋒ ⍭
Services: ▣ ☗ ⓐ ▦ → ⅃ ⅀
Notes: No cars by tents, no single sex groups

TOWYN (NEAR ABERGELE)   SH97

Ty Mawr Holiday Park ⌂ 65%

Towyn Road LL22 9HG
☎ 01745 832079 🖹 01745 827454
🅔 admin.tymawr@parkresorts.com
🅦 www.park-resorts.com

Dir: On A548, 0.25m W of town

★ ♣ £6-£25 ♣ £6-£25 ▲ £3-£23

Open Etr-Oct (rs Apr (excluding Etr)) Booking Advisable at all times Last arrival midnight Last departure 10.00hrs
A very large coastal holiday park with extensive leisure facilities including sports and recreational amenities, and club and eating outlets. The touring facilities are rather dated but clean. A 18-acre site with 282 touring pitches, 470 static.
Free evening entertainment

Leisure: ⌇ ♦ ⅊
Facilities: ♠ ☉ ⅊ ✳ ⅃ ⅀ ⍭
Disabled facilities: special caravans, toilets & showers
Services: ✗ ♨ ▣ ⓐ ☗ ⅄ ⌀ → ∪ ⅃18 ◎ ⅀
Notes: No single sex groups or groups of young people

🟦 🟦 🟦 🟦 🅢

PRESTATYN SJ08

Presthaven Sands 69%

Gronant LL19 9TT
☎ 01745 856471
🌐 www.havenholidays.com

Dir: Off A548 1.5m E of Prestatyn

🚐

Open Mar-Nov Booking Advisable at all times Last arrival 22.00hrs Last departure noon
Set beside two miles of superb sandy beaches and dunes, this large holiday centre offers extensive leisure and sports facilities and lively entertainment for all the family. The park land-train runs between reception and the leisure complex, with its clubs, pools, restaurants, shops, hair salon, launderettes and pub. The tourers have their own good toilet block in a separate area from the statics. A 130-acre site with 220 touring pitches, 672 static.

Leisure: 🏊 🎾 🗑 🎣 🛝 🎮

Facilities: 🛡

Services: ✖ 🍴 🛒 🔌 ♉

ABERSOCH SH32

Deucoch Touring Park ►►► 67%

Sarn Bach LL53 7LD
☎ 01758 713293
Dir: From Abersoch take Sarn Bach Rd, at crossroads turn R, campsite on R after 800yds

★ 🚐 £15 🚐 £11.50 ▲ £10.50

Open Mar-Oct Booking Advisable school hols Last arrival 22.00hrs Last departure 11.00hrs
A sheltered site with sweeping views of Cardigan Bay and the mountains, just a mile from Abersoch and a long sandy beach. The facilities block is well maintained, and this site is of special interest to watersports enthusiasts and those touring the Llyn Peninsula. A 5-acre site with 68 touring pitches, 9 hardstandings.

Leisure: 🛝

Facilities: 🛡 ⊙ 🗑 ☀ ♉ 🖭 🗑

Disabled facilities: toilet cubicle

Services: 🚐 🖭 → ∪ 🍴 18 ☀ ✈ 🛒

Notes: Families only

GWYNEDD

ABERSOCH SH32

Bryn Bach Caravan & Camping Site
▶▶▶ 71%

Tyddyn Talgoch Uchaf Bwlchtocyn LL53 7BT
☎ 01758 712285
🄔 brynbach@abersochholidays.co.uk
🆆 www.abersochholidays.co.uk

Dir: Take Sarn Bach road from Abersoch for approx 1m, turn L at sign for Bwlchtocyn. Follow road and site is approx 1m on L

★ 🚐 £13-£17 🚎 £13-£17 ▲ £8-£15

Open Mar-Oct Booking Advisable at all times Last arrival 22.00hrs Last departure 11.00hrs
This well run, elevated park overlooks Abersoch Bay, with lovely sea views towards the Snowdonia mountain range. Pitches are well laid out in sheltered paddocks, with well-placed modern facilities. Fishing, watersports, golf and beach access are all nearby.
A 4-acre site with 30 touring pitches, 2 static. Private shortcut to beach, boat storage

Leisure: 🄰
Facilities: ⬤ ⊙ ✳ ⌂ 🎠
Disabled facilities: disabled toilet, ramp, tactile paving
Services: 🕿 ↯ 🖥 → ∪ ⌂18 ⅙ ⤴ △ 🅛
Notes: Families & couples only

BALA SH93

Tytandderwen Caravan Park
▶▶▶ 65%

LL23 7EP
☎ 01678 520273 📄 01678 521393
Dir: From B4401 take B4391 then unclass rd signed Tytandderwen

🚐 🚎 ▲

Open Mar-Oct Booking Advisable peak periods
A secluded family park with superb views, and fishing on site in the River Dee. A large modern facilities block includes laundry, dishwashing and disabled unit, and this is an ideal base for watersports, walking and climbing. A 8-acre site with 55 touring pitches, 60 static.

Leisure: ⬤ 🄰
Facilities: ⬤ ⊙ 🖳 ✳ ⌁ 🎠
Disabled facilities: wc/shower & wash basin
Services: 🕿 🚐 🖥 🍴 ⌕ ⊘ 🖥 → ⌂ 9 ⅙ ⤴ 🍴 △ 🅛

Camping & Caravanning Club Site ▶▶▶ 69%

Crynierth Caravan Park Cefn-Ddwysarn LL23 7LN

☎ 01678 530324

ⓦ www.campingandcaravanningclub.co.uk

Dir: A5 onto A494 to Bala. Through 'Bethal' and 'Sarnau' villages. Pass 'Cefn-Ddwysarn' sign. R up lane before red phone box. Site 400yds on L

★ ⊞ £12.95-£16.35 ⊞ £12.95-£16.35

▲ £12.95-£16.35

Open Mar-Nov Booking Advisable bank hols & peak periods Last arrival 21.00hrs Last departure noon

A quiet pleasant park with interesting views and high class facilities, set back from the main road in a very secluded position. Lake Bala offers great appeal for the water sports enthusiast, as does the nearby River Tryweryn, a leading slalom course in white-water rafting. A 4-acre site with 50 touring pitches, 8 hardstandings.

Leisure: ⚑

Facilities: ⬛⊙⬛⬛✳⬛⬛⬛

Disabled facilities: toilet, shower, washbasin, razor point & hand dryer

Services: ⬛⬛⬛⬛⬛⬛⬛→⬛

⬛ ⬛ ⬛ ⬛ ⬛

Pen-y-Garth Caravan & Camping Park ▶▶▶▶ 67%

LL23 7ES

☎ 01678 520485 🖨 01678 520401

ⓔ stay@penygarth.com

ⓦ www.penygarth.com

Dir: Leave A494 in Bala onto B4391. After 1m fork R at sign to Rhosygwaliau. Site is 600yds on R

★ ⊞ £8.95-£10.50 ⊞ £8.95-£10.50

▲ £7.95-£9.95

Open Mar-Oct Booking Advisable bank hols & Jul-Aug Last arrival 22.00hrs Last departure noon

A good park in an area of great tranquility, attractively landscaped amongst trees and natural scenery. There are excellent views of Mount Arenag and the Berwyns, and nearby Bala is an ideal centre for water sports, walking and climbing. A 20-acre site with 63 touring pitches, 54 static.

Table tennis, 10-acre recreation, dish washing room

Leisure: ⚫ ⚑

Facilities: ⬛⊙⬛⬛✳⬛⬛⬛

Services:

⬛ ⬛ ⬛ ⬛ ⬛ ⬛

GWYNEDD

Trawsdir Touring & Caravan Park
▶▶▶ 72%

Caerddaniel Caravan Park Llanaber LL42 1RR
☎ 01341 280999 🖹 01341 280740
🅱 enquiries@barmouthholidays.co.uk
🅦 www.barmouthholidays.co.uk

Dir: 3m N of Barmouth on A496, just past Wayside pub on R

★ ⊞ £15-£23 ⊞ £13-£18 ▲ £10-£15

Open Mar-Oct Booking Advisable Etr, Whitsun & Jul-Aug Last arrival 21.00hrs Last departure noon

A good quality park on a working sheep farm with views to the sea and hills, and very accessible to motor traffic. The modern facilities are very clean and well maintained, and tents and caravans have their own designated areas divided by dry-stone walls. A site with 50 touring pitches.
Milk/bread etc available from reception

Leisure: ⚠
Facilities: ⬛⊙⬛✳🔌⬛
Disabled facilities: shower & toilet
Services: ⬛⬛⬛⬛⬛→∪⬛⬛
Notes: Families & couples only

Hendre Mynach Touring Caravan & Camping Park ▶▶▶▶ 75%

Llanaber Road LL42 1YR
☎ 01341 280262 🖹 01341 280586
🅱 mynach@lineone.net
🅦 www.hendremynach.co.uk

★ ⊞ £9-£18 ⊞ £9-£18 ▲ £6-£20

Open Mar-9 Jan (rs Nov-8 Jan shop closed) Booking Advisable bank hols & Jul-Aug Last arrival 22.00hrs Last departure noon

A lovely site with immaculate facilities, situated off the A496 on the northern outskirts of Barmouth and near to the railway, with almost direct access to promenade and beach. Caravanners should not be put off by the steep descent, as park staff are always on hand if needed. The toilet facilities are modern and excellent, and pitches have TV and satellite hook-up as well as water and electricity. A small café serves light meals and takeaways. A 10-acre site with 240 touring pitches, 50 hardstandings.
50 TV hook ups

Leisure: ⚠
Facilities: ⬛⊙⬛✳🔌⬛⬛
Disabled facilities: toilet, washbasin, shower
Services: ⬛✖⬛⬛⬛⬛⬛→∪⬛⬛
Notes: No single sex groups

GWYNEDD

BETWS GARMON   SH55

Bryn Gloch Caravan & Camping Park ▶▶▶▶ 77%

LL54 7YY
☎ 01286 650216 📄 01286 650591
📧 eurig@easynet.co.uk
🌐 www.bryngloch.co.uk

Dir: On A4085 7m SE of Caernarfon

★ ⊞ £12-£16 ⊞ £12-£16 ▲ £12-£14

Open all year Booking Advisable school & bank hols Last arr 23.00hrs Last dep 17.00hrs *An excellent family-run site with immaculate modern facilities, and all level pitches in beautiful surroundings. The park offers the best of two worlds, with its bustling holiday atmosphere and the peaceful natural surroundings. The 25 acres of level fields are separated by mature hedges and trees, guaranteeing sufficient space for families wishing to spread themselves out. There are plenty of walks in the area, and a constant source of interest is the babbling stream, Gwyrfai. A 12-acre site with 160 touring pitches, 20 hardstandings and 40 static.* Family bathroom, mother & baby room

Leisure: ♠ ⋒ ☐
Facilities: 🛁 ♠ ⊙ ☜ ✳ ☜ 🖳 🎣 🎋 ☍
Disabled facilities: toilet, shower & washbasin
Services: 🎲 🛒 ☰ 🚽 🍴 🍼 ⊿ 🖽 → ∪ ⌒18 ✦ ⊿ ◎ 🔲 🔲 🔲 🔲 🔲 🔲

BRYNCRUG   SH60

Woodlands Holiday Park ▶▶▶ 68%

LL36 9UH
☎ 01654 710471 📄 01654 710100
Dir: 2m from Tywyn on B4405 road to Tal-y-Llyn

★ ⊞ fr £10 ⊞ fr £10

Open Etr & Apr-Oct Booking Advisable Jul-Aug Last arrival 22.00hrs Last departure 11.00hrs *A large holiday park and country club with mainly statics and chalets, and a small, separate touring section. The club offers bar meals, elegant lounges, a cosy inglenook fireplace, a small restaurant, and a large function room for music, dancing and entertainment. A 2-acre site with 20 touring pitches, 10 hardstandings and 122 static.* Entertainment in high season

Leisure: ₹ ♠ ⋒ ☐
Facilities: ♠ ⊙ ☜ 🖳 ☐ 🎣 🎋
Services: ✕ 🛒 ☰ ☷ 🍼 → ∪ ⌒18 🛍 ⊿ ◎ ◭ 🔲 🔲 🔲 🔲 🔲

CAERNARFON — SH46

Ty'n yr Onnen Mountain Farm Caravan & Camping ►►► 64%

Waunfawr LL55 4AX
☎ 01286 650281 📄 01286 650043

Dir: At Waunfawr on A4085, turn down unclass road opposite church. Site is signposted

🚐 🚏 Å

Open Spring bank hol-Oct (rs Etr & Mayday bank hol open if weather premitting) Booking Advisable Spring bank hol & Jul-Aug Last arrival 21.00hrs Last departure 10.00hrs
A gently-sloping site on a 200-acre sheep farm, set in magnificent surroundings with mountain views. This secluded park is well equipped, with quality toilet facilities. Access is by single track unclassified road. A 4-acre site with 20 touring pitches, 4 static.
Fishing & nature park

Leisure: ⚓ ⚲ ⌂

Facilities: ⇥ 🕭 ⊙ 🔍 ☼ ⚲ 🎣 🎋 �🐾

Disabled facilities: toilets

Services: 🆃 🚐 🔌 🗑 🕳 → ∪ ↾18 ↘ 🥪 ♪ 🔘△ 🛒

CAERNARFON — SH46

Riverside Camping ►►► 73%

Seiont Nurseries Pont Rug LL55 2BB
☎ 01286 678781 📄 01286 677223
🅔 brenda@riversidecamping.freeserve.co.uk
🅦 www.riversidecamping.co.uk

Dir: 2m from Caernarfon on R of A4086, also signed Seiont Nurseries.

🚐 £10-£12 🚏 £10-£12 Å £10-£12
Open Etr-end Oct Booking Advisable Jul-Aug & BH's Last arrival anytime Last departure 20.00hrs
Set in the grounds of a large garden centre beside the small River Seiont, this park is approached by an impressive tree-lined drive. Facilities are very good, and include a café/restaurant and laundry. A 4.5-acre site with 60 touring pitches, 2 hardstandings.
Family shower room & baby changing facilities

Leisure: ⚲

Facilities: 🕭 ⊙ 🔍 ☼ 🐾

Disabled facilities: toilet, shower & washbasin

Services: ✗ 🍴 🚐 🗑 → ∪ ↾18 ↘ ♪ 🔘 △ 🛒

Notes: No fires, no loud music, dogs must be kept on leads

DINAS DINLLE SH45

Dinlle Caravan Park ►►►► 73%

LL54 5TW

☎ 01286 830324 📠 01286 831526
📧 enq@thornleyleisure.co.uk
🌐 www.thornleyleisure.co.uk

Dir: Turn R off A499 at sign for Caernarfon Airport. 2m W of Dinas Dinlle coast

★ 🚐 £7-£15.50 🚐 £7-£15.50 ▲ £7-£15.50

Open May-Aug (rs Mar-Apr & Sep-Nov club, shop, swimming pool restricted hours) Booking Advisable Spring bank hol & Jul-Aug Last arrival 23.00hrs Last departure noon
A very accessible, well-kept grassy site, adjacent to sandy beach, with good views to Snowdonia. The park is situated in acres of flat grassland, with plenty of room for even the largest groups. A lounge bar and family room are comfortable places in which to relax, and children are well provided for with an exciting adventure playground. The beach road gives access to the golf club, a nature reserve, and to Air World at Caernarfon Airport. A 11-acre site with 175 touring pitches, 167 static.

Leisure: ⚊ ⚊ ⚊
Facilities: ⚊ ⊙ ⚊ ☀ ⚊
Disabled facilities: toilet & showers
Services: ⚊ ⚊ ⚊ ⚊ ⚊ ⚊ ⚊ → ∪ ⚊ ⚊
Notes: No single sex groups

DYFFRYN ARDUDWY SH52

Murmur-yr-Afon Touring Park ►►► 69%

LL44 2BE

☎ 01341 247353 📠 01341 247353
📧 mills@murmuryrafon25.freeserve.co.uk

Dir: On A496 N of village

★ 🚐 £8-£16.75 🚐 £8-£16.75

▲ £5.50-£14.75

Open Mar-Oct Booking Advisable bank hols Last arrival 22.00hrs Last departure 11.30hrs
A pleasant family-run park alongside a wooded stream on the edge of the village, and handy for large sandy beaches. Expect good, clean facilities, and lovely views of rolling hills and mountains. A 4-acre site with 67 touring pitches, 30 hardstandings.

Leisure: ⚊
Facilities: ⚊ ⊙ ⚊ ☀ ⚊ ⚊ ⚊ ⚊
Disabled facilities: fully equipped disabled unit Grade 3.
Services: ⚊ ⚊ ⚊ → ∪ ⚊ ⚊

LLANDWROG SH45

White Tower Caravan Park
▶▶▶▶ 68%

LL54 5UH
☎ 01286 830649 📄 01286 830649
📧 whitetower@supanet.com
🌐 www.whitetower.supanet.com

Dir: 1.5m from village along Tai'r Eglwys road. From Caernarfon take A487 Porthmadog road. Cross over rdbt, then take 1st R. Park 3m on R

★ 🚐 £9.50-£15 🚐 £9.50-£15 ▲ £9.50-£15

Open Mar-15 Jan (rs Mar-mid May & Sep-Oct bar open wknds only) Booking Advisable bank hols & Jul-Aug Last arrival 23.00hrs Last departure noon
There are lovely views of Snowdonia from this park located just 2 miles from the nearest beach at Dinas Dinlle. A well-maintained toilet block has key access, and the hard pitches have water and electricity. Popular amenities include an outdoor heated swimming pool, a lounge bar with family room, and a games and TV room. A 6-acre site with 104 touring pitches, 80 hardstandings and 54 static.

Leisure: 🎯 ◣ 🎮 ▢
Facilities: 🏪 ⊙ 🏴 ✳ 📞
Disabled facilities: toilet, shower & wash basin, ramp access & toilet in club
Services: 🛢 🛒 🚗 🔌 🍽 🔥 🚿 🚽 → ∪ ⌂18 🔧 ♨
△ ≛

🟦 🟦 🟦 🟦 🟦

PORTHMADOG SH53

Greenacres 🏅 70%

Black Rock Sands Morfa Bychan LL49 9YB
☎ 08457 125931
🌐 www.british-holidays.co.uk

Dir: After Porthmadog high street, turn between Woolworths and the post office towards Black Rock Sands. After 2m, park entrance on L

★ 🚐 🚐

Open 22 Mar-28 Oct Booking Advisable at all times Last arrival 18.00hrs Last departure 10.00hrs
A quality holiday park on level ground just a short walk from Black Rock Sands, and set against a backdrop of Snowdonia National Park. All touring pitches are on hardstandings surrounded by closely-mown grass, and near the entertainment complex. A full programme of entertainment, organised clubs, indoor and outdoor sports and leisure including a high-level 'ropeworks' adventure course, pubs, shows and cabarets all add to a holiday here. A 121-acre site with 58 touring pitches, 370 static.

Leisure: 🎯 🎮 ◣ 🎮
Facilities: 📞 ≛
Services: ✗ 🛒 🚗 🔌 🍽 → ∪ ⌂9 🚿 🔧 ♨
Notes: No single sex groups or groups of under 18's

PWLLHELI SH33

Abererch Sands Holiday Centre
▶▶▶ 66%

LL53 6PJ
☎ 01758 612327 🖶 01758 701556
📧 enquiries@abererch-sands.co.uk
🌐 www.abererch-sands.co.uk

Dir: On the Porthmadog to Pwllheli road A497,
1m from Pwllheli

🏖 🚐 🅰

Open Mar-Oct Booking Advisable school &
bank holidays Last arrival 21.00hrs Last
departure 21.00hrs
*Glorious views of Snowdonia and Cardigan
Bay can be enjoyed from this very secure,
family-run site adjacent to a railway station
and a 4-mile stretch of sandy beach. A large
heated indoor swimming pool, snooker room,
pool room, fitness centre and children's play
area make this an ideal holiday venue. A 85-
acre site with 70 touring pitches, 70
hardstandings and 90 static.*
Snooker room, fitness room

Leisure: ⚲ ⚲ 𝄞
Facilities: 🏠 ⊙ ⚲ ⚒ ❄ 𝄞 🐾 🛒
Disabled facilities: wc & wash basin
Services: 🔲 ⚡ ⚲ 🔋 🛢 ⊘ 🔲 → ∪ ⋒18 ⅄ 🍴
🥨 ⚱

Notes: No single sex groups

▭▭ ▭▭ ▭▭ 🔀 🆂

FISHGUARD SM93

Fishguard Bay Caravan
& Camping Park ▶▶▶ 70%

Garn Gelli SA65 9ET
☎ 01348 811415 🖶 01348 811425
📧 enquiries@fishguardbay.com
🌐 www.fishguardbay.com

Dir: Take A487 Fishguard-Cardigan road.
Caravan park is 3m from Fishguard, signposted
and on L

★ 🚐 £11-£13 🚐 £11-£13 🅰 £10-£12

Open Mar-9 Jan Booking Advisable Jul-Aug
Last departure noon
*Set high up on cliffs with outstanding views of
Fishguard Bay, and the Pembrokeshire Coastal
Path running right through the centre. The
park is extremely well kept, with three good
toilet blocks, a common room with TV, a
lounge/library, decent laundry, and well-
stocked shop. A 5-acre site with 50 touring
pitches, 50 static.*
View point

Leisure: ⚲ 𝄞 ▭
Facilities: 🏠 ⊙ ⚲ ❄ ⚲ 🛒
Services: 🔲 ⚡ 🔲 🛢 ⊘ 🔲 → ∪ ⅄ ⚱ 🍴

▭▭ ▭▭ ▭ 🔀 🆂

ST DAVID'S SM72

Caerfai Bay Caravan & Tent Park
▶▶▶ 76%

Caerfai Bay SA62 6QT
☎ 01437 720274 ▤ 01437 720577
✉ info@caerfaibay.co.uk
🌐 www.caerfaibay.co.uk

Dir: At St David's turn off A487 at Visitor
Centre/Grove Hotel. Follow signs for Caerfai
Bay. R at end of road

★ ⚏ £8.50-£13.50 ⚏ £7-£13.50 ▲ £7-£9.50

Open Mar-mid Nov Booking Advisable school
hols Last arrival 21.00hrs Last departure
11.00hrs

*Magnificent coastal scenery and an outlook
over St Bride's Bay can be enjoyed at this
delightful site, just 300 yards from a bathing
beach. The refurbished facilities include four
en suite family rooms which are an asset to
the park. There is a farm shop very close by. A
10-acre site with 117 touring pitches, 4
hardstandings and 32 static.*
Family washrooms

Facilities: ⚏⊙⚏⚏⚏⚏
Disabled facilities: toilet, shower &
washbasin
Services: ⚏⚏⚏⚏⚏⚏→⚏⚏⚏⚏
Notes: No single sex groups

⬛ ⬛ ⬛ ⚏

TAVERNSPITE SN11

Pantglas Farm Caravan Park
▶▶▶ 69%

SA34 0NS
☎ 01834 831618 ▤ 01834 831193
✉ neil.brook@btinternet.com
🌐 www.pantglasfarm.com

Dir: Turn off the A477 to Tenby at Red Roses
cross roads onto the B4314 to Tavernspite. Take
middle road at the village pumps. Pantglas is
0.5m on the L

★ ⚏ £10.25-£12.50 ⚏ £10.25-£12.50
▲ £6-£7.50

Open Etr-17 Oct Booking Advisable Spring
bank hol & Jul-Aug Last arrival 23.00hrs Last
departure 10.30hrs

*A quiet family-run site in a rural setting, with
a welcoming attitude towards children, and a
large play area for them. In rolling countryside
with views towards Carmarthen Bay, with a
lounge bar that offers occasional
entertainment in high season. A 10-acre site
with 86 touring pitches, 3 hardstandings.*
Year round caravan weekly storage

Leisure: ⚏ ⚏
Facilities: ⚏⊙⚏⚏⚏⚏⚏
Disabled facilities: toilet & washroom
Services: ⚏⚏⚏⚏⚏⚏→⚏⚏⚏
Notes: No single sex groups, children must
be supervised/controlled at all times

Well Park Caravan & Camping Site
▶▶▶ 70%

SA70 8TL

☎ 01834 842179 📠 01834 842179

ⓔ enquiries@wellparkcaravans.co.uk

ⓦ www.wellparkcaravans.co.uk

Dir: Off A478 on R approx 1.5m before Tenby

★ ⛐ £10-£20 ⛟ £10-£20 ▲ £10-£16

Open Mar-Oct (rs Mar-mid May & mid Sep-Oct bar, launderette, baby room may be closed)
Booking Advisable Spring BH & Jul-Aug Last arrival 22.00hrs Last departure 11.00hrs
A very well-run park with good landscaping from trees, ornamental shrubs, and attractive flower borders. The friendly resident owners keep the toilets clean and sparkling, and amenities include a launderette and indoor dishwashing, games room with table tennis, and an enclosed and well-equipped play area. The site is ideally placed between Tenby (1m) and Saundersfoot (1.5m), with a 15-minute walk to Waterwych Bay and the Pembrokeshire Coastal Footpath. A 10-acre site with 100 touring pitches, 14 hardstandings and 42 static.
TV hookups

Leisure: ⚓ ⚲ ▱

Facilities: ⋒ ⊙ ⚑ ⚴ ⚘ ⚅ ⊞ ⋒

Services: ⊶ ⚘ ⛽ ⚄ ⚑ ⚶ ⊞ → U ⏱18 ⚓ ⚶
⚶ ◎ ⚱

Notes: No single sex groups

Wood Park Caravans ▶▶▶ 70%

New Hedges SA70 8TL

☎ 0845 129 8314

ⓔ enquiries@woodparkcaravans.co.uk

ⓦ www.woodparkcaravans.co.uk

Dir: At rdbt 2m N of Tenby follow A478 towards Tenby, then take 2nd R & R again

★ ⛐ £10-£16.50 ⛟ £10-£16.50

▲ £7-£15.50

Open Spring BH-Sep (rs Etr-Spring BH & Sep-Oct bar & launderette may not open) Booking Advisable Spring BH & Jul-Aug Last arrival 22.00hrs Last departure 10.00hrs
Nestling in beautiful countryside between the popular seaside resorts of Tenby and Saundersfoot, and with Waterwynch Bay just a 15-minute walk away. This peaceful site provides a spacious and relaxing atmosphere for holidays. The slightly sloping touring area is partly divided by shrubs into three paddocks. A 10-acre site with 60 touring pitches, 90 static.

Leisure: ⚓ ⚲

Facilities: ⋒ ⊙ ⚑ ⚘ ⚅ ⋒

Services: ⚘ ⛽ ⚄ ⚑ ⚶ ⊞ → U ⏱18 ⚓ ⚶ ⚶ ⚱

Notes: No single sex groups, 1 car per unit only, small dogs only accepted, no dogs Jul-Aug & Bank Hols

Trefalun ▶▶▶▶ 72%

Devonshire Drive St Florence SA70 8RD
☎ 01646 651514 📠 01646 651746
📧 trefalun@aol.com
🌐 www.trefalunpark.co.uk

Dir: 1.5m NW of St Florence & 0.5m N of B4318

★ 🚐 £10.50-£16.50 🚗 £10.50-£16.50
▲ £9-£14.50

Open Etr-Oct Booking Advisable bank hols & Jul-Aug Last arrival 20.00hrs Last dep noon
Set within 14 acres of sheltered, well-kept grounds, this park nestles among some of Pembrokeshire's finest scenery. This quiet country park offers well-maintained level grass pitches separated by bushes and trees, with plenty of space to relax in. Children will enjoy the enclosed play area, and can feed the park's friendly pets. Plenty of activities are available at the nearby Heatherton Country Sports Park, including go-karting, indoor bowls, golf and bumper boating. A 7-acre site with 90 touring pitches, 29 hardstandings and 10 static.

Leisure: 🎡
Facilities: 🏪⊙🎣☀️🔔🚻
Disabled facilities: seperate toilet & shower facilities
Services: 🔌🚐📷🛢️🍴🔆→ ∪Μ18🏊🎱🎵
🔋◎♿ Notes: No single sex groups
🖭 🖭 🖭 🔚

Kiln Park Holiday Centre 🏖️ 72%

Marsh Road SA70 7RB
☎ 01834 844121 📠 01834 845159
📧 gary.turner@bourneleisuregroup.co.uk

Dir: On A4139

★ 🚐 🚗 ▲

Open Mar-Oct (rs Mar-mid May & Sep-Oct fewer venues available) Booking Advisable all times Etr-Sep Last arrival 22.00hrs Last departure 10.00hrs
A large holiday complex complete with leisure and sports facilities, and plenty of entertainment for all the family. There are bars and cafés, and plenty of security. This touring, camping and static site is on the outskirts of town, with a short walk through dunes to the sandy beach. The well-equipped toilet block is very clean. A 103-acre site with 240 touring pitches, 620 static.
Entertainment complex, bowling & putting green

Leisure: ⚡🎾🏊🎣🎡
Facilities: 🔱🏪⊙🎣☀️🔔🛒🖨️🚻🐕
Disabled facilities: showers, toilets & bathrooms
Services: 🖳✖️🚮🚐📷🛢️🍴⊘→ ∪Μ18🏊🎱
🎵◎♿ Notes: No dogs when camping during Jul & Aug 🖭 🖭 🖭 🔚 🔚

Bishops Meadow Caravan Park
▶▶▶ 67%

Bishops Meadow Hay Road LD3 9SW
☎ 01874 61 ▤ 01874 614922
🅴 enquiries@bishops-meadow.co.uk

Dir: From A40 take A470 Hereford road. Turn L onto B4602

🐕 🐕 Å

Open Mar-Oct Booking Advisable BH's
A rural park close to the Brecon Beacons and with spectacular views. The family-owned and run park offers a heated outdoor swimming pool, an adjacent all-day restaurant, and a lounge bar open in the evenings. Facilities are very well kept, and the town is about one mile away. A 3.5-acre site with 82 touring pitches, 24 hardstandings.

Leisure: ⚲ ♦ ⚙

Facilities: ⇥ ♃ ☉ ❄ ⌂ ♿ 🐕 ⌁

Disabled facilities: toilet & shower

Services: 🆃 ✕ ⇥ ♨ ♀ 🔊 🍴 🆄 🆅 → 🆄 ⌁18 🍴 🍽
🍴 🅶

▨▨ ▨▨ ▨▨ ⑪ ▨▨ ▨ 🅂

Brynich Caravan Park
▶▶▶▶ 77%

Brynich LD3 7SH
☎ 01874 623325 ▤ 01874 623325
🅴 holidays@brynich.co.uk
🆆 www.brynich.co.uk

Dir: 2km E of Brecon on A470, 200mtrs from jct with A40

★ 🐕 £13-£16 🐕 £13-£16 Å £10-£13

Open 18 Mar-30 Oct Booking Advisable bank & school hols Last arrival 22.00hrs Last departure noon
A very attractive and well-appointed site with commanding views of the Brecon Beacons. Colourful flower beds create a lovely display, and a well-stocked shop is very popular. There is a superb restaurant/bar in a 17th-century barn, and a large soft indoor play area and outdoor boules pitch. A walk along the canal leads to the charming town of Brecon. A 20-acre site with 130 touring pitches, 25 hardstandings.
Off-licence

Leisure: ⚙

Facilities: ⇥ ♃ ☉ ♨ ❄ ⌂ ♿ ⩩ 🐕 ⌁

Disabled facilities: 2 complete rooms, toilet, shower, basin, bath & grab rail

Services: 🆃 ✕ ⇥ ♨ ⩗ 🔊 🍴 ⌁ 🆅 → 🆄 ⌁18
🍽 🍴 🍴 ⟁

Notes: No gazebos, motorized scooters. Only environmental ground sheets

▨▨ ▨▨ ▨▨ ▨ 🅂

BRECON   SO02

Pencelli Castle Caravan & Camping Park ▶▶▶▶ 78%

Pencelli LD3 7LX
☎ 01874 665451 ▤ 01874 665452
ⓔ pencelli.castle@virgin.net
ⓦ www.pencelli-castle.co.uk

Dir: Turn off A40 2m E of Brecon onto B4558, follow signs to Pencelli

★ 🚐 £12-£14 🚲 £12-£14 ▲ £6-£7

Open all year Booking Advisable bank & school hols Last arrival 22.00hrs Last departure noon 🏕

Lying in the heart of the Brecon Beacons National Park, this charming park offers peace, beautiful scenery and high quality facilities. The park is bordered by the Brecon and Monmouth Canal, and there are barge trips from the nearby marina. Attention to detail is superb, and the well-equipped heated toilets with en suite cubicles are matched by a drying room for clothes and boots, full laundry, and shop. A 10-acre site with 80 touring pitches, 40 hardstandings.
Bike hire

Leisure: 🏕

Facilities: ⬥⊙🔍✳💧💧🔒🖾

Disabled facilities: toilets, shower, hand & hair dryers

Services: 🆃🔌🚾🅱💧⊘🖾→∪🌂🎵

Notes: 🏕 No radios or music

▭▭ ▭▭ ▭▭ ▭▭ 💿

BRONLLYS   SO13

Anchorage Caravan Park ▶▶▶ 69%

LD3 0LD
ⓔ 01874 711246 ▤ 01874 711711
ⓦ www.ukparks.co.uk/anchorage

Dir: 8m NE of Brecon on A438, in village of Bronllys.

★ 🚐 fr £9 🚲 fr £9 ▲ fr £9

Open all year (rs Nov-Mar TV room closed) Booking Advisable BH's & Aug Last arrival 23.00hrs Last departure 18.00hrs

A well-maintained site with a choice of south-facing, sloping grass pitches and superb views of the Black Mountains, or a more sheltered lower area with a number of excellent super pitches. The site is a short distance from the water sports centre at Llangorse Lake. A 8-acre site with 110 touring pitches, 8 hardstandings and 101 static.
Baby bathroom, post office & hairdresser

Leisure: 🏕 🏓

Facilities: ⬥⬥⊙🔍✳💧💧🖾🏕

Disabled facilities: toilet & bath

Services: 🆃🔌🅱💧⊘🖾→∪🎵

LLANBRYMAIR SH80

Cringoed Caravan Park ▶▶▶ 71%

The Birches SY19 7DR
☎ 01650 521237 📠 01650 521237
[E] cringoedcaravan.park@virgin.net

Dir: Off A470 onto B4518, park 1.25m on R

★ 🚐 £11-£15 🚌 £11-£15 ⛺ £10-£12

Open 7 Mar-7 Jan Booking Advisable BH's Last arrival 22.00hrs Last departure noon
On the banks of the River Twymyn, a family-run park set amongst beautiful hillside and open scenery just 30 minutes' drive from the coastal resort of Aberdovey. An ideal location for touring the many local attractions, and with bright, well-maintained toilet facilities. A 20-acre site with 35 touring pitches, 4 hardstandings and 31 static.

Leisure: 🔍 ⛩
Facilities: 🚿 🔌 ✳ 📞 🐕
Services: 🔄 🗑 🔋 🌿 → ✈ 🎣 ⛳ ⛵

LLANGORS SO12

Lakeside Caravan Park ▶▶▶ 65%

LD3 7TR
☎ 01874 658226 📠 01874 658430
[E] holidays@lakeside.zx3.net
[W] www.lakeside-holidays.net

Dir: Leave A40 at Bwlch onto B4560 towards Talgarth, site signed towards lake in centre of Llangors village

★ 🚐 £7.50-£9.50 🚌 £7.50-£9.50
⛺ £7.50-£9.50

Open Jun-Sep (rs Mar-May & Oct Pool, clubhouse, restaurant, shop limited) Booking Advisable Etr, May wk, summer school hols Last arrival 21.30hrs Last departure 10.00hrs
Next to Llangors common and lake, this attractive park has launching and mooring facilities and is an ideal centre for water sports enthusiasts. Popular with families, and offering a clubhouse/bar, with a well-stocked shop and café/takeaway next door. Boats and windsurf equipment can be hired on site. A 2-acre site with 40 touring pitches, 72 static.
Boat & bike hire, windsurfing & fishing

Leisure: 🔍 ⛩
Facilities: 🚿 ⊙ 🔌 ✳ 📞 ⛳ 🏪 ⛩ 🐕
Services: [T] ✕ 🧺 🔄 🗑 🍷 🔋 🌿 → U ✈ 🎣 ⛵

VISA Barclays CONNECT DELTA [S]

POWYS

TALGARTH SO13

Riverside International ▶▶▶ 68%

Bronllys LD3 0HL
☎ 01874 711320 📠 01874 712064
✉ riversideinternational@bronllys1.freeserve.co.uk
🕸 www.riversideinternational.co.uk

Dir: On A479 opposite Bronllys Castle

★ 🏕 £12.50-£13.50 🚐 £12.50-£13.50
⛺ £10-£13.50

Open Etr-Oct Booking Advisable BH's & Jul-Aug Last arrival 22.00hrs Last departure 16.00hrs

A well-appointed touring park in a pretty, elevated position with magnificent views of the Black Mountains and the Brecon Beacons. The leisure centre facilities with heated indoor swimming pool, jacuzzi, and well-equipped gym are available to site users at special rates. Trout fishing is also available on site, and there are some pitches beside the river. A 9-acre site with 80 touring pitches.

Leisure facilities, sauna, jacuzzi, sunbed & gym

Leisure: ⚓ ⚭ Ⓜ

Facilities: 🖎 ⊙ ℐ ⚙ ℄ ⅃ ☴

Disabled facilities: toilet & shower

Services: 🆃 ✖ 🖤 ⚙ 🖥 🖩 🔃 🔜 → ∪ ⅄ ℐ

Notes: 🐕 💳 💳 ⚑ 🅢

SWANSEA SS69

Riverside Caravan Park ▶▶▶ 64%

Ynys Forgan Farm Morriston SA6 6QL
☎ 01792 775587 📠 01792 775587

Dir: Leave M4 J45 towards Swansea, and turn L into private road signed to park

🏕 🚐 ⛺

Open all year (rs winter months pool & club closed) Booking Advisable bank & main school hols Last arrival midnight Last departure noon

A large and busy park close to the M4 but in a quiet location beside the River Taw. This friendly site has a licensed club and bar with high-season entertainment and weekend lunches served. It makes a good base for touring Mumbles and Gower beaches. A 5-acre site with 90 touring pitches, 256 static.

Fishing on site by arrangement

Leisure: ⚓ ⚭ Ⓜ ⎙

Facilities: 🖎 ⊙ ℐ ☀ ℄ ⅃ ☴ ☴

Disabled facilities: toilet & washing facilities

Services: 🆃 🖤 ⚙ 🖥 ⚘ ⅄ ℐ ⌀ 🖩 → ∪ ℳ18 ⅄ ⚌

ℐ Notes: Dogs by arrangement only (no aggressive dog breeds permitted), no single sex groups 💳 💳 💳 ⚑ 🅢

LLANTWIT MAJOR   SS96

Acorn Camping & Caravan Site
▶▶▶ 67%

Ham Lane South CF61 1RP
☎ 01446 794024 📠 01446 794024
📧 info@acorncamping.co.uk
🌐 www.acorncamping.co.uk

Dir: B4265 to Llantwit Major following camping signs. Approach site through Ham Manor residential park

★ 🚐 £8-£9 🚙 £8-£9 ⚊ £8-£9

Open Feb-8 Dec Booking Advisable BH's, school holidays Last arrival 22.00hrs Last departure noon

A peaceful country site in level meadowland, with some individual pitches divided by hedges and shrubs. About 1 mile from the beach, which can be approached by a clifftop walk, and the same distance from the historic town of Llantwit Major. A 4.5-acre site with 90 touring pitches, 5 hardstandings and 15 static.

Leisure: ⚉ ⚌

Facilities: ⚊⊙🔧☀☾🛢

Disabled facilities: toilet, shower, washbasin, suitable holiday caravan, ramps

Services: 🔲💧🔌🗑🔘 → ∪ ⚒

Notes: No noise between 11pm-7am

EYTON   SJ34

The Plassey Leisure Park
▶▶▶▶▶ 78%

The Plassey LL13 0SP
☎ 01978 780277 📠 01978 780019
📧 enquiries@theplassey.co.uk
🌐 www.theplassey.co.uk

Dir: Leave A483 at Bangor-on-Dee exit, along B5426 for 2.5m. Follow signs to site

★ 🚐 £13.50-£19 🚙 £13.50-£19

⚊ £13.50-£19

Open Mar-Oct Booking Advisable wknds, bank & school hols Last arrival 21.00hrs Last departure 18.00hrs

A lovely park set in several hundred acres of quiet farm and meadowland in the Dee Valley. The superb toilet facilities include individual cubicles for total privacy, while the farm buildings have been converted into a restaurant, coffee shop, beauty studio, and various craft outlets. There is plenty here to entertain the whole family. A 10-acre site with 110 touring pitches, 45 hardstandings. Sauna, badminton, fishing & 9-hole golf

Leisure: ⚉ ⚉ ⚌

Facilities: ⚊⊙🔧☀🛢🏛🍴

Disabled facilities: toilet & shower

Services: 🔲✖💧🔌🚱🛢🔘🗑🔘 → ∪🅿18

🎪 ⚒ Notes: No footballs, bikes, or skateboards, dogs must be kept on leads, no single sex groups

ANTRIM

Sixmilewater Caravan Park
▶▶▶ 70%

Lough Road BT41 4DQ
☎ 028 9446 4131 📠 028 9446 2968
📧 forum@antrim.gov.uk

Dir: 1m from Antrim town centre, follow signs for Antrim Forum, Loughshore Park. On Dublin road take turn for Lough road, passing Antrim Forum on R. Park at end of Lough Rd

★ 🚐 £9-£12 🚐 £9-£12 ▲ £7-£9

Open Etr-Sep Booking Advisable all dates Last departure noon
A pretty tree-lined site in a large municipal park, within walking distance of Antrim and the Antrim Forum leisure complex yet very much in the countryside. The modern toilet block is well equipped, and other facilities include a laundry and electric hook-ups. A 9.61-acre site with 42 touring pitches, 18 hardstandings.
Watersport, angling stands & launching facilities

Facilities: 🏪 ⊙ ⚲ 🚿 🎠

Disabled facilities: toilets & showers

Services: ✗ 🖾 🖾 → ↑ 18 🛎 🗑 🖢 ♨

Notes: Max stay 7 nights, no noise between 23.00hrs -7.00hrs, dogs must be kept under control and on leads

BALLYMONEY

Drumaheglis Marina & Caravan Park ▶▶▶▶ 69%

36 Glenstall Road BT53 7QN
☎ 028 2766 6466 📠 028 2766 7659
📧 info@ballymoney.gov.uk
🌐 www.ballymoney.gov.uk

Dir: Signed off A26, approx 1.5m outside Ballymoney towards Coleraine, off B66 S of Ballymoney

★ 🚐 £14 🚐 £14 ▲ £10

Open 31 Mar-1 Oct Booking Advisable BH's & summer months Last arrival 20.00hrs Last departure 13.00hrs
Exceptionally well designed and laid out park beside the Lower Bann River, with very spacious pitches and two quality toilet blocks. Ideal base for touring Antrim or for water sports enthusiasts. A 16-acre site with 53 touring pitches, 53 hardstandings.
Ski school, marina berthing, banana boat, table tennis

Leisure: 🎠

Facilities: 🏪 ⊙ ⚲ ✳ ⚲ 🚿 🎠 🃏

Disabled facilities: toilets & shower room

Services: 🖾 🛢 → ∪ ↑ 9 🗑 🖾 🖢 ♨

Notes: Dogs must be kept on leads

BUSHMILLS

Ballyness Caravan Park
▶▶▶▶ 75%

40 Castlecatt Road BT57 8TN
☎ 028 2073 2393 📠 028 2073 2713
📧 info@ballynesscaravanpark.com
🌐 www.ballynesscaravanpark.com

Dir: 0.5m S of Bushmills on B66

★ 🚐 fr £13 🚎 fr £13 ⛺ fr £9

Open 17 Mar-Oct Booking Advisable Jun-Aug
& Etr Last arrival 21.00hrs Last departure
noon
*A quality park with superb toilet and other
facilities, on farmland beside St Columb's Rill,
the stream that supplies the famous nearby
Bushmills distillery. The friendly owners built
this park with the discerning camper in mind.
There is a pleasant walk around several
ponds, and the park is peacefully located
close to the beautiful North Antrim coast. A
12-acre site with 36 touring pitches, 30
hardstandings and 30 static.*

Leisure: 🅰

Facilities: 🚾🌂⊙🖉✳🕻🔭

Disabled facilities: shower, washbasins
& toilet with hand rails

Services: 🔲🚐🕯🚰🛢🔌🔳→🍴🎱🔧🔌

Notes: No single sex groups

▦ 🌆 📶 💷

DUNDONALD

Dundonald Touring Caravan Park
▶▶▶ 69%

111 Old Dundonald Road BT16 1XT
☎ 028 9080 9100 📠 028 9048 9604
📧 sales@castlereagh.gov.uk

Dir: From Belfast City Centre follow M3 &
A20 to City airport. After airport onto A20
to Newtownards, then follow signs to
Dundonald & Ulster Hospital. Before
hospital turn R at sign for Dundonald Ice
Bowl. Follow signs and site 0.25m

★ 🚐 £13 🚎 £13 ⛺ £7

Open Apr-Sep (rs Oct-Mar Open on request,
closed 25 Dec) Booking Advisable Jul-Aug Last
arrival 23.00hrs Last departure noon
*A purpose-built park in a quiet corner of
Dundonald Leisure Park on the outskirts of
Belfast. This peaceful park is ideally located
for touring County Down, and exploring the
capital. A 1.5-acre site with 22 touring
pitches, 22 hardstandings.*
Discount at ice rink, bowling, indoor play area

Leisure: 🅰

Facilities: 🌂⊙🖉✳🕻🛒🔭🎏

Disabled facilities: toilet, shower & access
to buildings

Services: ✗🛒🚐🔌→∪🍴🎱🎗🔧🔳

Notes: Dogs must be kept on leads

▦ 🌆 📶 💷

KESH

Lakeland Caravan Park ▶▶▶ 68%

Drumrush Boa Island Road BT93 1AD

☎ 028 6863 1578

Dir: 2.5m outside Kesh on the Boa Island road, Drumrush

🏠 🚐 ⛺

A busy site focusing on watersports, ideally located on the edge of Lower Lough Erne, and enjoying elevated views and loughside walks. Facilities include marina berths, a sauna, a fully-licensed bar and restaurant, and a private beach and bathing area. A 30-acre site with 50 touring pitches, 140 static.

Facilities: 🏠 ⚲ ☏

Services: ✖ 🕾 🖩 �‍

DUNGANNON

Dungannon Park ▶▶▶ 70%

Moy Road BT71 6DY

☎ 028 8772 7327 ▤ 028 8772 9169

✉ dungannonpark@utvinternet.com

Dir: 1m from A4 on A29, 1m from Dungannon

★ 🏠 £10-£12 🚐 £10-£12 ⛺ £7-£8

Open Mar-Oct Booking Advisable all wknds & BH's Last arrival 20.30hrs Last departure noon *Modern caravan park in a quiet area of a public park with fishing lake and excellent facilities, especially for disabled. A 2-acre site with 20 touring pitches, 12 hardstandings. Vending machine*

Leisure: ⚲ ⚠ ▢

Facilities: 🏠 ⊙ ⚲ ☏ 🚿 🏛 🎋 ↑

Disabled facilities: shower & toilets, angling & accessible walking paths

Services: 🕾 🖽 → ∪ ┌18 ↓ ☃ ⤸ 🖩

🖳 🖳 5